Real Analysis

Dr Anderson, who was born in Edinburgh, studied at the Queen's University of Belfast, where he obtained the degrees of BA and PhD. After holding a teaching assistantship at Belfast University, Dr Anderson, in 1962, joined the staff of Nottingham University, where he is Lecturer in Mathematics. He has written several papers on Classical Analysis, and is currently interested in problems of mathematical education.

ANDERSON, Johnston Andrew. Real Analysis. Gordon and Breach, 1969. 345p il 68-21945. 28.00; professional ed., 11.00
Recent years have seen a barrage of new, purportedly introductory, analysis books. It is hoped that this book will not get lost among them; for it is truly an *introductory* real analysis book. The currently popular treatment of topological properties, such as in M. Rosenlicht's *Introduction to Analysis* (1968), is omitted. This results in a self-contained, traditional treatment of the usual topics of one-variable calculus which requires very little background on the part of the reader. In a way, then, it resembles G. H. Hardy's *A Course of Pure Mathematics* (1959). The style is unhurried with many illustrations, examples, and counter-examples. Especially noteworthy is the careful explanation in Chapter One of the principles of logic involved in proof and the reference to these principles in later chapters when they are being applied. Thus the book should prove to be a valuable reference both to students in elementary calculus and to those taking more high powered real analysis courses. Recommended as a valuable addition to undergraduate libraries.

Real Analysis

J. A. Anderson, BA, PhD
Lecturer in Mathematics, University of Nottingham

LOGOS PRESS LIMITED
LONDON

© J. A. Anderson 1969

Published by
LOGOS PRESS LIMITED

in association with
ELEK BOOKS LIMITED
2 All Saints Street, London, N.1.

Library of Congress Catalog Card Number 68-21945
Printed in Great Britain by J. W. Arrowsmith Ltd., Bristol 3

Contents

THE GREEK ALPHABET

Lower case	Upper case	Name	English equivalent
α	A	alpha	a (as in h*a*t)
β	B	beta	b
γ	Γ	gamma	g
δ	Δ	delta	d
ε,	E	epsilon	e (as in g*e*t)
ζ	Z	zeta	z
η	H	eta	a (as in g*a*y)
θ	Θ	theta	th (as in *th*ick)
ι	I	iota	i (as in f*i*ll)
κ	K	kappa	k
λ	Λ	lambda	l
μ	M	mu	m
ν	N	nu	n
ξ	Ξ	xi	x
ο	O	omicron	o (as in g*o*t)
π	Π	pi	p
ρ	P	rho	r
σ	Σ	sigma	s
τ	T	tau	t
υ	Υ	upsilon	u (as in t*ou*r)
φ, φ	Φ	phi	f (as in *ph*oto)
χ	X	chi	ch (as in lo*ch*)
ψ	Ψ	psi	ps (as in *p*sychology)
ω	Ω	omega	o (as in *o*ver)

Preface

This book is based on a course of lectures given at Nottingham University, and is primarily designed to provide a basic introduction to the concepts and techniques of Analysis for first-year university undergraduates. Analysis is often found difficult by such students, and therefore I have made some effort to motivate, not only the concepts, but also the methods of proof used in the theorems, and further, to include frequent worked exercises and illustrative examples. This book also includes, as an introductory chapter, an account of logic and methods of mathematical argument, so that the logical principles underlying proofs may be better understood. Frequent use, too, is made of the counterexample, to show that conditions imposed or hypotheses assumed are, in fact, necessary. It is hoped that the worked exercises, the illustrative examples and the semi-informal comments will serve as a self-tutor for the student to supplement the "hard" facts of the main text.

One reason why Analysis is found difficult at university is that the methods and, to some extent, the concepts, are unfortunately not within the normal experience of a sixth-form school student. This book has therefore been written also in the hope that it may find its way into sixth-form libraries, and help to bridge the gap between school and university mathematics. Of course, some of the material will not be very suitable for sixth-form teaching, but with some pre-digestion by the teacher, most of the contents of Chapters 1, 2, 3, 7, 9 (and parts of Chapter 8) should be within the scope of sixth-forms. It seems to me important that the sixth-former, intending to read mathematics at university, should have had some contact with the kind of rigorous Analysis he will meet, and also with the logical methods of proof he will have to use.

The modern trend in Mathematics, and in Analysis in particular, is to seek to discover unifying concepts, and to emphasise the essential underlying structures. These structures are of two varieties, algebraic and topological. Analysis is mainly concerned with the latter. It is therefore tempting to set an account of Elementary Analysis in the wider framework of a discussion of spaces with a metric topology, but I have resisted this temptation, because I think it would defeat the purpose behind this book, which, as I have said, is intended to appeal not only to university undergraduates, but also to students in sixth-forms and colleges of technology. These readers will be familiar with some of the basic facts about the real numbers, and with the ideas of elementary calculus. I wish to draw on this experience and on intuition nourished by this experience to lead the reader forward, in a natural way, to the various aspects of functions of the real line. Subsequently, when he comes to consider topological spaces as an abstract concept, he will be familiar with a particular realisation. I think that, to appreciate the unity of a subject, it is better to see different facets individually first, and then as a whole later, rather than the other way round.

I have therefore discussed Analysis in a fairly traditional way; there is no discussion on the topology as such of the real line, nor of compactness nor connectedness; there is no discussion of the Heine–Borel Theorem nor of the Bolzano-Weierstrass Theorem. However, I have indicated how some of the theorems in the book are particular aspects of more general results.

In this book, theorems are designated by the number of the section in which they appear, and a letter; thus, Theorem 6.8–D will be the fourth theorem in Section 8 of Chapter 6. This is to distinguish more readily between theorems and Examples, which are numbered by section and number within the section; for instance, Example 6.8.4 is the fourth example in Section 8 of Chapter 6. The word "Example" in this context is used to mean both "worked exercise" and "illustrative example". Definitions are not numbered, except in Chapter 1, where there is considerable cross-reference. The conclusions of theorems and examples are indicated by a lozenge ◆.

My thanks are due to many of my colleagues at Nottingham; to Dr. Margaret Jackson who read the entire manuscript and made many helpful suggestions; to Dr. Kathleen Collard, for a detailed criticism of Chapter 1; to Dr. Gordon Fullerton, for comments and suggestions on Chapters 2, 3 and 8; to several research students for spotting minor errors, though the final form of the book and any errors remaining are my sole responsibility; to Miss Helen Hill, Mrs. Joan Wisdish and others for sterling work in typing the manuscript; to my wife for assistance with the index, and to Miss Alison Anderson and Logos Press for their patience, helpfulness and efficiency.

Nottingham   Johnston A. Anderson
January, 1969

Part One: Basic Machinery

Chapter 1 may be thought of as a kind of prologue. We have called this part of the book *Basic Machinery*, and we shall see that the contents of this chapter provide the logical means of processing the material that comes in the rest of the book. This chapter and its contents will therefore have a deep seated influence on the book, although it cannot be said to be part of the main subject matter.

We begin with an account of very basic set theory, and show how this leads naturally into an examination of elementary logic. This provides us with an opportunity to recount the principal methods of mathematical argument. Applications of these, of course, occur at every stage of the succeeding chapters, and indeed, apply not only to Analysis, but to all other branches of mathematics. We conclude with further remarks on the theory of sets.

The principles of logic and argument have been set down in considerable detail, because a full understanding of the techniques of Analysis can come only if the underlying logical foundations are completely grasped. The reader may consequently find this a difficult and perhaps at times tedious, chapter; in some ways, it is probably the most difficult chapter of the book. **Perhaps his best plan is to read it through fairly quickly and subsequently make reference to it as he reads the real "meat" of the book;** by this means, he will discover its value and find his patience rewarded, in that he will master it more and more as he sees its applications.

Chapter 1 differs from the subsequent chapters in two other minor ways. Firstly, in this chapter only, the definitions are numbered as there is considerable cross-reference. Secondly, the exercises, as they occur, are placed at the end of the corresponding sections; in the other chapters, the exercises are all gathered together at the conclusion of the chapter.

Sets, Logic and Mathematical Argument

1.1 Sets

We begin by describing some intuitive ideas about sets. Much of the mathematics that we will be concerned with involves the study of the relationships of one set with another, and it is therefore advisable that we should spend some time laying down the fundamental properties of sets.

Intuitively, by a **set**, we mean any collection of objects—a set may consist of people, of numbers, of points; it may consist of objects we can see and handle, or of abstract objects. The objects which make up, or belong to, a set are called its **elements**, or its **members**, or occasionally, its **points**.

The theory of sets has been systematically studied only since about 1880, when G. Cantor formulated the basic definitions and axioms. We follow him in remarking that a set must consist of definite, "well-defined" elements; that is to say, if we have in mind some particular collection, then we call it a "set" if, given any object, we can decide whether it belongs to the collection we are interested in, or whether it does not. This seemingly obvious property is violated by some objects; we can illustrate this by an example due to Bertrand Russell. If we have a set, let us call it S, then, since S is itself an object, either S will belong to the set S (itself) or (the object) S will not belong to (the set) S. Now, think of a new collection, Σ; let Σ be the collection of all those sets S which do not belong to themselves. On the face of it, this seems a perfectly respectable way to construct a new set Σ. But suppose Σ were an object in the universe; we could ask the same question of Σ: does Σ belong to Σ, or not? If Σ does belong to Σ, then by the defining property of the collection Σ, Σ is a set which does not belong to itself i.e. Σ does not belong to Σ! On the other hand, if Σ does not belong to Σ, then Σ is a collection which does not belong to itself, which is precisely the qualification needed for membership of Σ! Either way, we contradict ourselves. The only way out of this impasse is to say that Σ is not in our "universe"; it is not a set, because we are unable to decide whether every object belongs to Σ or not.

There is a more concrete realisation of this "paradox", which may be helpful to the reader. Suppose we have a large library. There will almost certainly be a catalogue of the books in the library. Now, since the catalogue is a book in the library, the catalogue may list itself, or it may not. We now consider all catalogues which do not list themselves; if there were lots of these, we might be tempted to compile a catalogue C which lists all those catalogues which do not list themselves. Now, does the catalogue C list itself, or not? If the reader pursues this to its conclusion, he will discover that no such catalogue as C can exist.

We therefore see that there are pitfalls in a deep study of set theory. We cannot, in the space of this book, go into a systematic and axiomatic treatment of set theory; but this can, and has, been done. We shall take it, as an axiom, that sets do exist, and that they contain "well-defined" objects. The reader may feel that this is, in some sense, cheating. Very well, let us look at the problem of language, and how we define the meanings of words. If we look up a word in a dictionary, its meaning is given, using other words. Look up the meaning of each of these words; some may have no "meaning" (for instance, "the" is described as "the definite article", which does not help at all!), while others are defined in terms of yet other words. Since the total number of words is finite, we will eventually find a word which appears in the definition of itself (indeed, observe what we have said about "the" above). For instance, take the word "straight". According to the dictionary, this means "without bend", so we look up "bend"; a "bend" is defined to be a "curve", and upon looking up "curve", we see that it is "a line no part of which is straight". If we put all these definitions together, we see that we obtain a circular definition; "straight" means "straight"! Fortunately, we have an intuitive idea of what "straightness" is, and equally fortunately, most of us have the same idea. So we can afford to leave it undefined, apart from synonyms, and yet avoid misunderstanding.

We adopt the same sort of viewpoint in this chapter. A *set* is what we would intuitively think of as a collection of objects, and we add on the condition that its elements be well-defined, to act as a guide to what are sets in our sense.

We shall denote sets by upper case letters, like $A, B, X, Y, \ldots$. We shall also, in talking about sets, have in mind a "universal set", which is a repository of all objects relevant to the discussion.* It is often denoted by E, or by S, and occasionally, by U. It is usually clear in any discussion which is the universal set.

Elements of a set are denoted by lower case letters like $a, b, x, y, \ldots$. It is convenient to have abbreviations for the phrases "is an element of" or "belongs to", and for their opposites "is not an element of", "does not belong to". The standard abbreviation for the first two is "$\in$";

---

* It is *not* the set of all objects whatever; Russell's paradox shows that this leads to serious logical difficulties.

for the latter two, it is "$\notin$". Thus,

$x \in A$: (the element) x belongs to (the set) A ;
$y \notin B$: (the object) y is not an element of (the set) B.

1.2 Comparison of Sets

Two sets may contain the same kind of objects, e.g. they may both be sets of numbers, or they may contain objects of different kinds, e.g. a set of points on a line and a set of postage stamps. In this section, we look primarily at sets containing the same kind of objects. What we say can be applied to sets of differing kinds of objects; but they do not have any *useful* meaning. Firstly, we examine two set *relations*; they say how two sets may be compared.

Definition 1.2–1.   Suppose A and B are sets; if each element of A is also an element of B, we say that A is a **subset** of B. Symbolically, we write

$$A \subset B \qquad (\text{or } B \supset A).$$

Some authors use the notation $A \subseteq B$.
This is read as "A is contained in B".

Example 1.2.1.   The set of all male human beings is a subset of the set of all human beings.

Example 1.2.2.   Let A be the set consisting of the first five numbers 1, 2, 3, 4, 5; let B be the set consisting of the odd digits. Then, A is not a subset of B. For, although the numbers 1, 3 and 5 in A also belong to B, the numbers 2 and 4 are not odd digits, and so do not belong to B.

Note.   We write $A = \{1, 2, 3, 4, 5\}$, $B = \{1, 3, 5, 7, 9\}$. See also Section 1.5.

Definition 1.2–2.   If A and B are two sets such that $A \subset B$ and also $B \subset A$, then we say that A and B are **equal**: $A = B$. A and B are thus equal if and only if their elements coincide completely.

Example 1.2.3.   Let A be the set consisting of all even integers between 1 and 9; let B be the set whose elements are the numbers 2, 4, 6 and 8. Then, $A = B$.

Exercise.   Let A be the set $\{\{1\}, \{1, 2\}, \{1, 2, 3\}\}$; which of the following relations are true?

(a) $\{1\} \subset A$;
(b) $\{1\} \in A$;
(c) $\{\{1\}\} \in A$;
(d) $\{\{1\}\} \subset A$;
(e) $\{2, 3\} \notin A$;
(f) $\{2, 3\} \not\subset A$;

(g) $\{\{2, 3\}\} \not\subset A$;
(h) $\{\{1, 3\}\} \subset A$;
(i) $\{1, 2, 3\} \in A$;
(j) $\{\{1, 2\}\} \subset A$;
(k) $\{\{1\}, \{1, 2\}\} \in A$;
(l) $\{\{1\}, \{1, 2\}\} \subset A$.

1.3 Combinations of Subsets

As well as comparing sets, we can also combine them in various ways to form new sets.

Definition 1.3–1.   Let A and B be two sets; then, the **union** of A and B is the new set consisting of all elements which belong to A, or to B (or both). This set has the symbol $A \cup B$.

Definition 1.3–2.   Let A and B be sets; the **intersection** of A and B is the new set consisting of all elements which belong to *both* A and B. It has the symbol $A \cap B$.

Definition 1.3–3.   Let A be a subset of a set E; the **complement of A in E** is the subset of E consisting of all those objects in E which do not belong to A. We denote this subset by $\mathscr{C}_E(A)$.

Note.   The subscript "E" is deliberately used. Suppose $A \subset B$ and $B \subset E$ (so that $A \subset E$, also). $\mathscr{C}_E(A)$ means "the set of all elements in E which do not belong to A", while $\mathscr{C}_B(A)$ means "the set of all elements in B which do not belong to A". Since $B \subset E$, there may well be elements of E which are not in B, and hence not in A. So $\mathscr{C}_B(A) \subset \mathscr{C}_E(A)$, and these need not be equal. This is why it is important to use the subscript, unless the context is quite clear.

Example 1.3.1.   Let $A = \{1, 2, 3\}, B = \{1, 2, 3, 4\}, E = \{1, 2, 3, 4, 5\}$. Then, $\mathscr{C}_B(A) = \{4\}$, while $\mathscr{C}_E(A) = \{4, 5\}$.

1.4 Venn Diagrams

A helpful device in the study of relations between sets is the Venn Diagram. In this, the "universal" set is depicted as a rectangle, and the sets under immediate discussion by circular disks within this rectangle. Then, the composite set is shaded to show its relation to the primitive sets. We illustrate the ideas of Sections 1.2 and 1.3 in the figures below.

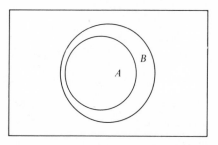

Fig. 1.4.1. $A \subset B$.

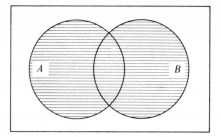

Fig. 1.4.2. $A \cup B$.

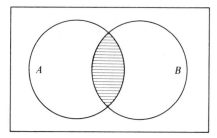

Fig. 1.4.3. $A \cap B$.

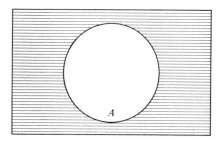

Fig. 1.4.4. $C_E(A)$.

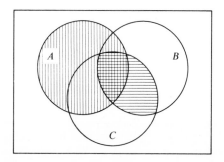

Fig. 1.4.5. $A \cup (B \cap C)$ is the total shaded area; $B \cap C$ is shaded horizontally, A vertically.

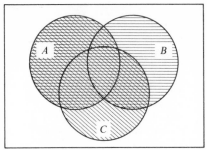

Fig. 1.4.6. $(A \cup B) \cap (A \cup C)$. $A \cup B$ is shaded horizontally, $A \cup C$ is shaded diagonally, $(A \cup B) \cap (A \cup C)$ is the cross-hatched area, which the reader will see coincides with the total shaded area of Fig. 1.4.5.

The idea can, of course, be extended to depict relations between three sets. For instance, Figs. 1.4.5 and 1.4.6 show how to obtain $A \cup (B \cap C)$ in two ways, thus showing that $A \cup (B \cap C) = (A \cup B) \cap (A \cup C)$ (see Theorem 1.11–B).

1.5 Set Builders

In order to explore further the concepts we have defined above, we now look at some simple logical ideas which underlie them.

In a typical mathematics textbook, we might find such phrases as

$$x^2 - 1 = 0,$$
17 is a divisor of 85,
for all integers k, $k(k + 1)$ is even.

We shall be considering these in this and subsequent sections, and so we begin by defining some of the words we shall use. The second phrase above is an example of a *statement*. We define a **statement** to be a collection of words and symbols (if we like, a *sentence*) which makes an assertion i.e. we can decide, from our experience, whether the sentence is true or false. Statements are either **true** or **false**, and it is the characteristic of a statement that we can, in any particular case, decide which of these it is. Thus, the second phrase above is a true statement, because we know from experience that 17 does divide 85.

The first phrase above is not a statement; we cannot decide whether "$x^2 - 1 = 0$" is true or false. At least, not until we know what "x" is; this phrase is called a *condition on x*. This section is particularly devoted to the consideration of such objects.

The last phrase seems to fall somewhere between the two just mentioned. It involves an "unknown", namely k, like the x of the first example, but yet it appears to make an assertion; it asserts that the product of any two successive integers is even. (Put this way, it looks even more like an assertion!). In fact, phrase three is again a statement, and it is again true; for of two successive integers, one must be even, and the product of an even and an odd integer is always even. Statements like this, which are made up of a condition ("$k(k+1)$ is even") and a "quantifier" ("for all integers k") are very important in mathematics. However, we shall not deal with them here, but in a later Section, 1.9.

We turn therefore to consideration of phrases like "$x^2 - 1 = 0$". The letter x here is a symbol; just as in Section 1.1 we used x to denote an element of a set, so here x again denotes an element of some (as yet unspecified) set. But it does have a special significance. The number 2 is an element of the set of integers; it is a definite, unambiguous, particular element. In the formula above, however, x is used as a general element—it can be replaced by any member at all of the relevant set. The letter x has been described in various ways at various times; it has been called a *variable*, a *place-holder*, a *stand-in*, and a *representative*. The word "variable" seems ambiguous, for although x can be replaced by any element of the set in question, it does not vary, in the sense that, once a replacement is made, we must stick to that choice for the duration of that argument. The word *symbol* has attractions in this context, but "symbol" is used in too many ways already.

We shall use the word **dummy** in this book. It has, perhaps, only a subjective superiority; but the reader is at liberty to adopt any other word he feels subjectively happier about.

If we go back to our formula, the set from which replacements for x are allowed may be the set of integers, or the set of positive integers, or the set of all fractions, and so on. Whatever the set happens to be, let us denote it by E, for the purposes of discussion.

We first observe that, if we replace the dummy x by an element of E, we obtain a statement. For instance, if E is the set of integers, and we replace x by the integer -1, we obtain the (true) statement "$(-1)^2 - 1 = 0$". If we replace x by the integer 2, on the other hand, we get the (false) statement "$2^2 - 1 = 0$".

If E is a set, and x is a dummy which can be replaced by any element of E, we say that x is a **dummy** with **domain** E, or simply, x has **domain** E.

If E is a set, and x has domain E, then a **condition on** x is an assertion about x which becomes a true or false statement when x is replaced by a definite element of E. Thus "$x^2 - 1 = 0$" is a condition on x, where x is a dummy whose domain is the set of integers.

Next, if $A \subset E$, then to say x has domain A means that the dummy x may be replaced only by elements of A.

Throughout this section, we shall use the notation $p(x), q(x), \ldots$ to denote conditions on x. This is not the same as the function-value notation, which we shall encounter in Chapter 3.

Example 1.5.1. Let E be the set of all integers. Then, if $p(x)$ is "$2^x > 8$", $p(x)$ is a condition on x, where x is a dummy with domain E.

$p(1)$ is the (false) statement "$2 > 8$"; $p(5)$ is the (true) statement "$2^5 > 8$", and so on.

Example 1.5.2.   Let A be the set of all male human beings. If $q(y)$ is "y is the son of the Prime Minister", then $q(y)$ is a condition on y, where y has domain A.

Note.   It does not matter what letter we use for the dummy; x would have done just as well.

Example 1.5.3.   Let x be a nonzero integer. Let $r(x)$ be "x divides xy", where y is any integer. Then, $r(x)$ is *not* a condition on x; for we can say that $r(x)$ is true, hence it is a statement. On this occasion, we have an example of ellipsis. The statement should read "for all nonzero integers x, x divides xy, where y is any integer". This has been camouflaged by writing the "for all . . ." part (in a different way) as a separate sentence. So this example belongs to Section 1.9. However, this kind of camouflage is very common in mathematics, and the reader should be alert to try to spot statements which are ostensibly conditions.

We observe in Example 1.5.1, that when we replace x by a particular element of the set E, we obtain a statement. Some of these may be true, others may be false. We can therefore divide the set E in two.

Definition 1.5–1.   Let $p(x)$ be a condition on x, where x has domain E. Let A denote the subset of E whose elements make $p(x)$ a true statement when they are substituted for x. Then, A is called the **solution set** of $p(x)$, and the elements of A are said to *satisfy* $p(x)$.

Example 1.5.4.   If E is the set of all integers, and $p(x)$ is the condition "$x^2 - 1 = 0$", then the solution set of $p(x)$ is the set whose elements are -1 and $+1$.

Example 1.5.5.   Let E, $p(x)$ be as in Example 1.5.1. The solution set of $p(x)$ is the set of all integers which exceed 3, i.e. the numbers $4, 5, 6, \ldots$

At this point, we introduce a new terminology. The solution set A of a condition $p(x)$ is the subset of E consisting of all those elements of E which satisfy $p(x)$; we write

$$A = \{x \in E : p(x)\}.$$

This is a coded abbreviation, and it translates as follows:

Code	Meaning
A	the set A
$=$	is (or "equals")
$\{\ \}$	the (sub)set consisting of
$x \in E$	all those elements x in E
$:$	such that
$p(x)$	the condition $p(x)$ is satisfied

We thus describe A in two ways; we can say exactly what its elements are, and secondly, we can say how they arise (as the solution of a condition). We read the code above as "A is the set of all x in E such that $p(x)$".

Expressions like $\{x \in E : p(x)\}$ are called **set-builders**, because that is exactly what they do; they "build" the solution set of the enclosed condition.

Sets can be defined, as we have said, either by using the set 1-1 builder notation or by listing its elements. In the latter case, they are included within braces. Thus, $\{1, 2, 3\}$ is the set whose elements are the numbers 1, 2, 3. Both forms can be used together:

$$\{-1, 1\} = \{x \in \text{integers} : x^2 - 1 = 0\}$$
$$\{4, 5, 6, \ldots\} = \{x \in \text{integers} : 2^x > 8\} = \{x \in \text{integers} : x \geqslant 4\}.$$

Often, however, we use the set-builder notation to give a label to a set, for purposes of easy reference in arguments. Thus,

$$\text{"let } A = \{x \in \text{integers} : x^3 - 3x + 2 \geqslant 0\}\text{"}$$

is a device to avoid using the long expression on the right in the course of an argument. For this reason, we shall now look at some special sets in the next section.

Exercises 1

1. Let A be the set of all words in English which contain the letter "a", B the set of all words in English which contain the letter "b", and so on. Thus, "is" $\notin A$, "are" $\in A$. What is $A \cup B$? What is $A \cap B$? Can you express the set of all English words in terms of $A, B, C, \ldots$? Is $A \subset B$? Is $B \subset A$? Is there *any* inclusion relation between any of the sets $A, B, C, \ldots$?

2. Let A be the set of letters which occur in the word "calculus", B the set of letters occurring in "algebra". What is $A \cup B$? What is $A \cap B$?

3. If Z denotes the set of all integers, what are the elements of the following sets?
   (a) $[\mathscr{C}_Z\{3, 5, 7\}] \cap \{2, 3, 5, 6, 8\}$
   (b) $\{1, 5, -9, -2\} \cup \{4, -9, 7, 6\}$
   (c) $\{36, 54\} \cup [\mathscr{C}_Z\{18, 36, 54\}]$
   (d) $\{-1, 3, 5, 7\} \cap [\mathscr{C}_Z\{2, 7, 1, 4, -5\}]$
   (e) $[\mathscr{C}_Z\{2, 4, 6\}] \cup \{2, 4, 6\}$
   (f) $\mathscr{C}_Z[\{3, 1, 7, 4\} \cup \{8, 2, 9, 5\}]$
   (g) $[\mathscr{C}_Z\{8, 2, 9, 5\}] \cap [\mathscr{C}_Z\{3, 1, 7, 4\}]$.

4. Simplify the definitions of the following composite sets; R is the set of all real numbers.
   (a) $\{x \in R : -1 \leqslant x < 3\} \cup \{y \in Z : 0 \leqslant y \leqslant 3\}$
   (b) $\{x \in Z : x \geqslant 0\} \cap \{y \in R : -1 < y \leqslant 1\}$

(c) $\mathscr{C}_R\{x \in R : x^2 \geqslant 2\} \cup \mathscr{C}_R\{y \in R : y^3 \leqslant 3\}$
(d) $\{x \in R : x^2 < 5\} \cap \{y \in R : y^2 > 5\}$
Simplify the following solution sets:
5. $\{x \in R : x^3 - 5x^2 + 6x = 0\}$ (Ans. $\{0, 2, 3\}$)
6. $\{x \in Z : x^2 + 3x + 2 \geqslant 0\}$.
Answer to question 1, last part: Yes; $Q \subset U$.

1.6 Some Special Sets

Although, as we mentioned earlier, we denote sets by upper case letters $A, B, \ldots$, there are some special sets which have a letter reserved for their exclusive use. Since we use these frequently, we list them here, with their special letters.

(i) N is the set consisting of all positive integers, or "natural numbers" $1, 2, 3, \ldots$; N stands for "number".

(ii) Z is the set consisting of all integers (positive, negative and zero); Z is from "Zahl", German for "integer".

(iii) Q is the set consisting of all rational numbers, or "rationals"; Q is used because a rational number is the "quotient" of integers.

(iv) R is the set consisting of all real numbers; R for "real".

(v) C is the set consisting of all complex numbers; C for "complex". We observe that $N \subset Z \subset Q \subset R \subset C$.

There is another special set, not yet mentioned. Consider the sets

(a) $\{x \in E : x \neq x\}$,
(b) $\{x \in Q : x^2 = 2\}$,
(c) $\{x \in R : x^2 = -1\}$,
(d) $\{1, 3, 5, 7, 9\} \cap \{2, 4, 6, 8\}$;

in all these cases, we might be tempted to say "no such set exists"; for no object can be unequal to itself; there is no *rational* whose square is 2 (Theorem 2.6–A); there is no *real* number whose square is -1; there is no digit common to the sets $\{1, 3, 5, 7, 9\}$ and $\{2, 4, 6, 8\}$. Alternatively, we could say that the sets in (a), (b), (c), (d) contain no elements, or are "empty". It is this latter course we adopt, because it seems quite unreasonable to make a quantitative distinction between solution sets of conditions, in that we would call $\{x \in E : p(x)\}$ a "set" if there is an element of E which satisfies $p(x)$, but would say that it is not a set, or does not exist, when no element of E satisfies $p(x)$.

(vi) The **empty** set (also called the **null** set) is denoted by $\varnothing$.

We use $\varnothing$, rather than 0, to avoid confusion with the integer 0. This is illustrated in the following example.

Example 1.6.1. $\{-2, -1, 0\} \cap \{1, 2, 3\} = \varnothing$, for there is no element common to the sets; $\{-2, -1, 0\} \cap \{0, 1, 2\} = \{0\}$, for the number zero, 0, is an element of both.

We illustrate an example of an empty set in Fig. 1.6.1.

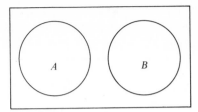

Fig. 1.6.1. $A \cap B = \emptyset$.

So, to say that the solution set of $p(x)$ is $\emptyset$ is to say that the condition $p(x)$ on x is never satisfied by an element in the domain of x. It is a distinguishing characteristic of the empty set $\emptyset$ that it is a subset of every set, and alone has this property.

Exercise. Which of the following statements are true?

(i) $0 \in Z$; (ii) $\emptyset \in Z$; (iii) $\{\emptyset\} \subset Z$; (iv) $0 \subset Z$; (v) $\emptyset \subset Z$; (vi) $\emptyset \subset \{0\}$; (vii) $\{0\} \in Z$; (viii) $0 \in \{\emptyset\}$; (ix) $\{0\} \subset Z$; (x) $\emptyset \in \{\{0\}, \{\emptyset\}\}$; (xi) $0 \in \{0\}$. [*TFFFTTFFTFT*]

1.7 Elementary Logic

In this section, we shall deal only with statements, and various combinations of these. We shall be primarily concerned with combinations effected by the use of such words as "and", "or", "not", "if... then...".

Since a statement is not a condition on a dummy, we shall use single letters $p, q, r, \ldots$ to denote statements. The fact that we use p instead of $p(x)$ indicates that we are considering statements and not conditions. Conditions will be dealt with in the next section. Therefore, p might be "John Smith is tall", q could be "John Smith is thin". In ordinary language, we get such combinations of these as "John Smith is tall and thin", "John Smith is not tall" and so on. The purpose of this section is to give a general analysis of these connectives and their effect on the combined statement.

Now, if p is a statement, then in view of our remark in Section 1.5, this statement p will be either true or false. We use T for "true", F for "false", and call these *truth-values*. For instance, the statement p given by "$2+2 = 4$" has the truth-value T, while "$3+3 = 7$" has the truth-value F. If, however, we want to discuss statements in an abstract way, we will not know which truth-value is appropriate, and so what we do is to tabulate all possibilities.

If we wish to deal with a combination of two statements, p and q, then we must consider all the possible cases which can arise. p may be either true or false, and q likewise, so that for a combination involving both there are *four* possible cases to consider. We then tabulate these in a "truth-table"; we list the various possible combinations of the truth values of p and q, and then opposite these, we fill in the truth value of the combined statement, which is determined by the connective used and the values of p, q. Thus,

Situations	p	q	Combination of p and q
1	T	T	?
2	T	F	?
3	F	T	?
4	F	F	?

Our problem in this section is to insert suitable values in the last column for the various combinations.

We begin with the connective "or". We shall use this in the inclusive sense ("Do you have any brothers or sisters?" meaning "brothers or sisters, or both?") rather than the exclusive sense (illustrated by phrases such as "man or woman", "yes or no?"). We call "or" the *disjunction*, and we define its truth-table as in the following definition, to conform to our normal usage of the inclusive "or".

Definition 1.7–1. The truth-table of the **disjunction** "p or q" is given by

p	q	p or q
T	T	T
T	F	T
F	T	T
F	F	F

That is, "p or q" is true whenever at least one of p, q is true.

Example 1.7.1. The statement

"John Smith is tall or thin"

is true if John Smith *is* tall, or if he *is* thin (or both).

Example 1.7.2. The statement

"$2+2 = 5$ or London is in England"

is true (by line 3 of the truth-table above).

We can connect two statements by the word "and". The connective "and", denoted by &, is called a *conjunction*. We define the truth-table of "p & q" in an obvious way.

Definition 1.7–2. The truth-table of the **conjunction** p & q is given by

p	q	$p \& q$
T	T	T
T	F	F
F	T	F
F	F	F

So, $p \& q$ is true if both p is true and q is true, and is false otherwise. We make the definition in such a way as to be consistent with everyday usage.

Example 1.7.3.   The statement

$$\text{"} 2 + 2 = 5 \text{ and London is in England"}$$

is false; but

$$\text{"} 2 + 2 = 4 \text{ and London is in England"}$$

is true.

Another very important "connective" is the word "not". This does not combine two statements, but it forms a new statement from an existing one, and so we put it with the others. Since we have only one basic statement, we have only two possible truth-values. The word "not", called a *negation*, denoted by $\sim$, is defined to reverse them.

Definition 1.7–3.   The truth table of the **negation** " $\sim p$ " is given by

p	$\sim p$
T	F
F	T

Example 1.7.4.   Let p be "It is raining"; $\sim p$ is "It is not raining." Clearly, if p is true, $\sim p$ is false, and *vice versa*.

We can, of course, perform secondary combinations of two statements. For if p, q are statements, $p \& q$ is a statement, and so $\sim (p \& q)$ is a statement. This is a secondary combination, arising from the original statements by *two* combinations. We look at some of these involving "or", "&" and " $\sim$ "; we can construct $\sim (p \text{ or } q)$, $\sim (p \& q)$, $\sim p$ or $\sim q$, $\sim p \& \sim q$, for example. We look at the truth tables of these secondary combinations.

p	q	$p \& q$	$\sim (p \& q)$	p or q	$\sim (p \text{ or } q)$
T	T	T	F	T	F
T	F	F	T	T	F
F	T	F	T	T	F
F	F	F	T	F	T

The fourth column is derived from the third by using Definition 1.7–3, and similarly the sixth from the fifth. On the other hand, we have

p	q	$\sim p$	$\sim q$	$\sim p \,\&\, \sim q$	$\sim p$ or $\sim q$
T	T	F	F	F	F
T	F	F	T	F	T
F	T	T	F	F	T
F	F	T	T	T	T

Here, column five follows from columns three and four by Definition 1.7–2, column six likewise, using Definition 1.7–1.

An examination of the tables will show that the tables for $\sim(p \,\&\, q)$ and $(\sim p$ or $\sim q)$ are exactly the same; the tables for $\sim(p$ or $q)$ and $(\sim p \,\&\, \sim q)$ are also identical. Whatever truth values p and q have, these pairs of combined statements agree in their derived value. This has nothing to do with whether p and q are actually true or false, but is a consequence of the logical system. So we can make a new definition.

Definition 1.7–4. Two statements are called **logically equivalent** (or just **equivalent**) if their truth-tables are identical. We use the device ⇔ to indicate logical equivalence.

The remarks above permit us to formulate a theorem.

Theorem 1.7–A. If p, q are statements, then

    (a) $\sim(p \,\&\, q) \Leftrightarrow \sim p$ or $\sim q$
    (b) $\sim(p$ or $q) \Leftrightarrow \sim p \,\&\, \sim q$.

The proof consists of showing that the truth-tables on either side of ⇔ are identical, as we have done above.

Example 1.7.5. The negation of the statement

"He is tall and thin"

is the statement

"He is not tall or he is not thin."

Yet another connective for making new statements from old, but of a slightly different appearance, is the *conditional* "if . . . , then . . .", denoted by "→".
We define the truth-table as follows.

Definition 1.7–5. The truth-table of the **conditional** $p \to q$, read as "if p, then q" is given by

p	q	$p \to q$
T	T	T
T	F	F
F	T	T
F	F	T

so that $p \to q$ is true in every case except when q is false and p is true.

We again emphasise that we have *defined* the truth-table to be this way, and we can define a combination in any way we choose. Nevertheless, it is clearly helpful to base our definition on our intuitive feelings as far as possible, as we have done with "$\sim$" and "&" and "or". The intuitive justification for Definition 1.7–5 is that we would wish a true statement to lead to a true statement, but not a false one. So we define the first two lines of the table with this in mind. On the other hand, if p is false, anything can happen; consider the following arguments:

(i) If $p:1 = 2$ (F)
       $(p):2 = 1$ (F)
     then $q:3 = 3$ (T)

(ii) If $p:1 = 2$ (F)
        $(p):1 = 2$ (F)
      then $q:2 = 4$ (F)

From the false hypothesis p, we can derive either a true or false conclusion. So we define $p \to q$, whenever p is false, to be true, irrespective of q's value.

We can show that, having defined the conditional in this way, it is the same as a combination of p and q using other connectives.

Theorem 1.7–B.   Let p, q be statements; then

$$(p \to q) \Leftrightarrow \sim p \text{ or } q.$$

Proof.   We construct the truth table for "$\sim p$ or q":

p	q	$\sim p$	$\sim p$ or q
T	T	F	T
T	F	F	F
F	T	T	T
F	F	T	T

But this is the same truth table as Definition 1.7–5. So, by Definition 1.7–4, $\sim p$ or q is equivalent to $p \to q$.   ◆

Theorem 1.7–C.   If p, q are statements,

$$(p \to q) \Leftrightarrow (\sim q \to \sim p).$$

Proof.   Again, we construct the table for $\sim q \to \sim p$.

p	q	$\sim q$	$\sim p$	$\sim q \to \sim p$	$p \to q$
T	T	F	F	T	T
T	F	T	F	F	F
F	T	F	T	T	T
F	F	T	T	T	T

The last two columns are identical, so the theorem is proved.   ◆

This theorem has far-reaching consequences, as it provides a most useful method of proof. This we shall discuss in a subsequent section. Meanwhile it is useful to have a name for $\sim q \to \sim p$. We call the conditional $\sim q \to \sim p$ the **contrapositive form** of the conditional $p \to q$.

The conditional $q \to p$ is called the **converse form** of the conditional $p \to q$.

Theorem 1.7–D. $p \to q$ and $q \to p$ are *not* logically equivalent.

The proof is left to the reader; it consists of showing that $p \to q$ and $q \to p$ have different truth tables.

Another connective widely used in mathematics is the *bi-conditional* "... if and only if ...". It is denoted by "$\leftrightarrow$", which the reader should notice is different from "$\Leftrightarrow$", the sign of equivalence.

Let us consider the bi-conditional $p \leftrightarrow q$.

Take as a concrete example the sentence

"He is pleased if and only if he wins."

In usual language, this means "If he wins, he is pleased, and only if he wins" i.e. if he does *not* win, he is not pleased. In symbolic terms, using p for "he wins" and q for "he is pleased", the sentence above reads

"If p, then q, and, if not p, then not q"

i.e.

$$(p \to q) \,\&\, (\sim p \to \sim q).$$

Since Theorem 1.7–C tells us that $\sim p \to \sim q$ and $q \to p$ are logically equivalent, we obtain $(p \to q) \,\&\, (q \to p)$ for $p \leftrightarrow q$. We therefore *define* the bi-conditional $p \leftrightarrow q$ to have the same truth-table as $(p \to q) \,\&\, (q \to p)$.

Definition 1.7–6.   The **bi-conditional** $p \leftrightarrow q$ is defined to have the truth table given by

p	q	$p \leftrightarrow q$
T	T	T
T	F	F
F	T	F
F	F	T

So $p \leftrightarrow q$ is true whenever p and q have the same truth value, and is false when they have opposite truth values. In view of Definition 1.7–6, it is easy to obtain the following result.

Theorem 1.7–E. $(p \leftrightarrow q) \Leftrightarrow (p \to q) \,\&\, (q \to p)$.

Consider now the following combined statement: p or $\sim p$. If p is true, then the combined statement is true, by Definition 1.7–1; if p is false, $\sim p$ is true, by Definition 1.7–3 and so the combined statement is true, again by Definition 1.7–1. In tabular form, we have

p	$\sim p$	p or $\sim p$
T	F	T
F	T	T

So the truth-values of the final combined statement are always T. It is convenient to have a name for this phenomenon.

Definition 1.7–7. Suppose P is a statement which is a combination of other statements $p, q, \ldots$. If P always has the truth value T, whatever the truth-values of $p, q, \ldots$, then P is called a **tautology**. We sometimes say P is **logically true**.

Example 1.7.6. The statement P given by p or $\sim p$ is a tautology.

It could happen that a statement P always had the truth value F, whatever those of $p, q, \ldots$ might be. For example, examine the truth table of $p \,\&\, \sim p$:

p	$\sim p$	$p \,\&\, \sim p$	
T	F	F	$\left.\right\}$ by Definition 1.7–2
F	T	F	

Definition 1.7–8. Let P be a statement which is a combination of other statements $p, q, \ldots$. If P always has the truth value F, whatever those of $p, q, \ldots$ may be, then P is called a **self-contradiction**.

Example 1.7.7. The statement $p \,\&\, \sim p$ is a self-contradiction. Thus "It is raining, and it is not raining" is a self-contradiction. From these definitions, we can prove the following results.

Theorem 1.7–F. Suppose P, Q are two statements (combinations of statements $p, q, \ldots$). Then, $P \Leftrightarrow Q$ if and only if $P \leftrightarrow Q$ is a tautology.

Proof. We have to show that two statements are logically equivalent if and only if the bi-conditional is tautologous. Now, $P \Leftrightarrow Q$ if and only if P and Q have the same truth-table. By Definition 1.7–6, $P \leftrightarrow Q$ is true if and only if P, Q have the same truth-value, and false if and only if P, Q have opposite truth-values; hence, if P, Q have identical truth-tables, they have the same truth value at each stage, and hence $P \leftrightarrow Q$ is true, in every case i.e. $P \leftrightarrow Q$ is a tautology. Conversely, if $P \leftrightarrow Q$ is a tautology, then P and Q have the same truth value at every stage, i.e. their truth tables are identical, that is to say, $P \Leftrightarrow Q$. ◆

This theorem shows how the bi-conditional is bound up with logical equivalence. It is no accident that they have similar devices to denote them. In a similar way, we connect the conditional with logical implication.

Definition 1.7–9. Let P, Q be statements; we shall say that P **logically implies** Q (or merely that P **implies** Q), and write $P \Rightarrow Q$, if, and only if, the conditional $P \to Q$ is a tautology.

Example 1.7.8. Let p, q, r be statements. Then

$$\{(p \to q) \,\&\, (q \to r)\} \;\Rightarrow\; (p \to r).$$

Proof. We exhibit the truth table. This time, since p, q, r are independent, and can each take two values, the total number of possibilities is eight i.e. 2^3.

p	q	r	$p \to q$	$q \to r$	P $(p \to q) \,\&\, (q \to r)$	Q $p \to r$	$P \to Q$
T	T	T	T	T	T	T	T
T	T	F	T	F	F	F	T
T	F	T	F	T	F	T	T
T	F	F	F	T	F	F	T
F	T	T	T	T	T	T	T
F	T	F	T	F	F	T	T
F	F	T	T	T	T	T	T
F	F	F	T	T	T	T	T

The last column consists entirely of T's (since P is never true when Q is false), so $P \to Q$ is a tautology (Definition 1.7–7). That is, $P \Rightarrow Q$ by Definition 1.7–9.

Note, however, that P is not *equivalent* to Q. ◆

Exercises 2

1. Show that $(p \text{ or } q) \Leftrightarrow (q \text{ or } p)$; $p \,\&\, q \Leftrightarrow q \,\&\, p$.
2. Show that $(p \,\&\, q) \,\&\, r \Leftrightarrow p \,\&\, (q \,\&\, r)$ (Associativity Law).
3. Show that $p \text{ or } (q \,\&\, r) \Leftrightarrow (p \text{ or } q) \,\&\, (p \text{ or } r)$ (Distributive Law).
4. Show that $p \to (q \,\&\, r) \Leftrightarrow (p \to q) \,\&\, (p \to r)$ (Distributive Law).
5. Prove Theorem 1.7–D.
6. Prove Theorem 1.7–E.
7. Show that $p \,\&\, q \Rightarrow p \leftrightarrow q$.
8. Show that $p \,\&\, (q \text{ or } r) \Leftrightarrow (p \,\&\, q) \text{ or } (p \,\&\, r)$ (Distributive Law).
9. Does p imply $(p \,\&\, q)$?
10. Does p imply $(p \text{ or } q)$?
11. Show that $(p \,\&\, q) \to r \Leftrightarrow (p \to r) \text{ or } (q \to r)$.
12. Does $\{(p \,\&\, q) \to r\}$ imply $\{(p \to r) \,\&\, (q \to r)\}$?
13. Show that $\{(p \to q) \to r\} \Rightarrow \{(p \,\&\, \sim r) \to \sim q\}$.
14. How many of the following sentences can be simultaneously true?
    (i) Albert is tall.
    (ii) If Albert is tall, then he is not stupid.
    (iii) Either Albert is tall or he is stupid, but not both.
    (iv) Albert is stupid if and only if he is tall.
    (v) Albert is not stupid.
    (vi) Albert is tall, but he is not stupid.

1.8 Combinations of Conditions

We now go back to discussing conditions on x, where x is a dummy with domain E. If $p(x)$, $q(x)$ are conditions on x, let us call the solution sets of these conditions A and B respectively. Thus, if a is an element of

A, $p(a)$ is true; if $b \notin B$, $q(b)$ is false. The discussion of the last section provides a way of combining conditions, and for determining the solution set of the new condition. For example, consider the following everyday remark, "I never go out on days when it is raining or on days when it is foggy"; we can put this into symbolic form. Let E be the set of all days in the year, x be a dummy with domain E; let $p(x)$ be "x is a rainy day", $q(x)$ be "x is a foggy day". So,

$$A = \{x \in E : p(x)\} \text{ is the subset of all rainy days,}$$
$$B = \{x \in E : q(x)\} \text{ is the subset of all foggy days.}$$

It is easy to see that $A \cup B$ is the subset of days which are rainy or foggy (or both) i.e. $A \cup B = \{x \in E : p(x) \text{ or } q(x)\}$. Likewise $\{x \in E : p(x) \,\&\, q(x)\}$ is the subset of days which are rainy and foggy ("x is rainy and x is foggy"), that is, $A \cap B$. We can similarly work out $\mathscr{C}_E(A)$, $\mathscr{C}_E(B)$ and so on.

Let us therefore begin our investigation of combinations of conditions.

We begin, as in Section 1.7, with disjunction, and this gives us the new condition on x, "$p(x)$ or $q(x)$". What sort of solution set has "$p(x)$ or $q(x)$"? If we denote it by X, then

$$X = \{x \in E : p(x) \text{ or } q(x)\}.$$

We have to help us the truth table of Definition 1.7–1; for once we replace x by any element of E, $p(x)$ and $q(x)$ become statements. Now when is the *statement* "p or q" true? The answer is, when either p or q or both are true; so we can say that "$p(x)$ or $q(x)$" is true whenever x is replaced by any element for which $p(x)$ is true, or $q(x)$ is true. In other words, the element k of E belongs to X whenever $p(k)$ is true, or $q(k)$ is true, (or both); but if $p(k)$ is true, $k \in A$, by definition of the term solution set. Likewise if $q(k)$ is true, $k \in B$. So $k \in X$ if and only if $k \in A$ or $k \in B$ (or both). By Definition 1.3–1, this means $k \in A \cup B$.

Hence, we have shown that the solution set of "$p(x)$ or $q(x)$" is the set $A \cup B$.

Next, let us consider the new combination "$p(x) \,\&\, q(x)$". If Y is the solution set of this condition,

$$Y = \{x \in E : p(x) \,\&\, q(x)\}.$$

So the element $y \in Y$ if y satisfies the condition $p(x) \,\&\, q(x)$ i.e. if $p(y) \,\&\, q(y)$ is true. Using Definition 1.7–2, we see that $p(y) \,\&\, q(y)$ is true if and only if both $p(y)$ and $q(y)$ are true i.e. if y belongs both to A and to B.

Thus, the solution set of "$p(x) \,\&\, q(x)$" is $A \cap B$.

If we go on to negation, we obtain the new condition "$\sim p(x)$". For instance, if $p(x)$ is "x is a rainy day", $\sim p(x)$ means "x is not a rainy day". (Compare this with the statements p, $\sim p$ of Example 1.7.4). The truth-table of Definition 1.7–3 tells us how to find the solution set of $\sim p(x)$.

If we denote it by T, then $T = \{x \in E : \sim p(x)\}$; so, $t \in T$ if t satisfies $\sim p(x)$ i.e. if $\sim p(t)$ is true. By Definition 1.7–3, this means $p(t)$ is false, so $t \notin A$. Conversely, if $t' \in A$, then $p(t')$ is true, and so $\sim p(t')$ is false. Hence $t' \notin T$. So T is precisely the set of elements of E which do not belong to A. That is, $T = \mathscr{C}_E(A)$.

We can illustrate these ideas by Venn Diagrams, as in Section 1.4 (Fig. 1.8.1).

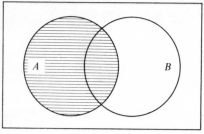

Solution set of $p(x)$

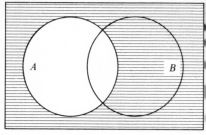

Solution set of $\sim p(x)$

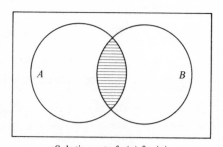

Solution set of $p(x)$ & $q(x)$

Fig.   1.8.1.

Example 1.8.1.   Using the set-builder notation, it is clear that we can write $A = \{x \in E : x \in A\}$, provided that E and A are sets in our sense. So we have the following examples of combinations of conditions. Here $p(x)$ is "$x \in A$", $q(x)$ is "$x \in B$".

$$A \cup B = \{x \in E : x \in A \text{ or } x \in B\}$$

$$A \cap B = \{x \in E : x \in A \ \& \ x \in B\}$$

$$\mathscr{C}_E(A) = \{x \in E : x \notin A\}.$$

This allows us to manipulate sets themselves, or conditions, whichever is more appropriate to the situation.

We have now seen how the combinations "$p(x)$ or $q(x)$" "$p(x)$ & $q(x)$", "$\sim p(x)$" are related to the ideas of union, intersection and complement described in Section 1.3. The reader may now ask : what sort of relation between conditions is associated with the ideas of set inclusion and set equality, as described in Section 1.2?

Let $p(x)$, $q(x)$ be conditions on x (x with domain E), with solution sets A, B. Suppose $A \subset B$. What can we say? Let v be an element of E; if $p(v)$ is true, then $v \in A$; since $A \subset B$, v is an element of B, by Definition 1.2–1, and so $q(v)$ is true. This means that $p(x)$ cannot be true and $q(x)$ be false. Hence, the second line in the truth table of the conditional (Definition 1.7–5) never applies. That is, $p(x) \to q(x)$ is always true, or to use the special term of Section 1.7, is a tautology. By Definition 1.7–9, this means that $p(x)$ logically implies $q(x)$ i.e. $p(x) \Rightarrow q(x)$.

Conversely, suppose $p(x) \Rightarrow q(x)$, where x is any element of E. This means (Definition 1.7–9) that $p(x) \to q(x)$ is always true. Now, an examination of Definition 1.7–5 reveals that if $p \to q$ is true, then p cannot be true and q false (line two of the truth-table). So if $p(x)$ is true, $q(x)$ must also be true. But this is just to say, if x is in A, x must also be in B, or $A \subset B$.

We can sum these two paragraphs up in the following theorem:

Theorem 1.8–A. Let $p(x)$, $q(x)$ be conditions on x with solution sets A and B. Then,

$$A \subset B \quad \text{if and only if} \quad p(x) \Rightarrow q(x).$$

Let us now go on to consider the relation $A = B$. We recall that, by Definition 1.2–2, this means $A \subset B$ and $B \subset A$. Let us consider the second of these in detail; to say $B \subset A$ means "if $x \in B$, then $x \in A$ also". But we can express this in the contrapositive form, viz., "if x is not in A, then x is not in B". So x is in B *only if* it is also in A. To see this visually, consider Fig. 1.8.2. The point c is not in A, and so it cannot be in B; on the other hand, a point need not be in B merely because it is in A (as the point a shows). But to be in B, the point must be in A. We therefore say that $x \in B$ only if it is in A, or that, for the point x to be in B, it is **necessary** for x to be in A.

The condition $x \in A$ is, however, not **sufficient** for x to be in B, as the point a shows. To say $x \in B$, we need more information than simply that $x \in A$.

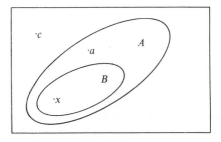

Fig. 1.8.2.

Observe on the other hand, that for x to be in A, it is sufficient (but not necessary) that x belongs to B.

We prove the following theorem, which is a parallel to the preceding result.

Theorem 1.8–B. Let $p(x)$, $q(x)$ be conditions on x, with solution sets A, B. Then

$$A = B \quad \text{if and only if} \quad p(x) \Leftrightarrow q(x).$$

Proof. Suppose first that $A = B$. Then,

$$A \subset B, \quad \text{and so (by Theorem 1.8–A),} \quad p(x) \to q(x)$$
$$\text{is logically true;}$$

also,

$$B \subset A, \quad \text{and (again by Theorem 1.8–A),} \quad q(x) \to p(x)$$
$$\text{is logically true.}$$

Therefore,

$$(p(x) \to q(x)) \,\&\, (q(x) \to p(x)) \quad \text{is logically true}$$
$$\text{(line 1 of Definition 1.7–2)}$$

that is,

$$p(x) \leftrightarrow q(x) \quad \text{is logically true}$$
$$\text{(by Theorem 1.7–E)}$$

which means that $p(x) \Leftrightarrow q(x)$, by Theorem 1.7–F.

Now suppose, on the other hand, that $p(x) \Leftrightarrow q(x)$. Then, $p(x) \leftrightarrow q(x)$ is a tautology, i.e. is logically true. Hence, looking at the truth-table in Definition 1.7–6, we see that this means the middle two lines cannot occur, if $p(x) \Leftrightarrow q(x)$. So, either $p(x)$ and $q(x)$ are *both* true, or they are *both* false. That is, if $p(x)$ is true then $q(x)$ is true, and if $q(x)$ is true then $p(x)$ is true i.e. $A \subset B$ and $B \subset A$, which means $A = B$. ◆

It is not really so surprising that the set relations $A \subset B$, and $A = B$ are closely connected with $\Rightarrow$ and $\Leftrightarrow$, which are logical relations. However, we have not yet exhausted all the connectives used in Section 1.7; there remain the "if ... then" and the "... if and only if ..." connectives, and in view of our earlier experience, we might expect the solution sets of these to be combinations of subsets, rather than comparisons of subsets. So, we now look at the solution sets of $p(x) \to q(x)$ and of $p(x) \leftrightarrow q(x)$. For we can combine conditions, as well as statements, by the use of "if ..., then ..." as well as by "and" and "or"! For instance,

"If x is tall, then x is thin"

where the domain of x is the set of men in Britain.

We again identify the solution set by using the truth-table (Definition 1.7–5). Let $W = \{x \in E : p(x) \to q(x)\}$. Then, as before, we can say, the element w of E belongs to W if w satisfies $p(x) \to q(x)$, i.e. if $p(w) \to q(w)$ is true. But $p(w) \to q(w)$ is true in every case except when $p(w)$ is true and $q(w)$ is false; in other words, in every case except when $w \in A$ and $w \notin B$. So, we find that $W = \mathscr{C}_E(A) \cup B$ (Fig. 1.8.3).

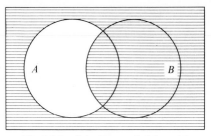

Fig. 1.8.3.   Solution set of $p(x) \to q(x)$.

We can also arrive at this using Theorem 1.7–B. Since "$p \to q$" and "$\sim p$ or q" have the same truth-table, we can say that

$$W = \{x \in E : \sim p(x) \text{ or } q(x)\}.$$

Now, using the Example 1.8.1, we see that $W = \mathscr{C}_E(A) \cup B$, as before.

For the bi-conditional $p(x) \leftrightarrow q(x)$, we proceed similarly. Let $V = \{x \in E : p(x) \leftrightarrow q(x)\}$; then, an element v belongs to V if and only if v satisfies $p(x) \leftrightarrow q(x)$, i.e. if and only if $p(v) \leftrightarrow q(v)$ is true. By Definition 1.7–6, this happens in two cases, when $p(v)$ and $q(v)$ are both true, i.e. $v \in A \cap B$, and when $p(v)$ and $q(v)$ are both false i.e. $v \in \mathscr{C}_E(A) \cap \mathscr{C}_E(B)$.

So, $V = (A \cap B) \cup (\mathscr{C}_E(A) \cap \mathscr{C}_E(B))$ (see Fig. 1.8.4). The reader should verify that, since Theorem 1.7–E is established, the set $(A \cap B) \cup (\mathscr{C}_E(A) \cap \mathscr{C}_E(B))$ is the same as $(\mathscr{C}_E(A) \cup B) \cap (\mathscr{C}_E(B) \cup A)$.

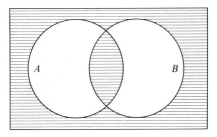

Fig. 1.8.4.

We have already seen, in Theorem 1.7–F and Definition 1.7–9, the relationship between equivalence ($\Leftrightarrow$) and the bi-conditional ($\leftrightarrow$) and between implication ($\Rightarrow$) and the conditional ($\to$). Since all of these logical ideas have now been shown to correspond to situations involving sets, we should naturally expect corresponding relationships between these set situations. For example, "$\Rightarrow$" is related to the inclusion $A \subset B$, "$\rightarrow$" to the set $\mathscr{C}_E(A) \cup B$; since "$\Rightarrow$" and "$\rightarrow$" are related by Definition 1.7–9, it follows that $A \subset B$ and $\mathscr{C}_E(A) \cup B$ should be in some way related. If we look at a Venn Diagram, with $A \subset B$ (Fig. 1.8.5), we can easily find $\mathscr{C}_E(A) \cup B$; it is shown as the total hatched area; as a comparison, the general situation of $\mathscr{C}_E(A) \cup B$ is illustrated in Fig. 1.8.6.

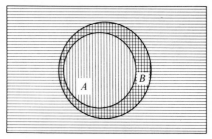

Fig. 1.8.5. $\mathscr{C}_E(A) \cup B$ when $A \subset B$.

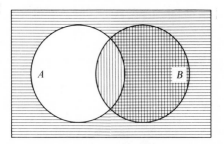

Fig. 1.8.6. $\mathscr{C}_E(A) \cup B$ in general.

So we obtain

Theorem 1.8–C.   Let A, B be subsets of E. Then,

$$A \subset B \quad \text{if and only if} \quad \mathscr{C}_E(A) \cup B = E.$$

Proof.   To say that $\mathscr{C}_E(A) \cup B = E$ is to say that the solution set of $p(x) \rightarrow q(x)$ is E. Therefore, $p(x) \rightarrow q(x)$ is true, for all x in E. So, $p(x) \rightarrow q(x)$ is a tautology, which means that $p(x) \Rightarrow q(x)$, and hence by Theorem 1.8–A, $A \subset B$. The converse is similar.   ◆

Likewise, we can show

Theorem 1.8–D.   If A, B are subsets of E, then

$$A = B \quad \text{if and only if} \quad \mathscr{C}_E(A) \cup B = \mathscr{C}_E(B) \cup A = E.$$

Alternatively, $A = B$ if and only if $(A \cap B) \cup (\mathscr{C}_E(A) \cap \mathscr{C}_E(B)) = E$.

As we remarked in the introductory paragraphs of Section 1.5, there are statements which are comprised of a condition on a dummy x, and a quantifier on x. It is now time to consider these kinds of statements.

Exercises 3

1. Instead of writing "P if and only if Q", we sometimes say "Q is necessary and sufficient for P". The bi-conditional is made up of the "if" part and the "only if" part. Which is necessary and which is sufficient?

2. Below we list various conditions P, Q. In which cases is Q necessary for P, sufficient for P, both necessary and sufficient, or neither?

Q	P
(a) $x^2 > 0$.	$x > 0$.
(b) $x^2 - 7x + 12 < 0$.	$1 < x < 2$.
(c) x is a rectangle.	x is a square.
(d) x is a square.	x is a rhombus.
(e) x is a rhombus.	x is a quadrilateral.
(f) x is a trapezium.	x is a parallelogram.

3. Find *sufficient* conditions for the following conclusions to be true. Which, if any, are also necessary?
   (a) $x^3 > 0$.
   (b) The triangle x is congruent to the triangle y.
   (c) x was present when the crime was committed.

4. Find *necessary* conditions for the following conclusions to hold.
   (a) $x^3 > 0$.
   (b) x is a rectangle.
   (c) x committed the crime.

5. Why is an alibi a good defence?

1.9 Quantifiers

Section 1.7 contained a brief account of basic methods of combining statements. As we have remarked, a condition on x is not a statement, although it becomes a statement as soon as x is replaced by a particular element from its domain. Thus, the condition

$$x^2 - 1 = 0 \quad \text{(where the domain of } x \text{ is } Z, \text{ say)}$$

becomes a statement as soon as we replace x by a definite integer:

replace x by $+2$; $4 - 1 = 0$ —a *false* statement;

replace x by -1; $1 - 1 = 0$ —a *true* statement.

These are examples of substitution, and they yield what we might describe as a particular, or "local", statement.

There are two other ways by which a condition on x can be turned into a statement. They involve the use of what are known as *quantifiers*.

Definition 1.9–1. The phrase "for all . . ." is called the **universal quantifier**. It is abbreviated by the symbol "$\forall$".

Let us see how it works; suppose $p(x)$ is a condition on x, where the domain of x is E. As a concrete example, we shall take $p(x)$ as $x^2 - 1 = 0$, and $E = Z$. Now apply the universal quantifier—we obtain the new formula,

$$\forall\, x \in E, \quad p(x);$$

in our example,

$$\forall\, x \in Z, \quad x^2 - 1 = 0,$$

or in words,

$$\text{"for all integers } x, \quad x^2 - 1 = 0\text{"}.$$

The reader will say, "Obviously false! Put $x = 2$, for instance." Here is the real point of this device. The fact that the reader is able to decide on the truth or falsehood of the formula shows that it is a statement. So again, a condition on x is made into a statement. It is a different kind of statement from those mentioned above—we might describe it as a general, or *global*, statement.

In the example we took, the statement was false, and this was shown by the simple expedient of producing a replacement for x which did not satisfy the condition. Such a replacement is called a **counterexample**.

Counterexamples play a most important role in mathematics. They provide a standard method of *disproving* a statement involving a universal quantifier. For, such a "universal" statement asserts that, for all elements x in some given set, a certain condition is satisfied. That is, no matter with which element of the set we replace x, we always obtain a true statement. A statement involving "for all . . ." is, in fact, a shorthand way of writing the conjunction of a number of particular statements. Take, for example, E to be the set $\{1, 2, 3, 4, 5\}$, $p(x)$ to be $(x^2 - 1) = (x - 1)(x + 1)$; then, "for all $x \in E$, $p(x)$" is equivalent to

$$[1 - 1 = (1 - 1)(1 + 1)]\,\&\,[4 - 1 = (2 - 1)(2 + 1)]\,\&\,[9 - 1 = (3 - 1)(3 + 1)]$$
$$\&\,[16 - 1 = (4 - 1)(4 + 1)]\,\&\,[25 - 1 = (5 - 1)(5 + 1)].$$

It is apparent, even when E contains as few as five elements, how hopelessly cumbersome the second form is.

But the connection between $\forall$ and $\&$ gives us a clue as to how to disprove a universal statement. Suppose $E = \{a, b, c, \ldots\}$. Then

$$\forall\, x \in E, \quad p(x) \Leftrightarrow p(a)\,\&\,p(b)\,\&\,p(c)\,\&\,\ldots.$$

To disprove this, we have to show that

$$\sim [\forall\, x \in E, \quad p(x)]$$

is true. That is, we must show that

$$\sim [p(a) \,\&\, p(b) \,\&\, p(c) \,\&\, \ldots]$$

is true. If we use an extended version of Theorem 1.7–A(a), we observe that this is the same as showing

$$\sim p(a) \quad \text{or} \quad \sim p(b) \quad \text{or} \quad \sim p(c) \quad \text{or} \quad \ldots$$

is true, which is the case if any one of the component statements is true. But if, say, $\sim p(a)$ is true, this means that $p(a)$ is false, and a does not satisfy the condition $p(x)$. The element a is therefore a counter-example.

Conclusion: We have disproved a universal statement by producing a counterexample. Therefore, a universal statement is false if and only if at least one of its component statements is false.

Another way of turning a condition on x into a statement is by the use of the existential quantifier.

Definition 1.9–2. The phrase "there is (are)... such that..." is called the **existential quantifier**; it is denoted by $\exists \ldots$ such that ....

Other forms are "there exists ... such that ..." or "For some ..., ..." or "there is at least one...". Again, we take the same condition $x^2 - 1 = 0$ as an illustrative example. On application of the existential quantifier, we have

$$\exists \, x \in E \quad \text{such that} \quad p(x), \tag{1}$$

or, in our example,

$$\exists \, x \in Z \quad \text{such that} \quad x^2 - 1 = 0$$

i.e.

"there is an integer x such that $x^2 - 1 = 0$."

The reader will admit that this is a statement (and further, that it is true). To show an existential statement like (1) true, we need only produce *one* replacement for x which satisfies the condition $p(x)$. On the other hand, to disprove (1), we must show that every replacement for x gives a false sentence.

Once again, we show how to justify this if $E = \{a, b, c, \ldots\}$. To show $\exists \, x \in E$ such that $p(x)$ is true, we could, in theory, test every element in E by substitution; then (1) would be true if $p(a)$ were true, or if $p(b)$ were true, or $p(c)$, or ....

Thus, parallel to the universal case, we see that (1) is equivalent to "$p(a)$ or $p(b)$ or $p(c)$ or ..."; the symbolism $\exists \ldots$ such that ... is a short-hand for a large number* of disjunctions. Hence, to disprove (1), we have to show $\sim (\exists \, x \in E$ such that $p(x))$ true. This is equivalent to showing

$$\sim (p(a) \quad \text{or} \quad p(b) \quad \text{or} \quad p(c) \quad \text{or} \quad \ldots)$$

* Possibly infinite; see the illustrative example above.

true, and by an extended version of Theorem 1.7–A(b), this means

$$\sim p(a) \,\&\, \sim p(b) \,\&\, \sim p(c) \,\&\, \ldots$$

is true, or $p(a)$, $p(b)$, $p(c)$, ... are *all* false.

So, an existential statement is false if and only if all the component statements are false.

In view of our remarks about the connection between "$\forall$" and "$\&$", "$\exists$" and "or", we can write

$$\sim [\exists \, x \in E \text{ such that } p(x)]$$

as

$$\forall \, x \in E, \quad \sim p(x).$$

We therefore obtain the following logical equivalences, which we shall call **rules of negation**.

Rule 1. $\sim [\forall \, x \in E, p(x)] \Leftrightarrow \exists \, x \in E$ such that $\sim p(x)$.

Rule 2. $\sim [\exists \, x \in E \text{ such that } p(x)] \Leftrightarrow \forall \, x \in E, \sim p(x)$.

These propositions on the negation of quantified conditions play a most important role in the development of mathematics. However, they also conform to everyday usage of language.

Example 1.9.1. Consider the condition on x given by

$$p(x) \text{ is "} x \text{ has a tail."}$$

Suppose the domain of $x = \{\text{set of all cats}\} = E$, say. Then the universal statement "$\forall \, x \in E, p(x)$" is

"for all x in the set of cats, x has a tail"

or, as we would more naturally phrase it,

"All cats have tails."

To find the negation of this statement, we apply Rule 1 :

$$\sim [\forall \, x \in E, p(x)]$$

becomes, in this case

"There is an x in the set of cats such that x does not have a tail."

Again, this is more naturally written as

"There is a cat which has no tail."

or

"Some cats do not have tails."

Not all statements in mathematics are as simple as this. It often happens that we have more than one dummy to consider, and this complicates the matter. For example, suppose x and y are dummies with domain R, and that the choice of a substitute for one does not restrict the other. Let $p(x, y)$ be the *condition on x and y* given by

$$x + y = 2.$$

If we replace x by a real number, we do not get a statement; for instance, replacing x by 1 we obtain $1 + y = 2$ (or $y = 1$), which is a condition on y, and as it stands is neither true nor false. The same is true if we use either of the quantifiers on the domain of x;

$$\forall\, x \in R, \quad x + y = 2,$$

$$\exists\, x \in R \quad \text{such that} \quad x + y = 2.$$

Neither of these formulae is a statement—they are both conditions on y. However, we have achieved something; we have reduced the formula from a condition on *two* dummies to a condition on *one* dummy. If we repeat the performance, we know that we will get a statement. We can get a statement from a condition on y in three ways: by substitution, or by the use of either quantifier. It follows, then, that the condition $p(x, y)$ on x and y can be turned into a statement by nine different methods. We tabulate these, for the example above, by way of illustration. As examples of substitution, we shall replace x by 1, and y by 2. The possibilities are

	Restrictive Operation on		Resulting Statement	Truth-Value
	y	x		
(1)	Sub. 2	Sub. 1	$1 + 2 = 2$	F
(2)	Sub. 2	$\forall$	$\forall\, x \in R, x + 2 = 2$	F
(3)	Sub. 2	$\exists$	$\exists\, x \in R$ s.t. $x + 2 = 2$	T
(4)	$\forall$	Sub. 1	$\forall\, y \in R, 1 + y = 2$	F
(5)	$\forall$	$\forall$	$\forall\, y \in R, \forall\, x \in R, x + y = 2$	F
(6)	$\forall$	$\exists$	$\forall\, y \in R, \exists\, x \in R$ s.t. $x + y = 2$	T
(7)	$\exists$	Sub. 1	$\exists\, y \in R$ s.t. $1 + y = 2$	T
(8)	$\exists$	$\forall$	$\exists\, y \in R$ s.t. $\forall\, x \in R, x + y = 2$	F
(9)	$\exists$	$\exists$	$\exists\, y \in R, \exists\, x \in R$ s.t. $x + y = 2$	T

In this case, we notice that only four of the nine possibilities are true. (If we change "substitution for y by 2" to "substitution for y by 1", (1) becomes true also.)

(3) is true because x can be replaced by 0;
(6) is true because we can replace x by $2 - y$, whatever y is;
(7) is true because y can be replaced by 1;
(9) is true because y can be replaced by 2 & x by 0 (for example).
On the other hand,
(1) is false because $3 \neq 2$;
(2) is false because we can replace x by, for example, 1;

(4) is false for a similar reason ($y = 2$);

(5) is false, because we can replace both x and y by 0;

(8) is false, because it requires $y = 2-x$, and this is different for every different replacement of x.

Our interest centres on (6) and (8). In (8), the existential quantifier occurs before the universal quantifier, and the result is false. But, in (6), where the universal quantifier precedes the existential quantifier, the result is a true statement. The order of occurrence of the quantifiers is therefore crucial. We shall see an important application of this in Section 4.1.

We can find the negation of a statement involving two or more quantifiers, in a similar way to the simple case. Consider the statement

$$\exists\, y \in A \quad \text{such that} \quad \forall\, x \in B, \quad p(x, y). \qquad (2)$$

Its negation is

$$\sim [\exists\, y \in A \quad \text{such that} \quad \forall\, x \in B, \quad p(x, y)],$$

which we may regard as

$$\sim [\exists\, y \in A \quad \text{such that} \quad q(y)],$$

where $q(y)$ is the condition on y given by "$\forall\, x \in B, \, p(x, y)$". By Rule 2, this is

$$\forall\, y \in A, \quad \sim q(y).$$

To complete the negation, we apply Rule 1 to $\sim q(y)$:

$$\sim q(y) \Leftrightarrow \sim [\forall\, x \in B, \, p(x, y)]$$
$$\Leftrightarrow \exists\, x \in B \quad \text{such that} \quad \sim p(x, y).$$

So the negation of our original statement (2) is

$$\forall\, y \in A, \quad \exists\, x \in B \quad \text{such that} \quad \sim p(x, y).$$

Similarly, the rules above show that

$$\sim [\forall\, x \in B, \exists\, y \in A \quad \text{such that} \quad p(x, y)]$$
$$\Leftrightarrow \exists\, x \in B \quad \text{such that} \quad \forall\, y \in A, \quad \sim p(x, y).$$

This allows us to propound the following rule:

Rule 3. To negate any statement involving quantifiers, change every "$\forall$" to "$\exists$... such that", every "$\exists$... such that" to "$\forall$", and negate the basic condition on the dummies involved.

Example 1.9.2. The negation of the (false) statement

$$\exists\, y \in R \quad \text{such that} \quad \forall\, x \in R, \quad x+y = 2$$

is the (true) statement

$$\forall\, y \in R, \quad \exists\, x \in R \quad \text{such that} \quad x+y \neq 2.$$

Exercises 4

1. Let A be the set of digits $\{0, 1, 2, 3, \ldots, 9\}$. Which of the following are true?
   (a) $\exists x \in A$ such that $x + 3 = 12$
   (b) $\forall x \in A, (x-4)^2 \leqslant 20$
   (c) $\forall x \in A, \exists y \in A$ such that $x + y < 10$
   (d) $\forall x \in A, \forall y \in A, x^2 + y^2 \leqslant 81$
   (e) $\exists x \in A$ such that $\forall y \in A, x - y \geqslant 1$
   (f) $\exists x \in A$ such that $\forall y \in A, y^2 - x^2 < 81$
2. Find the negation of the statements in Exercise 1.
3. Find a counterexample for the following statements: A is the set $\{2, 3, 4, 5, 6, 7\}$;
   (a) $\forall x \in A, x$ is a prime;
   (b) $\forall x \in A, x^2 - 9x + 8 < 0$;
   (c) $\forall x \in A, 3x + 2 \leqslant 20$;
   (d) $\forall x \in A, x$ is not a square.
4. The following are conditions on the dummy y, where the domain of both x and y is the set $\{0, 1, 2, \ldots, 9\}$. Find the solution set of the conditions.
   (a) $\exists x$ such that $3x + y < 11$
   (b) $\forall x, x + 2y \leqslant 9$
   (c) $\forall x, 2x + y \leqslant 9$
   (d) $\exists x$ such that $x + 3y < 11$.

1.10 Modes of Argument

In this section, we shall point out some of the most common principles of logical argument. These will, of course, occur throughout the remainder of the book. We begin by saying what an argument is. Let $p_1, p_2, \ldots, p_n$ and q be statements. Then, an **argument** is an assertion that the statements $p_1, \ldots, p_n$, called the **premises**, lead to the statement q, called the **conclusion**. We write this as

$$p_1, p_2, \ldots, p_n \vdash q.$$

We have said that an argument is an assertion; that is, it is itself a statement which may be true or false.

Definition 1.10–1. The argument $p_1, p_2, \ldots, p_n \vdash q$ is said to be **valid**, or true, if

$$p_1 \,\&\, p_2 \,\&\, p_3 \,\&\, \ldots \,\&\, p_n \Rightarrow q.$$

Equivalently, it is valid if $(p_1 \,\&\, p_2 \,\&\, \ldots \,\&\, p_n) \to q$ is a tautology.

Definition 1.10–2. An argument which is not valid is said to be false, or to be a **fallacy**.

The truth-values of the premises and conclusion have little bearing on the validity of the argument. We can illustrate this by means of examples.

Example 1.10.1. Let p_1 be "If London is in England, then Paris is in France", p_2 be "Paris is in France" and q be "London is in England". The argument $p_1, p_2 \vdash q$ has got a true conclusion, but we shall see that it is not a valid argument (see Theorem 1.10–E(a)).

On the other hand, consider

Example 1.10.2. Take

p_1 as "all cats have wings";
p_2 as "all winged creatures like fish";
q as "all cats like fish".

We shall see that this argument $p_1, p_2 \vdash q$ is valid, and the conclusion true, although both premises are false (Theorem 1.10–F).

Example 1.10.3. Take

p_1 as "Women cannot bring up children";
p_2 as "People who are logical are not made fun of";
p_3 as "People who cannot bring up children are always made fun of";
q as "Women are illogical".

Again, we shall see that $p_1, p_2, p_3 \vdash q$ is valid, although q is false.

Thus, in an argument, it is not the truth or falsehood of the statements appearing in the argument which determines its validity. Of course, in mathematics, we shall be concerned with the problem of showing that a conclusion q *follows from* premises $p_1, p_2, \ldots$. That is to say, we suppose $p_1, p_2, \ldots$ are all true, and we wish to deduce that q is true. If we use a valid argument, then $p_1 \& p_2 \& \ldots \to q$ is a tautology (i.e. is logically true); so, by Definition 1.7–5, if $p_1, p_2, \ldots$ are true, q must be true. Thus, the use of valid arguments *guarantees* the conclusion q.

So we turn to the problem of validity in a wider framework. The fact that an argument's validity is independent of the statements within it allows us to establish a fundamental principle of logic.

Theorem 1.10–A (Principle of Logical Substitution). Let P be a composite statement of the assertions $p, q, \ldots$. (An argument is an example of such a P.) If P is a tautology, then the statement obtained upon replacing $p, q, \ldots$ by any other assertions $p', q', \ldots$ is also a tautology.

Proof. Since $P(p, q, \ldots)$ is a tautology, it is true whatever truth values the particular statements $p, q, \ldots$ may have. Thus, it is irrelevant to the truth of P whether p be true or false. But if p' is any other statement, p' is also either true or false. So it does not affect the truth of P if p

is replaced by p', and likewise, if q is replaced by q', r by r', and so on; $P(p', q', r', \ldots)$ will be logically true.   ◆

Example 1.10.4.   Let $P(p, \sim p)$ be the composite statement "p or $\sim p$". Then, $P(p, \sim p)$ is a tautology (Example 1.7.6).

(a) Replace p by "the integer k is odd"; $\sim p$ is therefore "the integer k is even". We therefore, by Theorem 1.10–A, can obtain a new tautology: "the integer k is odd, or it is even".

(b) The reader should do the same when p is replaced by "It is raining".

The content of Theorem 1.10–A will underlie much of what we now say, for we shall exhibit valid arguments (which, by Definition 1.10–1, are equivalent to tautologies) in terms of dummies $p, q, r, \ldots$; then, by Theorem 1.10–A, we can replace these dummies by any statements which we may care to use.

We now go on to a very simple form of argument, one of great age. It is again a principle of substitution, and its use is mainly in conjunction with the universal quantifier.

Theorem 1.10–B (Principle of Substitution).   Let $p(x)$ be a condition on x, where the domain of x is E. Then, $\{\forall\, x \in E, p(x)\}$ is a statement, by Section 1.9. The argument

$$\{\forall\, x \in E, p(x)\}, \quad x_0 \in E \vdash p(x_0)$$

is valid.

Example 1.10.5.   The classical example of this argument is:

> All men are mortal;
> Socrates is a man;
> ⊢ Thus, Socrates is mortal.

Question.   Can you see a connection between Theorems 1.10–A and 1.10–B?

Another legitimate means of pursuing an argument is to employ the existential quantifier.

Theorem 1.10–C.   With the notation of Theorem 1.10–B, the argument

$$x_0 \in E, \quad p(x_0) \vdash \exists\, x \in E \quad \text{such that} \quad p(x)$$

is valid.

Both theorems follow from the definitions of $\forall$, $\exists$ respectively.

A more sophisticated form of argument is the following:

Theorem 1.10–D.   Let p, q be statements. Then, the argument $p, p \to q \vdash q$ is valid.

Proof.   We must show that $\{p \,\&\, (p \to q)\} \to q$ is a tautology, by Definition 1.10–1. We construct the appropriate truth-table:

p	q	$p \to q$	$p \,\&\, (p \to q)$	$\{p \,\&\, (p \to q)\} \to q$
T	T	T	T	T
T	F	F	F	T
F	T	T	F	T
F	F	T	F	T

Hence, $p \,\&\, (p \to q) \Rightarrow q$, and the theorem follows, by Definition 1.10–1. ◆

This result is called the **Law of Detachment**, or **modus ponens**. It is of fundamental importance (see pp. 37–38).

Closely related to Theorem 1.10–D are two fallacies;

Theorem 1.10–E.   The arguments
   (a) $p \to q,\; q \vdash p$
   (b) $p \to q,\; \sim p \vdash \sim q$
are fallacious.

Proof. We construct truth-tables for $\{(p \to q) \,\&\, q\} \to p$ and for $\{(p \to q) \,\&\, \sim p\} \to \sim q$, and show that these are *not* tautologous. Details are left to the reader.

Example 1.10.1 is a fallacy of the first type. Consider

Example 1.10.6.   "All cats like fish;
         John is not a cat;
         ⊢ Therefore, John does not like fish."

This is an example of the second type of fallacy.

We now look at a mode of argument which is, perhaps, as widely used as modus ponens.

Theorem 1.10–F.   The argument $p \to q,\; q \to r \vdash p \to r$ is valid.

The proof of this has already been given, in Example 1.7.8. This argument is called the **Law of Syllogism**; it is a chain procedure whereby we can progress from p to r by a series of intermediate steps. By repeatedly applying Theorem 1.10–F, we have an extended form with more "links", e.g.

$$p_1 \to p_2,\; p_2 \to p_3, \ldots, p_{n-1} \to p_n \vdash p_1 \to p_n.$$

Of equal importance is the "Extended Law of Syllogism", used with quantifiers and conditions. It takes the following form.

Theorem 1.10–F(a).   The argument

$$\{\forall\, x, p(x) \to q(x)\}, \quad \{\forall\, x, q(x) \to r(x)\} \vdash \{\forall\, x, p(x) \to r(x)\}$$

is valid.

Proof. We must show that

$$[\{\forall\, x, p(x) \to q(x)\} \,\&\, \{\forall\, x, q(x) \to r(x)\}] \Rightarrow \{\forall\, x, p(x) \to r(x)\}.$$

i.e.

$$[\{\forall\ x, p(x) \to q(x)\}\ \&\ \{\forall\ x, q(x) \to r(x)\}] \to \{\forall\ x, p(x) \to r(x)\} \qquad (1)$$

is a tautology.

Let a be any element of the domain of x. Then, by Theorem 1.10–B, if $\{\forall\ x, p(x) \to q(x)\}$ is true, $p(a) \to q(a)$ is true: likewise, if $\{\forall\ x, q(x) \to r(x)\}$ is true, then $q(a) \to r(a)$ is true; in this case, by Theorem 1.10–F, if $p(a) \to q(a)$ is true and $q(a) \to r(a)$ is true, $p(a) \to r(a)$ is true. But since this holds for any element a, this means $\forall\ x, p(x) \to r(x)$ is true, and so (1) is true. If either of $\{\forall\ x, p(x) \to q(x)\}$, $\{\forall\ x, q(x) \to r(x)\}$ is false, so is their conjunction, and so the conditional (1) is true. So the conditional (1) is always true i.e. is a tautology. ◆

Example 1.10.7. The argument

> "All cats have green eyes;
> Animals with green eyes like fish;
> ⊢ Hence, all cats like fish"

is a syllogism. So are those of Examples 1.10.2 and 1.10.3.

For, let $p(x)$ be "x is a cat", $q(x)$ be "x has green eyes", and $r(x)$ be "x likes fish".* The argument above has the form $\{\forall x, p(x) \to q(x)\}$, $\{\forall\ x, q(x) \to r(x)\} \vdash \{\forall\ x, p(x) \to r(x)\}$ which is valid by Theorem 1.10–F(a); so by Theorem 1.10–A, the argument in Example 1.10.7 is valid. Furthermore, it is valid whether or not all cats do like fish!

In mathematics, we shall be concerned with theorems and proofs. We have used these words already. Let us now make our terminology precise. Many of our theorems are of the form "If a, b and c, then d"; in other words, that a certain set of premises imply a certain conclusion. What, then, is a proof of such a theorem? We make the following definition.

Definition 1.10–3. Let P, Q be statements, or combinations of statements. A **proof** is an argument which shows that $P \Rightarrow Q$.

Thus, if the argument $P \vdash Q$ is valid, we say that we have *proved* that P implies Q.

Suppose we wish to assert that a conclusion q follows from a premise p_0. A typical proof or argument might be: we proceed from p_0 to an immediate consequence p_1. If the argument $p_0 \vdash p_1$ is valid, then $p_0 \to p_1$ is true (it is a tautology), and so, since the premise p_0 is assumed to be true, it follows by Theorem 1.10–D that p_1 is true. We now proceed from p_1 to an immediate consequence of it, p_2 say. If $p_1 \vdash p_2$ is valid, p_2 is true. Continuing in this way, we finally obtain $p_n \vdash q$. p_n is true, by the preceding step, $p_n \to q$ is true if $p_n \vdash q$ is valid, and so (Theorem 1.10–D) q is true. We have thus proved that if p_0 is true, q is true. The

---

* The domain of x is the set of all animals.

proof is therefore of the form

$$p_0, p_0 \Rightarrow p_1, p_1 \Rightarrow p_2, \ldots, p_{n-1} \Rightarrow p_n, p_n \Rightarrow q$$

$$\vdash p_0, p_0 \Rightarrow q \quad \text{(by the syllogism law)}$$

$$\vdash q \qquad\qquad \text{(by the detachment law)}.$$

This, which is an example of a *direct proof*, is usually written in the form

$$p_0 \Rightarrow p_1$$
$$\Rightarrow p_2$$
$$\ldots$$
$$\Rightarrow p_n$$
$$\Rightarrow q$$

We here combine each syllogism as we go along. Then, if p_0 is true, so is q. The proof usually terminates at "$\Rightarrow q$".

Note. Any valid argument containing $\rightarrow$ as a premise is valid when $\rightarrow$ is replaced by $\Rightarrow$. E.g. $p, p \Rightarrow q \vdash q$. Here if p is true, q is true ($p \Rightarrow q$ is always true). A direct proof is not always obvious. It may be difficult to select the right kind of immediate consequence of the premises. In such a case we resort to the method of *indirect* proof. We have already shown (Theorem 1.7–C) that $p \rightarrow q$ is logically equivalent to $\sim q \rightarrow \sim p$. Hence, the arguments $p \vdash q$ and $\sim q \vdash \sim p$ are either both valid or both fallacious. If $\sim q \vdash \sim p$ is valid, therefore, we can say that we have proved that q follows from p. In this method of proof, we assume the conclusion is false, and show that this implies the falsehood of the premise. This is a **contradiction** because premises are considered to be true.

Example 1.10.8. Prove that if x is an integer, and x^2 is odd, then x is odd.

Proof. Suppose, to the contrary, that x is not odd (i.e. is even). This is $\sim q$. Then,

$$\sim q : x \text{ is even} \Rightarrow x \text{ is of the form } 2k, \text{ where } k \text{ is an integer}$$
$$\Rightarrow x^2 = 4k^2$$
$$\Rightarrow x^2 = 2m \text{ where } m = 2k^2, \text{ an integer}$$
$$\Rightarrow x^2 \text{ is even } (\sim p).$$

So we have shown that $\sim q \Rightarrow \sim p$. Hence $p \Rightarrow q$, as required. The usual way of terminating the proof is to say,

$$\Rightarrow x^2 \text{ is even, a contradiction. Hence } x \text{ is odd.} \qquad \blacklozenge$$

The diamond indicates that the proof has come to an end.

There are other variations on this method of indirect proof. We sum up the three principal methods in Theorem 1.10–H. First we have

Theorem 1.10–G.

(i) $(p \to q) \Leftrightarrow (p \,\&\, \sim q) \to \sim p$;

(ii) $(p \to q) \Leftrightarrow (p \,\&\, \sim q) \to q$

(iii) $(p \to q) \Leftrightarrow (p \,\&\, \sim q) \to r \,\&\, \sim r$,

where r is any statement; $r \,\&\, \sim r$ is a self-contradiction. The proof is left to the reader.

As a consequence of this theorem, we have (for instance) that $p \to q$ is true if $(p \,\&\, \sim q) \to q$ is true and *vice versa*. In particular, if $(p \,\&\, \sim q) \Rightarrow q$, then $p \Rightarrow q$. Similarly, we obtain logical implications in the other two cases. So by Theorem 1.10–G, we deduce the following valid modes of argument:

Theorem 1.10–H. Let P denote the conjunction of the premises, q the conclusion. The following arguments are all valid:

(a) $P, \sim q, [(P \,\&\, \sim q) \to \sim P] \vdash q$

(b) $P, \sim q, [(P \,\&\, \sim q) \to q] \vdash q$

(c) $P, \sim q, [(P \,\&\, \sim q) \to r \,\&\, \sim r] \vdash q$.

Proof. As usual, this consists of showing that, for example,

(a) $[P \,\&\, \sim q \,\&\, \{(P \,\&\, \sim q) \to \sim P\}] \to q$

is a tautology. The details, which are straightforward, are left to the reader.

Now another consequence of saying that (a) is valid is to say that if $P, \sim q$, and $(P \,\&\, \sim q) \to \sim P$ are all true, then q is true. This will be the case if P and $\sim q$ are true and also $(P \,\&\, \sim q) \Rightarrow \sim P$. Hence, to prove that $P \Rightarrow q$, we can proceed in any of the following ways:

(A) We can use an additional hypothesis, $\sim q$, as well as the original premises P, to produce the contradictory statement $\sim P$. That is, we *assume* $\sim q$ is true; P is true (since it is a premise), and we show that together P and $\sim q$ *logically imply* the negation of P. In symbols this is just $P, \sim q, (P \,\&\, \sim q) \Rightarrow \sim P$; Theorem 1.10–H(a) asserts that this yields the required conclusion q.

(B) On the other hand, we can use the additional hypothesis $\sim q$ in addition to P to obtain a direct proof of q. We assume $P, \sim q$ and show that $(P \,\&\, \sim q) \Rightarrow q$. Theorem 1.10–H(b) guarantees that this argument gives the conclusion q, also.

(C) Finally, we can use the extra hypothesis $\sim q$, in addition to P, to produce a self-contradiction (i.e. a statement $r \,\&\, \sim r$). That is, we have $P, \sim q$, and we show that $(P \,\&\, \sim q) \Rightarrow r \,\&\, \sim r$. Theorem 1.10–H(c) now assures us that the conclusion q is true, as required. This method is known as *reductio ad absurdum*.

The benefit of the method of indirect proof is that, by assuming the extra hypothesis $\sim q$, we then have three possible paths which lead to the conclusion q. It suffices to deduce q, $or \sim P$, or a self-contradiction. Example 1.10.8 illustrates the use of method (A). Theorem 2.6–A is an example of method (C), where r is taken to be "p and q are integers with no common factor".

Note. Of course, there are many theorems in mathematics which have the form "a if and only if b", or "$a \Leftrightarrow b$". A proof of such a theorem is a *pair* of arguments, one showing that $a \Rightarrow b$, the other that $b \Rightarrow a$.

See also the Appendix to Chapter 2, for another method of mathematical argument.

Exercises 5

1. Prove Theorem 1.10–E.
2. Prove Theorem 1.10–G.
3. Prove Theorem 1.10–H.
4. Is the following argument valid? $p \to \sim q, r \to q, r \vdash \sim p$.
5. Which of the following arguments are valid?
   (a) $p \to q, r \to \sim q \vdash r \to \sim p$
   (b) $q \to \sim p, \sim r \to \sim q \vdash r \to \sim p$
6. Given the following premises, find a conclusion for which the argument will be valid:
   (a) $q \to \sim p, \sim r \to p$
   (b) $q \to \sim p, q$
   (c) $q \to \sim p, q, \sim p \to \sim r$
   (d) $p \to \sim q, r \to q$
7. Analyse the argument in the nursery rhyme:
       Jack Sprat could eat no fat, his wife could eat no lean,
   $\vdash$ And so, between the pair of them, they licked the platter clean."
   Can you think of any other examples?
8. Which of the following arguments are valid?
   (a)   Some happy people sing in the bath;
          Nobody who is unhappy is carefree;
          $\vdash$ Some people who sing in the bath are not carefree.
   (b)   If $x^2 + y^2 \leqslant 1$, then $-1 \leqslant x \leqslant 1$;
          $4x = 1$;
          $\vdash x^2 + y^2 \leqslant 1$.
   (c) X is never less than 3, unless y is greater than 4;
          If $y \leqslant 4$, then $Z^2 > X$;
          $\vdash Z^2$ is always less than 3.

1.11 The Algebra of Sets

In this section we list the more important results about sets. We indicate how these are proved in some sample cases, and from these,

it will be apparent why this section comes after Section 1.8.
We suppose A, B, C, are subsets of E.

Theorem 1.11–A. $A \cup B = B \cup A$ (i.e. the operation of union is independent of order).

Proof. $x \in A \cup B \Leftrightarrow x \in A$ or $x \in B$ (Definition 1.3–1)
$\qquad\qquad \Leftrightarrow x \in B$ or $x \in A$ (Exercises 2, No. 1)
$\qquad\qquad \Leftrightarrow x \in B \cup A$ (Definition 1.3–1).
So the conditions $x \in A \cup B$, $x \in B \cup A$ are equivalent. So by Theorem 1.8–B, their solution sets are equal i.e. $A \cup B = B \cup A$, by Example 1.8.1. $\qquad\qquad\blacklozenge$

Note. We see that the proof above depends on the *logical* relation $(p \text{ or } q) \Leftrightarrow (q \text{ or } p)$.

Theorem 1.11–B. $A \cup (B \cap C) = (A \cup B) \cap (A \cup C)$. (See Figs. 1.4.5, 1.4.6.)

Proof. $x \in A \cup (B \cap C) \Leftrightarrow x \in A$ or $x \in B \cap C$ (Definition 1.3–1)
$\qquad\qquad \Leftrightarrow x \in A$ or $\{x \in B \,\&\, x \in C\}$
$\qquad\qquad\qquad\qquad$ (Definition 1.3–2)
$\qquad\qquad \Leftrightarrow \{x \in A$ or $x \in B\}$ and $\{x \in A$ or $x \in C\}$
$\qquad\qquad\qquad\qquad$ (Exercises 2, No. 3)
$\qquad\qquad \Leftrightarrow x \in A \cup B \,\&\, x \in A \cup C$
$\qquad\qquad\qquad\qquad$ (Definition 1.3–1)
$\qquad\qquad \Leftrightarrow x \in (A \cup B) \cap (A \cup C)$
$\qquad\qquad\qquad\qquad$ (Definition 1.3–2).
The result follows again by Theorem 1.8–B and Example 1.8.1. $\quad\blacklozenge$

Theorem 1.11–C. (De Morgan) (a) $\mathscr{C}_E(A \cup B) = \mathscr{C}_E(A) \cap \mathscr{C}_E(B)$
$\qquad\qquad\qquad\qquad\qquad$ (b) $\mathscr{C}_E(A \cap B) = \mathscr{C}_E(A) \cup \mathscr{C}_E(B)$.

Proof of (a): $x \in \mathscr{C}_E(A \cup B) \Leftrightarrow x \notin A \cup B$ (Definition 1.3–3)
$\qquad\qquad \Leftrightarrow x \notin A$ and $x \notin B$ (Theorem 1.7–A(b))
$\qquad\qquad \Leftrightarrow x \in \mathscr{C}_E(A)$ and $x \in \mathscr{C}_E(B)$
$\qquad\qquad\qquad\qquad$ (Definition 1.3–3)
$\qquad\qquad \Leftrightarrow x \in \mathscr{C}_E(A) \cap \mathscr{C}_E(B)$ (Definition 1.3–2).
whence the result. $\qquad\qquad\qquad\qquad\qquad\qquad\qquad\blacklozenge$

Note. Again the proofs of the two theorems above depend on *logical* relations.

Exercises 6

Let A, B, C be subsets of E. Prove the following results.
1. $A \cap B = B \cap A$.
2. $A \cup (B \cup C) = (A \cup B) \cup C$
3. $A \cap (B \cap C) = (A \cap B) \cap C$
4. $A \cap (B \cup C) = (A \cap B) \cup (A \cap C)$

5. $A \cup E = E$
6. $A \cup \varnothing = A$
7. $A \cap \varnothing = \varnothing$
8. $\mathscr{C}_E(\mathscr{C}_E(A)) = A$
9. $A \subset B \,\&\, B \subset C \Rightarrow A \subset C$
10. $A \subset B \Rightarrow (C \cup A) \subset (C \cup B)$
11. $A \subset B \Rightarrow (C \cap A) \subset (C \cap B)$
12. $A \subset B \Leftrightarrow \mathscr{C}_E(B) \subset \mathscr{C}_E(A)$
13. $A \subset B \Leftrightarrow A \cup B = B$
14. $A \subset B \Leftrightarrow A \cap B = A$
15. Show that $A \cup B = \varnothing \Leftrightarrow A = \varnothing \,\&\, B = \varnothing$
16. Is it true that $A \cap B = \varnothing \Rightarrow A = \varnothing$ or $B = \varnothing$?
    Is it true that $A \cap B = \varnothing \Rightarrow A = \varnothing \,\&\, B = \varnothing$?

1.12 Product Sets

Suppose A and B are two sets. Then, we can form a new set from A and B by picking an element of A together with an element of B, and considering this pair as a single element of the new set. For example, suppose $A = \{1, 2, 3\}$, and $B = \{\alpha, \beta\}$. Then we can regard the pairs $(1, \alpha), (2, \alpha), (3, \alpha), (1, \beta), (2, \beta), (3, \beta)$ as the elements of the new set. However, we shall distinguish the set consisting of the six elements above from that whose elements are $(\alpha, 1), (\alpha, 2), (\alpha, 3), (\beta, 1), (\beta, 2), (\beta, 3)$. The totality of all possible pairs obtained by picking an element of A and *then* an element of B is called the *product* of A and B.

We now give the formal definitions.

Definition 1.12–1.   Suppose that (x, y) is a pair consisting of two elements x and y, possibly from the same set. If we prescribe that x shall be the first element in the bracket, y the second element then (x, y) is called an **ordered pair.**

Example 1.12.1.   In coordinate geometry, points of the plane are denoted by ordered pairs. The point $(4, 3)$ is the point whose abscissa is 4, and whose ordinate is 3. It is quite distinct from the point $(3, 4)$. The same two numbers occur in each bracket, but we distinguish the brackets by prescribing that the abscissa shall be given first. Points of the plane are given by (abscissa, ordinate)—in that order.

Example 1.12.2.   A second method of describing the position of a point in the plane is to give its distance from a certain fixed point (called the origin) and its bearing or direction relative to a certain fixed line through the origin (the zero line) (see Fig. 1.12.1). The point $(4, \pi/4)$ is the point whose distance from the origin is 4, and whose bearing is $\pi/4$. This again is an ordered pair; distance is given first, followed by the bearing. Whereas, in Example 1.12.1, both elements of the ordered pair (x, y) had domain R, in this case, the elements (r, θ) have different domains; the domain of r is the set $\{r \in R : 0 \leqslant r < \infty\}$, that of θ the set $\{\theta \in R : 0 \leqslant \theta < 2\pi\}$.

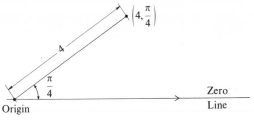

Fig. 1.12.1.

Definition 1.12–2. Let A, B be two sets, x and y dummies with domain A and B respectively. The collection of all ordered pairs (x, y) is called the **product** (set) of A and B and is denoted by $A \times B$. Thus, we have

$$A \times B = \{(x, y) : x \in A, y \in B\}.$$

The set $B \times A$ is the set of all ordered pairs (y, x) with $x \in A$, $y \in B$. It is therefore different from $A \times B$, except when $A = B$. When $A = B$, we sometimes talk about the set A^2, rather than $A \times A$. This, for example, is the usual notation for the real coordinate plane; it is denoted by R^2. We can define the product of three or more sets similarly; $A \times B \times C$ is the set of all ordered triples (x, y, z) with $x \in A$, $y \in B$, $z \in C$.

Example 1.12.3. The plane R^2 is a product set, being the product of the real numbers with themselves. For any point in R^2 is described by an ordered pair, as we saw in Example 1.12.1 (see Fig. 1.12.2).

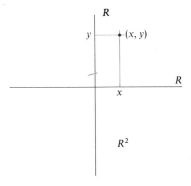

Fig. 1.12.2.

Example 1.12.4. Let A be the set of points lying on a circle of radius 1, B the set of points in the line segment $\{y \in R : 0 \leqslant y \leqslant 4\}$. Then, the product set $A \times B$ can be represented by the set of points on the surface of a cylinder of height 4 and diameter 2 (Fig. 1.12.3). We can define the usual relations between subsets of $A \times B$. For example,

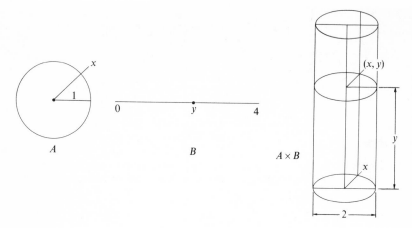

Fig. 1.12.3.

Definition 1.12–3. Let X, Y be subsets of $A \times B$. Then,
(a) $X \subset Y$ if and only if, $(x, y) \in X \Rightarrow (x, y) \in Y$, for all $(x, y) \in X$
(b) $X = Y$ if and only if, $(x, y) \in X \Leftrightarrow (x, y) \in Y$, for all $(x, y) \in X$.
These definitions are just those of Section 1.2 in the context of product sets.
We can also deduce results like the following.

Theorem 1.12–A. Suppose X, Y are subsets of $A \times B$, with $X \subset Y$. Write

$$A_X = \{x \in A : (x, y) \in X\}$$
$$A_Y = \{x \in A : (x, y) \in Y\},$$

and define B_X, B_Y similarly. Then,

$$A_X \subset A_Y, \qquad B_X \subset B_Y.$$

[If X is a proper subset of Y (i.e. $X \neq Y$), then $A_X \neq A_Y$ or $B_X \neq B_Y$ or both; but observe that one of the relations $A_X = A_Y$, $B_X = B_Y$ may be true]. The proof is left to the reader; the converse is false (Fig. 1.12.5).

A_X, B_X are called the **projections** of X on to A, B respectively (Fig. 1.12.4).

Note. The reader should observe, and indeed, verify by example for himself, that X need not equal $A_X \times B_X$; it is however, a subset of $A_X \times B_X$.

Corollary. If X, Y are subsets of $A \times B$, with $X = Y$, then $A_X = A_Y$, and $B_X = B_Y$. But conversely, $A_X = A_Y$ & $B_X = B_Y \nRightarrow X = Y$; in fact, it is not even the case that $A_X = A_Y$ & $B_X = B_Y \Rightarrow X \subset Y$ (or $Y \subset X$).

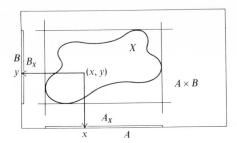

Fig. 1.12.4.

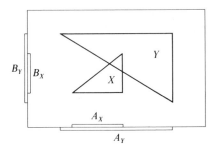

Fig. 1.12.5.

Exercises 7

1. The ordered pairs $(x + y, 3)$ and $(5, x - y)$ are equal. Find x and y.
2. Prove that $A = B \Leftrightarrow A \times B = B \times A$.
3. Show that $A \times B = \varnothing \Leftrightarrow A = \varnothing$ or $B = \varnothing$.
4. Suppose A, B are sets such that $A \times B \neq \varnothing$. Prove that

$$A \times B \subset X \times Y \Leftrightarrow A \subset X \ \& \ B \subset Y.$$

5. Let A_1, A_2 be subsets of A; B_1, B_2 be subsets of B. Show that
   (a) $(A_1 \times B_1) \cup (A_2 \times B_1) = (A_1 \cup A_2) \times B_1$;
   (b) $(A_1 \times B_1) \cap (A_2 \times B_2) = (A_1 \cap A_2) \times (B_1 \cap B_2)$.

Part Two: Raw Materials

Analysis is largely concerned with investigating what happens when we operate on sets with objects called *functions*, and Real Analysis is that branch in which the sets in question are sets of real numbers. The raw materials of our subject are therefore the set R of real numbers, and functions, and in the next two chapters, we give an account of these. In Chapter 2, we discuss the principal properties of the set R of real numbers, and in Chapter 3 we introduce and explore the idea of a function. In this third chapter, we give a quite general account of the concept of function, though such specific requirements for our purposes as real valued functions and sequences are included.

CHAPTER 2

The Real Numbers

2.1 Introduction

In the previous chapter, we introduced the general idea of a set. Throughout the rest of this book, we shall be principally concerned with the particular set R of real numbers, and with subsets of R. Therefore, it is essential that we know what are the basic properties of this set.

As far as this book goes, these properties fall into two distinct categories. There are those properties which we shall *assume* R to have, and there are those which we shall *prove* that R has. Ideally, of course, we should like to prove all the properties that R possesses; however, the justification of some of these really forms a subject on its own, and we cannot hope to include this within the scope of a book such as this.

To begin, therefore, we *state* which properties of the set R we are going to assume. It is important to remember that we will not have proved them. Having made these assumptions, we shall then deduce all the other results about the set R which we are likely to need. Obviously, it is more satisfactory if we reduce the number of assumptions we make as far as possible, and prove as many properties as we can. The list of ten assumed properties we give in Sections 2.2 and 2.3 represents a reasonable compromise along these lines. Properties which are not explicitly assumed in Section 2.2 and 2.3 and not explicitly proved in the rest of the chapter are left to the reader. They can, and should, be proved using the assumptions of Sections 2.2 and 2.3.

2.2 Algebraic and Order Properties

In this section, we list the basic facts about the "structure" of R. These all tell us about the internal workings of the set, and many of them are very familiar.

First of all, any two real numbers x and y can be added to give another real number, $x + y$. Likewise, x and y can be multiplied together to give the real number xy. These internal operations of addition and multiplication satisfy the following simple algebraic rules:

for all x, y, z in R,

(1) $x + y = y + x$, $xy = yx$ (Commutative laws)

(2) $x+(y+z) = (x+y)+z$

$\quad\quad x(yz) = (xy)z$ (Associative laws)

(3) $\quad x(y+z) = xy+xz$ (Distributive law)

The operations opposite to addition and multiplication, called subtraction and division, can also be performed in R, with the proviso that division by zero is not permitted. We have

(4) If x, y belong to R, then there is one, and only one, element z in R such that

$$x = y+z.$$

This single number z (which, when added to y, gives the real number x) is denoted by $x-y$. The number $y-y$ is denoted by 0, called **zero**. Note that, by definition of 0,

$$y = y+0$$

for any y in R. The number $0-y$ is written as $-y$.

(5) If x, y belong to R with $y \neq 0$, there is one and only one element z in R such that

$$x = yz.$$

This number z (which, when multiplied by y, gives the real number x), is denoted by x/y. The number y/y is denoted by 1; note that, by the definition of 1, we have, for all y in R, $y = y \cdot 1$.

These five properties tell us that the real numbers form a **field**.

Properties (1), (2) and (3) are, of course, very familiar, and we have all been accustomed to using them from a very early age. But consider what happens with the operation of subtraction; the statement

$$\text{"for all } x, y \text{ in } R, \quad x-y = y-x\text{"}$$

is false. So *subtraction* does not satisfy the commutative law (1). Likewise, the statement

$$\text{"for all } x, y, z \text{ in } R, \quad x-(y-z) = (x-y)-z\text{"}$$

is also false, so that subtraction does not satisfy the associative law either. In the same way, we can show that division is neither commutative nor associative. Thus, the properties (1), (2) and (3) enjoyed by addition and multiplication are not universal, and so are well worth pointing out.

The set R is equipped not only with the algebraic structure just described, but it also has an "ordering relation"; that is to say, if x, y are any two distinct real numbers, then we can compare them. Either x is **greater than** y, written $x > y$ (or equivalently, y is **less than** x, written $y < x$), or else y is greater than x. This ordering of the real numbers also obeys certain rules. We shall *assume* that it satisfies the following conditions:

(6) If x, y belong to R, then precisely one of the three statements

$$x < y, \quad x = y, \quad x > y$$

is true; this is called the *trichotomy law*. Trichotomy means *dividing into three parts.*

(7) If x, y, z belong to R, $x > y$ and $y > z$, then $x > z$; this is the transitivity law for order.

(8) If x, y, z belong to R, and $x > y$, then $x + z > y + z$.

(9) If x, y, z belong to R, $x > y$ and $z > 0$, then $xz > yz$.

Note that not all sets satisfy (6); the collection of subsets of a set E (with more than two elements) does not satisfy (6). We cannot say, in general, given two subsets A and B of E, that $A \subset B$ or $B \subset A$.

We note one or two refinements of the idea of ordering. It frequently happens that we are interested only in knowing, for example, that the real number x is *not less than* the real number y. By (6), this means $x = y$ or $x > y$. We abbreviate this disjunction by the sign $x \geqslant y$, read "x is greater than or equal to y". Therefore,

$$x \geqslant y \Leftrightarrow x = y \quad \text{or} \quad x > y.$$

An examination of the truth table for a disjunction (Definition 1.7–1) shows, for instance, that the statements "$3 \geqslant 2$" and "$2 \geqslant 2$" are both true; the first because "$3 > 2$" is true, the second because "$2 = 2$" is true.

Likewise, if x, y are real numbers, we write

$$x \leqslant y \Leftrightarrow x = y \quad \text{or} \quad x < y;$$

$x \leqslant y$ is read as "x is less than or equal to y". It is very easy to verify that

$$x = y \Leftrightarrow x \geqslant y \, \& \, x \leqslant y.$$

There are several other abbreviations which we shall introduce at this point. If x, y, z are real numbers, we write

$$x < y < z \Leftrightarrow x < y \, \& \, y < z$$
$$x \leqslant y \leqslant z \Leftrightarrow x \leqslant y \, \& \, y \leqslant z$$
$$x < y \leqslant z \Leftrightarrow x < y \, \& \, y \leqslant z$$
$$x \leqslant y < z \Leftrightarrow x \leqslant y \, \& \, y < z.$$

Next, if x, y are real numbers, we define

$$\max(x, y) = \begin{cases} x & \text{if } x \geqslant y \\ y & \text{if } x < y \end{cases}$$

and

$$\min(x, y) = \begin{cases} x & \text{if } x \leqslant y \\ y & \text{if } x > y. \end{cases}$$

This says that if x and y are distinct real numbers, then $\max(x, y)$ and $\min(x, y)$ are just the larger and smaller of x and y respectively. Thus, for example,

$$\max(2, 3) = 3,$$

and if x is a positive real number (a real number x is called **positive** if $x > 0$, **negative** if $x < 0$; we also use the term **non-negative**: x is non-negative if $x \geqslant 0$), then

$$\max(x, x^2) = \begin{cases} x & \text{if } x \leqslant 1 \\ x^2 & \text{if } x > 1 \end{cases};$$

because, if $x \leqslant 1$, $x^2 = x \cdot x \leqslant x \cdot 1 = x$, by (9) and (5), and if $x > 1$, then $x^2 = x \cdot x > x \cdot 1 = x$, also by (9) and (5).

By a similar method, if $x_1, \ldots, x_n$ is a finite set of real numbers, we can define the real numbers

$$\max(x_1, \ldots, x_n) \quad \text{and} \quad \min(x_1, \ldots, x_n).$$

Properties (1) to (9) above contain, with one exception, all the assumptions we are going to make about the set R. The remaining property (10) which we shall assume is discussed in the next section. Let us now show how, using the assumptions (1) to (9), we can deduce some other very familiar properties of R.

Example 2.2.1 (The Cancellation Law for addition). If x, y, z belong to R, and $x + z = y + z$, then $x = y$.

Proof. $x + z = y + z \Rightarrow (x + z) + (-z) = (y + z) + (-z)$

$\Leftrightarrow x + (z + (-z)) = y + (z + (-z))$ (Property 2)

$\Leftrightarrow x + 0 = y + 0$ (Definition of $-z$)

$\Leftrightarrow x = y$ (Definition of 0).   ◆

Note that we have proved more than we said we would; we have shown that $x + z = y + z$ if and only if $x = y$.

Example 2.2.2. For every real number x, $x \cdot 0 = 0$.

Proof. $0 + x \cdot 0 = x \cdot 0$ (Definition of 0)

$= x(0 + 0)$ (Definition of 0)

$= x \cdot 0 + x \cdot 0$ (Property 3)

which, by the cancellation law for addition, implies that $x \cdot 0 = 0$.   ◆

Example 2.2.3 (The Cancellation Law for multiplication). If x, y, z belong to R, $xz = yz$ and $z \neq 0$, then $x = y$.

Proof. $xz = yz \Rightarrow (xz)\dfrac{1}{z} = (yz)\dfrac{1}{z}$

$\Leftrightarrow x\left(z \cdot \dfrac{1}{z}\right) = y\left(z \cdot \dfrac{1}{z}\right)$ (Property 2)

$\Leftrightarrow x \cdot 1 = y \cdot 1$ $\left(\text{Definition of } \dfrac{1}{z}\right)$

$\Leftrightarrow x = y$ (Definition of 1).   ◆

Example 2.2.4. If x, y belong to R, and $xy = 0$, then $x = 0$ or $y = 0$.

Proof. Suppose that $y \neq 0$. Then,

$$xy = 0 = 0 \cdot y$$

which implies, by the preceding example, that $x = 0$.   ◆

Example 2.2.5. If x, y belong to R, and $x > y$, then $-y > -x$.

Proof. $x > y \Rightarrow x + (-x) > y + (-x)$ (Property 8)

$\Leftrightarrow 0 > y + (-x)$ (Definition of $-x$)

$\Rightarrow -y = (-y) + 0 > (-y) + (y + (-x))$ (adding $-y$ and using (8))

$\Leftrightarrow -y > ((-y) + y) + (-x) = 0 + (-x) = -x.$ ◆

Example 2.2.6. If x, y belong to R, and $x > y > 0$, then $x^2 > y^2$.

Proof. $x > y > 0 \Rightarrow x^2 = x \cdot x > x \cdot y$ and $x \cdot y > y \cdot y = y^2$
    (Property 9)

$\Rightarrow x^2 > y^2$ (Property 7).   ◆

We have written out these examples in detail to show quite clearly that these results have been proved using only properties (1) to (9) of the real numbers. The reader should do the same with Exercises 1 to 4 at the end of the chapter.

We also remark that it is easily deduced from the associativity and commutativity of addition that the sum of n real numbers is independent of the way in which they are added up. We therefore denote such a sum by

$$x_1 + \ldots + x_n,$$

omitting all brackets. We shall also denote such a sum by either of the symbols

$$\sum_{i=1}^{i=n} x_i \quad \text{or} \quad \sum_{i=1}^{n} x_i.$$

Σ is the Greek letter "S", standing for "sum", and the subscript i which appears is called a summation index. It is a dummy whose domain in this case is the set $\{1, 2, \ldots, n\}$. A similar comment can be made about the product of n real numbers $x_1, \ldots, x_n$. We shall denote such a product by

$$x_1 x_2 \ldots x_n \quad \text{or} \quad \prod_{i=1}^{i=n} x_i \quad \text{or} \quad \prod_{i=1}^{n} x_i.$$

Π is the Greek letter "P", standing for "product". In the special case when $x_1 = x_2 = \ldots = x_n \ (= x, \text{ say})$, we shall of course write nx and x^n instead of $\sum_{i=1}^{n} x_i$ and $\prod_{i=1}^{n} x_i$ respectively.

2.3 Completeness

The last section contained all but one of the assumptions we are going to make about the set R. We now describe the final property we are going to assume. It is a property of a different kind to those mentioned above, but is, nevertheless, a property which we would all probably regard as fairly obvious. However, see also the remark following Theorem 2.6–A.

Let us begin by describing this property geometrically; we are commonly used to depicting the set R of real numbers diagrammatically by the set of points on a horizontal straight line. In the traditional picture (Fig. 2.3.1), if x and y are distinct real numbers, with $x < y$, then the point representing y lies to the right of the point representing x. Conversely, if the point representing y lies to the right of the point representing x, then $x < y$.

$$x \qquad\qquad y$$

Fig. 2.3.1.

Consider the following assertion about the horizontal line L (Fig. 2.3.2).

Suppose L is composed of two parts S_1 and S_2, i.e. $L = S_1 \cup S_2$, where S_1 and S_2 are non-empty subsets of L with the property that every point of S_1 lies to the left of every point of S_2; then, there is a point p of L such that every point of L to the left of p belongs to S_1, while every point of L to the right of p belongs to S_2; p itself may belong to either S_1 or S_2.

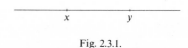

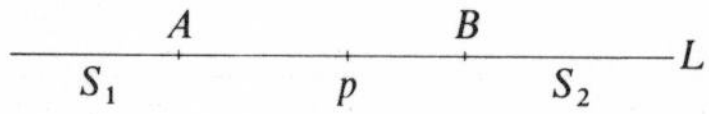

Fig. 2.3.2.

Thus, this assertion says that if the sets S_1, S_2 have the property described, then p divides L into two distinct parts with no point in common, one of which is S_1, and the other S_2. I hope the reader is prepared to concede that this assertion about the line L is borne out by his intuition or experience, for we are merely asserting that the line L has no gaps or holes, or, to put it another way, that the line L is "complete".

What does this tell us about the set R of real numbers? Translating this geometrical assertion into the language of Section 2.2, it says that R has the following completeness property:

(10) If $R = S_1 \cup S_2$, where S_1 and S_2 are non-empty subsets of R such that every number in S_1 is less than every number in S_2, then there is a real number μ such that every real number less than μ is in S_1, and every real number greater than μ is in S_2. The real number μ may belong to S_1 or to S_2 (but not both). If $\mu \in S_1$, it is called the **greatest element** of S_1; if $\mu \in S_2$, then it is the **least element** of S_2.

Example 2.3.1. Consider the sets

$$S_1 = \{x \in R : x < 0\}, \qquad S_2 = \{x \in R : x \geqslant 0\}.$$

Then, if $y \in S_1$, $z \in S_2$, we have

$$y < 0 \quad \text{and} \quad 0 \leqslant z \Rightarrow y < z \quad \text{(by (7))}.$$

Thus, the sets S_1 and S_2 have the property that every point of S_1 is less than every point of S_2. Also, we note that if $x \in R$, then $x < 0, x = 0$, or $x > 0$ by (6). If $x < 0$, then $x \in S_1$; if $x = 0$ or $x > 0$, then $x \in S_2$. Hence, $R = S_1 \cup S_2$. By (10), we should be able to conclude that there is a number μ such that

$$y < \mu \Rightarrow y \in S_1 \quad \text{and} \quad z > \mu \Rightarrow z \in S_2.$$

We leave the reader to verify that the real number 0 satisfies these requirements, and is the least element of S_2. ◆

Remark. This concludes the list of assumptions we shall make about R. We take it, henceforth, that R possesses properties (1)–(10). That is to say, we assume that the set R is a **complete ordered field**. But this is *all* we shall assume. Any other property of R (for instance, those described in Theorem 2.5–A and Theorem 2.6–B) can or will be proved using these assumptions and deductions from them, as we have already done in the examples of Section 2.2. One final remark here concerns terminology. In view of the geometric representation of the set R by points on a horizontal line, we shall use the terms *set R of real numbers* and *the real line* interchangeably, and likewise the terms *real number* and *point*.

2.4 Some Fundamental Inequalities

We shall be concerned a lot with calculations involving inequalities. Many of these arise when we are dealing with the absolute value of a real number, which we now define.

Definition. The **modulus** or **absolute value**, of a real number x, denoted by $|x|$, is defined by

$$|x| = \begin{cases} x & \text{if } x \geqslant 0 \\ -x & \text{if } x < 0 \end{cases}$$

$$= \max(x, -x).$$

We see that, for all x, $|x| \geqslant 0$; for $x < 0 \Rightarrow -x > 0$. So, $|x|$ is a non-negative real number, with $|x| = 0 \Leftrightarrow x = 0$. Geometrically, it represents the distance from the point representing x to the point representing 0 (Fig. 2.4.1).

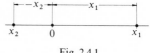

Fig. 2.4.1.

If x and y are real numbers, then $|x - y|$ is the distance between the points representing x and y on the real line (Fig. 2.4.2). Note that $|x - y| = |y - x|$ geometrically; and it is easy to show that $|-x| = |x|$, using the above definition.

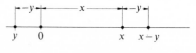

Fig. 2.4.2.

We first prove the following result about absolute values.

Theorem 2.4–A.   If a is a non-negative real number, and x is any real number, then

$$|x| \leqslant a \Leftrightarrow -a \leqslant x \leqslant a.$$

Proof.   We have $|x| = \max(x, -x)$, so that

$$|x| \leqslant a \Leftrightarrow x \leqslant a \,\&\, -x \leqslant a$$

$$\Leftrightarrow x \leqslant a \,\&\, -a \leqslant x \qquad \text{(by Example 2.2.5)}$$

$$\Leftrightarrow -a \leqslant x \leqslant a. \qquad\qquad\qquad ◆$$

Following this, we prove the result sometimes known as the "triangle" law.† It says that the modulus of a sum does not exceed the sum of the moduli.

Theorem 2.4–B. If x and y are any two real numbers, then

$$|x+y| \leqslant |x| + |y|. \qquad (1)$$

Proof. By definition,

$$x \leqslant |x| \ \& \ -x \leqslant |x| \ \Rightarrow \ -|x| \leqslant x \leqslant |x| \qquad \text{(using Example 2.2.5)}$$

Similarly, $-|y| \leqslant y \leqslant |y|$,
and so, adding,

$$-(|x|+|y|) \leqslant x+y \leqslant |x|+|y|$$

$$\Leftrightarrow |x+y| \leqslant |x|+|y|, \qquad \text{by Theorem 2.4–A.} \qquad \blacklozenge$$

It is simple to verify that if x and y have the same sign, then equality occurs in (1), while if x and y have opposite signs, then $|x+y| < |x|+|y|$.

Another important inequality concerns the relation between the modulus of a difference and the difference of the moduli.

Theorem 2.4–C. If x, t are real numbers, then

$$\|x| - |t\| \leqslant |x-t|.$$

Proof. We note that $|-y| = |y|$ for any y in R. So, in (1), if we replace y by $-y$, we obtain, for all x, y in R,

$$|x-y| \leqslant |x|+|y|.$$

This being true for all y in R, write $y = x-t$ (so defining t). Then, we have, for all x, t in R,

$$|t| \leqslant |x| + |x-t| \ \Leftrightarrow \ -|x-t| \leqslant |x|-|t|. \qquad (2)$$

On the other hand, if we write $-x$ for x in (1), we have

$$|y-x| \leqslant |y|+|x| \qquad \text{(for all } x, y \text{ in } R).$$

Now, write $x = y-w$. Then, for all y, w in R,

$$|w| \leqslant |y| + |y-w| \ \Leftrightarrow \ -|y-w| \leqslant |y|-|w|. \qquad (3)$$

In (3), y and w are merely dummies with domain R. So we can replace the dummy letter y by the dummy letter t, and the dummy letter w by

† This terminology arises from vectors. If A represents the end of the vector x, B the end of the vector y, then C represents the end of the vector $x+y$. The distance OA corresponds to $|x|$ (the distance from O to x) $OB = AC$ corresponds to $|y|$, and OC to $|x+y|$. Then, in the triangle OAC, $OC \leqslant OA + AC$.

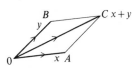

the dummy letter x. We obtain, by (3), for all $x, t \in R$,

$$-|t-x| \leqslant |t|-|x| \Leftrightarrow |x|-|t| \leqslant |x-t|.$$

Combining this with (2), we have

$$-|x-t| \leqslant |x|-|t| \leqslant |x-t|$$

$$\Leftrightarrow \|x|-|t\| \leqslant |x-t|, \qquad \text{by Theorem 2.4–A.} \qquad \blacklozenge$$

2.5 Bounds

There are some subsets of R which have the property that no element of the subset exceeds some fixed real number. To put this in another way, the subset does not contain unlimitedly large numbers. We say that such a subset is *bounded above*. In this section, we shall investigate the properties of such subsets. We begin with the formal definition.

Definition. A number s is called an **upper bound** of a subset E of R if every element of E is less than, or equal to, s; if the subset E has an upper bound, we say that E is **bounded above**.

Symbolically, this definition becomes: E is bounded above $\Leftrightarrow \exists s \in R$ such that $\forall x \in E, x \leqslant s$.

We observe that if s is an upper bound of E, and $t > s$, then t is also an upper bound of E; for clearly, by property (7),

$$x \leqslant s, \forall x \in E, \& s < t \Rightarrow x \leqslant t, \forall x \in E.$$

The converse of this is false. If t is an upper bound of E, and $s < t$, then it does not follow that s is an upper bound of E. We shall see this illustrated in the following examples. First, however, we note how we can show that a number w is not an upper bound. We have w is not an upper bound of $E \Leftrightarrow \sim [\forall x \in E, x \leqslant w]$

$\Leftrightarrow \exists x \in E$ such that $\sim [x \leqslant w]$ (by Rule 1 of Section 1.9)

$\Leftrightarrow \exists x \in E$ such that $x > w$ (property 6 of Section 2.2).

Example 2.5.1. The set $\{1, 2, 3, 4\}$ is bounded above. 4 is an upper bound; so is 5, and so also are 73 and $96\frac{1}{2}$. Observe, though, that no number **less than** 4 can be an upper bound. For if $w < 4$, then we have $4 > w$, where 4 is a member of the set, and so, by the remark immediately preceding this example, w is not an upper bound.

Example 2.5.2. If $a < b$, the set $\{x \in R : a \leqslant x \leqslant b\}$ is called a **closed interval**, and is denoted by $[a, b]$. This set is bounded above. The number b is an upper bound, for clearly, $x \leqslant b, \forall x \in [a, b]$. So, too, is $b+r$, where $r > 0$. But again, no number less than b is an upper bound of the set. For we see that if $w < b$, then $b > w$ and b is an element of the set.

In these examples, there is a member of the subset itself which is an upper bound. This member is, of course, the greatest element of the subset. However, this situation does not always happen, as we now see.

Example 2.5.3. If $a < b$, the set $\{x \in R : a < x < b\}$ is called an **open interval**, and is denoted by (a, b). This set is bounded above. Again, we notice that, $\forall\, x \in (a, b)$, $x \leqslant b$ (in fact, $x < b$), and so b is again an upper bound. This time, b is not an element of the subset, but yet no number less than b is an upper bound. For, suppose $w < b$. We distinguish two cases, $w < a$, and $a \leqslant w < b$.

(i) If $w < a$, then $\frac{1}{2}(a+b) > w$, and $\frac{1}{2}(a+b)$ is a point of (a, b) (Fig. 2.5.1), so that w is not an upper bound.

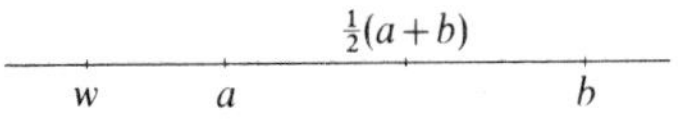

Fig. 2.5.1.

(ii) If $a \leqslant w < b$, consider the point $\frac{1}{2}(w+b)$. On the one hand,

$$\frac{1}{2}(w+b) < \frac{1}{2}(b+b) = b \quad \text{(since } w < b\text{),}$$

while on the other hand,

$$\frac{1}{2}(w+b) > \frac{1}{2}(w+w) = w \quad \text{(since } b > w\text{)}$$

so that

$$a \leqslant w < \frac{1}{2}(w+b) < b$$

i.e. there is a point of (a, b) greater than w (Fig. 2.5.2), and w is not an upper bound of (a, b).

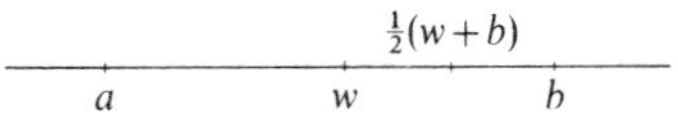

Fig. 2.5.2.

We have shown, incidentally, that the set (a, b) does *not* have a greatest element. For, if $a < w < b$, i.e. if w is an element of (a, b), then $\frac{1}{2}(w+b)$, which exceeds w, also satisfies $a < \frac{1}{2}(w+b) < b$. That is, if w is any element of (a, b), we can produce a bigger one, and this clearly implies that (a, b) has no greatest element. So, in Example 2.5.3, the set has no greatest member, no upper bound is an element of the set, and no element of the set is an upper bound.

Example 2.5.4. The set of numbers of the form $-1/n$, where $n \in N$, is bounded above. Since for all n, $-1/n$ is negative, every positive number is an upper bound. So also is 0, for $-1/n < 0$ for all n in N. No number less than 0 is an upper bound of the set. For, if $w < 0$, there is† an integer n in N such that $-1/n > w$. This set also has no greatest element, since for every n in N, $-[1/(n+1)] > -1/n$. Again,

---

† This assertion depends on the Archimedean property of the set R, which we shall establish in Theorem 2.6–B.

then, no element of the set is an upper bound, and no upper bound is an element of the set.

Example 2.5.5.   The set $\{2, 4, 6, 8, \ldots\}$ of even positive integers is not bounded above; for if w is any real number, there is† a positive integer n with $2n > w$.

If the reader looks again at Examples 2.5.1–2.5.4, he will observe that in each case, we pointed out a number μ which was an upper bound, and such that no number less than μ was an upper bound. These were 4, b, b and 0 respectively. We might call these the "least" upper bounds of their respective sets. It is a fundamental property of R that, for every non-empty subset of R which is bounded above, the collection of upper bounds has a least member. This fact was discovered by the German mathematician, Richard Dedekind (1831–1916), and is called the **Dedekind property** of R. It is by no means obvious, since we have already seen examples of collections which have no greatest element (Examples 2.5.3, 2.5.4), and clearly, we can construct sets which have no least element. For instance, the set (a, b) of Example 2.5.3 has no least element. We therefore have the following important theorem.

Theorem 2.5–A.   Let E be a non-empty subset of R which is bounded above. Then, the set of upper bounds of E has a least element.

Proof.   Every real number either is, or is not, an upper bound of E. Therefore, we can divide the set R of real numbers into two subsets S_1 and S_2 whose union is R:

$$S_1 = \{x \in R : x \text{ is not an upper bound of } E\},$$

$$S_2 = \{x \in R : x \text{ is an upper bound of } E\}.$$

We wish to prove that S_2 has a least element. By the completeness property (10) of R, we can, under certain conditions, conclude that if R is the union of two subsets, then either one of the subsets has a greatest element, or the other has a least element. So, if we can show that S_1 and S_2 satisfy the conditions of property (10), i.e. that (i) S_1 and S_2 are non-empty, and (ii) every number in S_1 is less than every number in S_2, we can conclude that either S_1 has a greatest element, or else S_2 has a least element. If we can then, in addition, show that (iii) S_1 does not have a greatest element, we will plainly have achieved our target. Our task, therefore, is to prove (i), (ii) and (iii), which we now do.

Proof of (i).   Since E is non-empty, E contains an element a, say. If x is any real number less than a (e.g. $x = a - 1$), then x is not an upper bound of E. So, x belongs to S_1, which is thus non-empty. By hypothesis, E is bounded above; this means, by definition, that E has an upper bound, and so S_2 is non-empty.

---

† This assertion depends on the Archimedean property of the set R, which we shall establish in Theorem 2.6–B.

Proof of (ii). Let x be any element of S_1, y any element of S_2. Since x is not an upper bound of E, there is a number b in E greater than x. Since y is an upper bound of E, $b \leqslant y$. Hence, $x < b \leqslant y$ i.e. $x < y$, which proves (ii).

Proof of (iii). Let $x \in S_1$. Then, x is not an upper bound of E, and so there is a number c in E greater than x. Now, $\frac{1}{2}(x+c) < c$, which means that $\frac{1}{2}(x+c)$ is not an upper bound of E, i.e. $\frac{1}{2}(x+c) \in S_1$. Furthermore, $\frac{1}{2}(x+c) > x$, and so, given any element of S_1, we can produce an element of S_1 which is larger. It follows that S_1 does not have a greatest element, and the proof of the theorem is therefore complete.   ◆

Theorem 2.5–A tells us that there is a *least* upper bound of a set E which is bounded above. We accordingly introduce a new definition.

Definition.   Let E be a non-empty subset of R which is bounded above. The least upper bound of E is called the **supremum** of E, and is denoted by sup E or by l.u.b. E.

It follows that if E is a non-empty subset of R which is bounded above, then sup E satisfies the following conditions:

(i) for all x in E, $x \leqslant$ sup E (this says that sup E is an upper bound of E);

(ii) given any positive real number ε, there is an element x_0 of E such that

$$x_0 > \text{sup } E - \varepsilon$$

(this says that no number less than sup E is an upper bound—so that sup E is the *least* upper bound).

It often happens that we wish to establish that a number α is the supremum of a set E. To do this, we must show that α satisfies *both* conditions (i) and (ii) above. That is, we must show that

(i′) for all x in E, $x \leqslant \alpha$ (that α *is* an upper bound);

(ii′) if $\varepsilon > 0$, there is an element x_0 in E such that $x_0 > \alpha - \varepsilon$ (no number less than α is an upper bound). Then, E is bounded above, and $\alpha = \text{sup } E$.

We have done precisely this in Examples 2.5.1–2.5.4. We have there shown that 4, b, b and 0 are the respective suprema. In each case, we proved that a certain number was an upper bound, and no number less than this was an upper bound.

Note.   It is especially important *not* to identify sup E with the *greatest element* of the set E. If the set E *has* a greatest element, then this element is also sup E (as in Examples 2.5.1, 2.5.2). But, as we have seen, there are sets which do not have a greatest element, though sup E nevertheless exists. (See Examples 2.5.3, 2.5.4).

We therefore make the following explicit warning.

Warning.   sup E may, or may not, be a member of the set E. We can say what happens in these alternative cases, however:

(a) sup E is an element of E $\Leftrightarrow$ E has a greatest element m. Then, $m = $ sup E (Examples 2.5.1, 2.5.2).

(b) sup E is not an element of E $\Leftrightarrow$ E has no greatest element (Examples 2.5.3, 2.5.4).

We now show how Theorem 2.5–A can be applied to prove that any positive real number has a unique positive square root.

Theorem 2.5–B. Let a be a positive real number. Then, there is precisely one positive real number b such that $b^2 = a$.

Proof. Let E be the set $\{x \in R : x \geqslant 0 \ \& \ x^2 \leqslant a\}$. Since 0 belongs to E, E is non-empty. Also, E is bounded above. For, suppose $x \in E$; then, $0 \leqslant x^2 \leqslant a$: if $a \leqslant 1$, then $x^2 \leqslant 1$, and therefore $x \leqslant 1$; while, if $x > 1$, then $x < x^2 \leqslant a$. It follows, then, that for all x in E,

$$x \leqslant \max(1, a),$$

and so E is bounded above. By Theorem 2.5–A, therefore, E has a supremum, say sup $E = b$. It is clear that $b \geqslant 0$; we shall prove that $b^2 = a$.

Suppose first that $b^2 < a$, and let ε be a real number satisfying $0 < \varepsilon < 1$. Then,

$$(b+\varepsilon)^2 = b^2 + 2b\varepsilon + \varepsilon^2$$
$$< b^2 + 2b\varepsilon + \varepsilon \qquad (0 < \varepsilon < 1 \Rightarrow \varepsilon^2 < \varepsilon)$$
$$= b^2 + \varepsilon(2b+1).$$

If ε satisfies the condition $\varepsilon < (a-b^2)/(2b+1)$ (and this can be done, since $a > b^2$ by hypothesis), then $(b+\varepsilon)^2 < a$ i.e. $b+\varepsilon$ is an element of E, and it clearly exceeds b, so contradicting the definition of b as sup E. Hence, our hypothesis that $b^2 < a$ is untenable, and so $b^2 \geqslant a$.

Suppose, then, that $b^2 > a$. Then,

$$(b-\varepsilon)^2 = b^2 - 2b\varepsilon + \varepsilon^2 > b^2 - 2b\varepsilon \quad (\text{since } \varepsilon^2 > 0).$$

If ε satisfies the condition $\varepsilon < (b^2-a)/2b$ (and this is possible, since we are now supposing that $b^2 > a$), then $(b-\varepsilon)^2 > a$; further,

$$b - \varepsilon > b - \frac{b^2 - a}{2b} = \frac{b^2 + a}{2b} > 0$$

and so, since $b-\varepsilon$ is not an upper bound of E (by definition of b as sup E), there is an element x_0 in E such that

$$x_0 > b - \varepsilon$$
$$\Rightarrow x_0^2 > (b-\varepsilon)^2 \qquad (\text{using Example 2.2.6 since } b-\varepsilon > 0)$$
$$\Rightarrow x_0^2 > a,$$

contradicting the fact that $x_0 \in E$. Hence, the hypothesis that $b^2 > a$ is untenable. By property (6) of Section 2.2, therefore, we have $b^2 = a$.

Finally, we must show that there is only one such number b. Suppose that b and c are positive real numbers such that $b^2 = c^2 = a$. Then,

$$0 = b^2 - c^2 = (b-c)(b+c)$$

$$\Rightarrow b - c = 0, \qquad \text{by Example 2.2.4, since } b + c \neq 0,$$

$$\Leftrightarrow b = c.$$

Thus, there is precisely one positive number whose square is a.　◆

If a is a positive real number, the unique positive real number b such that $b^2 = a$ is denoted by $\sqrt{a}$ or by $a^{\frac{1}{2}}$.

Our concern so far has been with subsets of R which are bounded above. We could have discussed subsets which are bounded below. We now give the definitions and results for these, and we shall see there is an obvious symmetry about the two concepts.

Definition. A number s is called a **lower bound** of a subset E of R if every member of E is greater than or equal to s, i.e.

for all x in E, $x \geqslant s$.

If the set E has a lower bound, then it is said to be **bounded below**. E is bounded below $\Leftrightarrow \exists s \in R$ such that, for all x in E, $x \geqslant s$.

Let us now look at what we called the "symmetry" above. Suppose E is a non-empty subset of R, and write

$$E' = \{y \in R : y = -x, \text{ for some element } x \text{ of } E\}.$$

If $s \in R$, then

$$x \geqslant s \text{ for every } x \in E \Leftrightarrow -x \leqslant -s \text{ for every } x \in E$$

$$\Leftrightarrow y \leqslant -s \text{ for every } y \in E'$$

Hence, s is a lower bound of $E \Leftrightarrow -s$ is an upper bound of E'. From this, and Theorem 2.5–A, we can deduce at once that the set of lower bounds of the subset E has a greatest element.

Definition. Let E be a non-empty subset of R which is bounded below. The greatest lower bound of E is called the **infimum** of E, and is denoted by inf E or by g.l.b. E.

Again, from the symmetry of the concepts of upper and lower bounds, we can say that, if E is a non-empty subset of R which is bounded below, then inf E satisfies the following conditions, and is the only real number to do so (we sometimes say "inf E is 'characterised' by these conditions"):

(i) for all x in E, $x \geqslant$ inf E (inf E is a lower bound of E)

(ii) for every $\varepsilon > 0$, there is an element x_0 in E such that

$$x_0 < \inf E + \varepsilon$$

(no number greater than inf E is a lower bound).

Similar remarks apply to $\inf E$ as were contained in the note and warning above concerning $\sup E$.

Some subsets are both bounded above and bounded below. We introduce a term to cover this situation.

Definition. A subset E of R is said to be **bounded** if it is bounded above and bounded below; otherwise, it is called **unbounded**.

Remark. We note that the following terminology is used; a set E which is not bounded above is called **unbounded above**, and a set which is not bounded below is called **unbounded below**. We have, then, from the definition above, and Theorem 1.7–A(a),

E is bounded $\Leftrightarrow$ E is bounded above & E is bounded below

E is unbounded $\Leftrightarrow$ E is unbounded above or E is unbounded below.

Theorem 2.5–C. A subset E of R is bounded if and only if there is a number K such that, for all x in E,

$$|x| \leqslant K.$$

Proof. (1) Suppose there is such a number K; then, for all x in E,

$$-K \leqslant x \leqslant K$$

by Theorem 2.4–A. Hence, K is an upper bound of E, and $-K$ is a lower bound. By definition, this means E is bounded.
(N.B. K is not necessarily $\sup E$, nor $-K$ necessarily $\inf E$).
(2) Conversely, suppose E is bounded. Then, E is bounded above, and so, if α is an upper bound of E, we have, for all x in E,

$$x \leqslant \alpha.$$

Also, E is bounded below, and so, if β is a lower bound of E,

$$\beta \leqslant x \quad \text{for all } x \text{ in } E.$$

Let $K = \max(\alpha, -\beta)$. Then, for all x in E, we obtain

$$-K \leqslant \beta \leqslant x \leqslant \alpha \leqslant K \Rightarrow |x| \leqslant K, \qquad \text{again by Theorem 2.4–A.} \quad \blacklozenge$$

2.6 Rational and Irrational Numbers

A real number is said to be **rational** if it is of the form p/q, where p, q are integers, with q nonzero. We note that if p, q, r are integers with $rq \neq 0$, then p/q and pr/qr are the same real number.

Real numbers, which are not rational, are called **irrational**. We begin this section by showing that such objects exist, and we do this by producing an example of a real number which cannot be written in the form p/q, where p, q are integers, with q nonzero.

Theorem 2.6–A. $\sqrt{2}$ is irrational (i.e. if $x \in R$ and $x^2 = 2$, then x is irrational).

Proof. This proof is by contradiction, using method (C) of Section 1.10. Suppose $\sqrt{2}$ is rational. (This is the "$\sim q$" of Theorem 1.10–H(c)). Then, we can write $\sqrt{2} = m/n$, where m, n are integers, and we suppose m and n have no common factor (this last remark is going to be the "r" of Theorem 1.10–H(c)). Then, $m^2/n^2 = 2 \Leftrightarrow m^2 = 2n^2$, and so m^2 is even. Now, the square of an odd integer is always odd (proof ?), and so m must be even—we can therefore write $m = 2k$, where k is an integer. Hence, $m^2 = 4k^2 = 2n^2 \Rightarrow n^2 = 2k^2 \Rightarrow n^2$ is even. As before, this means that n is even, which contradicts the hypothesis that m, n have no common factor (m, n both even $\Leftrightarrow m, n$ have the common factor 2). Thus, from "P" and "$\sim q$", we have obtained "r & $\sim r$". By Theorem 1.10–H(c), it follows that $\sqrt{2}$ is irrational.   ◆

We recall that in Section 2.3, we assumed that the set R was "complete" (property (10)). We also suggested then that it was a fairly obvious property. Consider the set Q of rationals; let

$$S_1 = \{x \in Q : x^2 < 2\}, \qquad S_2 = \{x \in Q : x^2 > 2\}.$$

Then, $Q = S_1 \cup S_2$, and if $x \in S_1$, $y \in S_2$, then $x < y$. But, S_1 has no greatest element, and S_2 no least (proof ?); note that, by Theorem 2.6–A, $\sqrt{2}$ does not belong to either S_1 or S_2. So the set Q of rationals does *not* have the completeness property (10). This makes the property well worth mentioning in Section 2.3.

Later in this Section, we shall show that between any two real numbers, no matter how close together they may be, we can find numbers that are rational, and numbers that are irrational. This is often described by saying that the sets of rationals and irrationals are each "dense" in R. However, in order to accomplish this, we require knowledge of another important property of R, called the Archimedean property (allegedly recognised by Archimedes (287–212 B.C.)). This is the property which says, in effect, that if we lay *enough* people end to end, they will stretch from, say, London to Edinburgh.

Theorem 2.6–B. R possesses the **Archimedean property**, i.e. if x and y are any two real numbers, with $x > 0$, then there is a positive integer n such that $nx > y$.

Proof.   The result is geometrically obvious. If x and y are points on the real axis, with $x > 0$, the theorem says there is a point representing a positive integral multiple of x to the right of the point representing y, or that any length can be exceeded by a (large) number of smaller lengths (see Fig. 2.6.1).

Fig. 2.6.1.

We shall, however, have to prove this using only properties (1)–(10) of R, and the consequences so far deduced from these.

It seems highly unlikely that we can offer a direct proof e.g. construct an integer n with the desired property. [If the reader thinks all we need do is take n to be the first integer after y/x, he must think again; this is exactly the same problem as we're trying to prove!] So, we fall back again on the method of contradiction.

Suppose, then, that $nx \leqslant y$ for every positive integer n. Then, y is an upper bound of the set E of positive integral multiples of x. By Theorem 2.5–A, E has a least upper bound, α say. Thus,

$$\alpha \geqslant nx \text{ for every positive integer } n,$$

$$\Rightarrow \alpha \geqslant (m+1)x \text{ for every positive integer } m^*$$

$$\Rightarrow \alpha - x \geqslant mx \text{ for every positive integer } m,$$

$$\Rightarrow \alpha - x \text{ is an upper bound of } E.$$

Since $\alpha - x < \alpha$, this contradicts the definition of α as sup E. Hence there is an integer n_0 such that $n_0 x > y$.   ◆

We now prove that between any two real numbers there is a rational number. In the subsequent theorem, we show there is also an irrational with this property.

Theorem 2.6–C.   If x, y are real numbers, and $x < y$, there is a rational number r such that $x < r < y$.

Proof.   We split the proof into two parts, when $x > 0$ and when $x \leqslant 0$. We first consider the case $x > 0$. Informally speaking, what we do is as follows: suppose q is some fixed positive integer. The points $0, 1/q, 2/q, \ldots$ are equally spaced along the real axis at distance $1/q$ apart. Moreover, the points p/q represent rational numbers. If we can show there is such a point between x and y, we have proved the result. Intuitively, we see this will happen if we make the spacing $1/q$ less than $y - x$. We now move on to the formal proof. In this, we do two things; we show that we *can* make $1/q$ less than $y - x$, (this is very easy), and then we show that this does in fact give the required result.

By hypothesis, $y - x > 0$, and therefore, by Theorem 2.6–B, there is a positive integer q with $q(y - x) > 1$ i.e. $(1/q) < y - x$. As we said, this stage is very easy! Going on to the second stage, we note, again by Theorem 2.6–B, that there is a positive integer n with $n > qx$; let p be the smallest such integer. Now, if $p = 1$, then, since $x > 0$, $p - 1 = 0 < qx$, while if $p \geqslant 2$, $p - 1$ is a positive integer, and by the definition of p, $p - 1 \leqslant qx$; thus, for all positive integers p, $p - 1 \leqslant qx$.

---

* This line says that $\alpha \geqslant kx$ for $k = 2, 3, 4, \ldots$ which clearly follows from the inequality $\alpha \geqslant nx$ for $n = 1, 2, 3, 4, \ldots$.

Hence,

$$qx < p = (p-1)+1$$
$$< qx + q(y-x)$$
$$= qy$$

i.e. $qx < p < qy \Leftrightarrow x < (p/q) < y$.

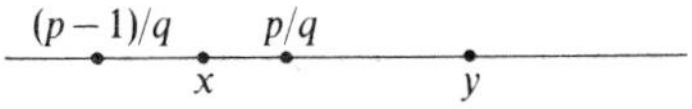

Fig. 2.6.2.

If $x \leqslant 0$, then by Theorem 2.6–B, there is a positive integer k such that $k = k \cdot 1 > -x$ i.e. such that $k + x > 0$. Hence, by the proof for the previous case, there is a rational number s such that

$$k + x < s < k + y \Rightarrow x < s - k < y,$$

and here, of course, $s - k$ is a rational number. ◆

Theorem 2.6–D. If x, y are real numbers with $x < y$, there is an irrational number z such that $x < z < y$.

Proof. By Theorem 2.6–C, there is a rational number r with $x < r < y$. It will clearly suffice to prove there is an irrational number z such that $x < z < r$. There are two possible cases to consider: x rational, and x irrational. The second of these is easy; the sum of a rational and an irrational number is irrational (proof ?), so if x is irrational, $z = \frac{1}{2}(x + r)$ is irrational, and of course $x < z < r$. When x is rational, $\frac{1}{2}(x + r)$ is also rational, and so this technique will not work. But if we could find an irrational close enough to x, this would do the trick. At present, the only irrational we know to exist is $\sqrt{2}$, so we try to use this in the proof somehow. Since $r - x > 0$, there is (by Theorem 2.6–B) a positive integer n such that

$$n(r-x) > \sqrt{2} \Leftrightarrow \frac{\sqrt{2}}{n} < r - x.$$

Let $z = x + \sqrt{2}/n$. Then, z is irrational, and $x < z < r$. ◆

APPENDIX

Mathematical Induction

We conclude this chapter with an account of another powerful and frequently used method of mathematical argument. This method is known as *induction* or *mathematical induction*, and it depends on a property of the natural numbers called the *well-ordering principle*. This property is not possessed by all sets (for example, it is not possessed by R);† however, since $N \subset R$, and the method depends on this property possessed by N, we include it here after the chapter on the real numbers.

Definition. Let E be an ordered set with the property that every subset of E has a least element (or first element). Then, E is said to be **well-ordered**.

Remark. The set N of natural numbers is well-ordered.

We now come to the principle of mathematical induction. Suppose that $P(n)$ is a condition on the natural number n, and that we wish to prove that "$\forall\, n \in N, P(n)$" is true. Because N is an infinite set, we cannot verify that $P(n)$ is true, for each $n \in N$. However, we have to assist us the following principle.

Principle of Mathematical Induction. Let S be a subset of N with the following properties;
(a) $1 \in S$,
(b) $k \in S \;\Rightarrow\; k+1 \in S$;
then, S is the set of natural numbers, i.e. $S = N$.

How does this help us? Denote by S the *solution set* of $P(n)$; then, if $1 \in S$ (i.e. if $P(1)$ is true) and if $k \in S \Rightarrow k+1 \in S$ (i.e. $P(k) \Rightarrow P(k+1)$), then by the principle of mathematical induction above, $S = N$ i.e. the solution set of $P(n)$ is N, or "$\forall\, n \in N, P(n)$" is true.

We can give a justification of the principle. Let $P(n)$ be a condition on n, where n has domain N. Suppose that
(a) $P(1)$ is true,
(b) $k \in N, P(k) \Rightarrow P(k+1)$.
We wish to deduce that, for all $n \in N$, $P(n)$ is true. Suppose this is not the case; that is, there are numbers $n \in N$ for which $P(n)$ is false. Denote the set of such $n \in N$ by A. Then, because A is a subset of N, and N is *well-ordered*, A has a least element, n_0. By (a), $n_0 \neq 1$; also, by definition of n_0 as the least element of N for which $P(n_0)$ is false, we have $P(1), \ldots, P(n_0 - 1)$ all true. But by (b), $P(n_0 - 1) \Rightarrow P(n_0)$, and so, since $P(n_0 - 1)$ is true, $P(n_0)$ is true by Theorem 1.10–D, which is a contradiction. Hence, "$\forall\, n \in N, P(n)$" is true.

The reader should also observe that, in the step $P(n_0 - 1) \Rightarrow P(n_0)$, $n_0 - 1 \geqslant 1$ since $n_0 > 1$ by (a), and so this implication is meaningful. If $P(1)$ is false, then $n_0 = 1$, and $P(n_0 - 1)$ is not defined.

Example 2.A.1.   Prove, by induction, that

$$1 + 2^2 + \ldots + n^2 = \tfrac{1}{6}n(n+1)(2n+1).$$

† *Note.* There is a difficult theorem in Logic which asserts that every set *can* be well-ordered. However, the ordering that results will not necessarily be that of the set as originally considered.

Proof. Here,

$$P(n) \text{ is } "1 + 2^2 + \ldots + n^2 = \tfrac{1}{6}n(n+1)(2n+1)".$$

(a) Consider $P(1)$. This is $1 = \tfrac{1}{6}(1.2.3)$, which is clearly true.
(b) We have, for any k,

$$P(k) \Leftrightarrow 1^2 + 2^2 + \ldots + k^2 = \tfrac{1}{6}k(k+1)(2k+1).$$

We obtain the left-hand side of $P(k+1)$ by adding $(k+1)^2$ to the left-hand side of $P(k)$. Hence, from $P(k)$ we obtain, adding $(k+1)^2$ to both sides,

$$
\begin{aligned}
1^2 + 2^2 + \ldots + k^2 + (k+1)^2 &= \tfrac{1}{6}k(k+1)(2k+1) + (k+1)^2 \\
&= \tfrac{1}{6}(k+1)[k(2k+1) + 6(k+1)] \\
&= \tfrac{1}{6}(k+1)(2k^2 + 7k + 6) \\
&= \tfrac{1}{6}(k+1)(k+2)(2k+3) \\
&= \tfrac{1}{6}r(r+1)(2r+1)
\end{aligned}
$$

with $r = k+1$, which is precisely $P(k+1)$. Thus, $P(k) \Rightarrow P(k+1)$, for each k. By the induction principle, "$\forall n, P(n)$" is true.

Example 2.A.2.   Prove, by induction, that for all $n \in N$, $3n^5 + 7n$ is divisible by 5.

Proof.   Here, $P(n)$ is "$3n^5 + 7n$ is divisible by 5".
(a) $P(1)$ is "$3 + 7$ is divisible by 5"; since 5 divides 10, $P(1)$ is true.
(b) Let us suppose that 5 divides $3k^5 + 7k$. Consider the expression

$$3(k+1)^5 + 7(k+1).$$

We write this as

$$
\begin{aligned}
&(3k^5 + 3 \cdot 5k^4 + 3 \cdot 10k^3 + 3 \cdot 10k^2 + 3 \cdot 5k + 3) + (7k + 7) \\
&= (3k^5 + 7k) + 5(3k^4 + 6k^3 + 6k^2 + 3k + 2).
\end{aligned}
$$

Now, 5 divides the first bracket $3k^5 + 7k$, by hypothesis. 5 clearly divides the second term, which is of the form $5a$. So 5 divides $3(k+1)^5 + 7(k+1)$. We have shown that if 5 divides $3k^5 + 7k$, then 5 divides $3(k+1)^5 + 7(k+1)$ i.e. that $P(k) \Rightarrow P(k+1)$. Hence, by the induction principle, "$\forall n \in N, P(n)$" is true.

Remark.   It sometimes happens that we wish to show that a condition $P(n)$ on n is true, for all n after a certain one. The principle of induction is easily adapted for this purpose. Suppose we wish to show that "$\forall n \geqslant n_0, P(n)$" is true. Then, it suffices to prove
   (i) $P(n_0)$ is true
   (ii) $\forall n \geqslant n_0, P(n) \Rightarrow P(n+1)$.

To see this, we note that the set $\{n \in N : n \geqslant n_0\}$ is well-ordered; also, if we write $m = n - n_0 + 1$, then m takes the values $1, 2, 3, \ldots$ as n takes the values $n_0, n_0 + 1, n_0 + 2, \ldots$ and *vice versa*. Denote by $Q(m)$ the condition $P(m + n_0 - 1)$. Then,

$$P(n_0) \text{ true } \Leftrightarrow \text{ (a) } Q(1) \text{ is true;}$$

$$\{\forall \, n \geqslant n_0 \; P(n) \Rightarrow P(n+1)\} \Leftrightarrow \text{(b)} \{\forall \, m, \, Q(m) \Rightarrow Q(m+1).\}$$

By the induction principle, applied to (a) and (b), "$\forall \, m \in N, \, Q(m)$" is true. That is, "$\forall \, n \geqslant n_0, \, P(n)$" is true.

Example 2.A.3. If $a > -1$, $a \neq 0$, show that

$$(1+a)^n > 1 + na$$

for $n = 2, 3, \ldots$.

Proof. Let $P(n)$ be $(1+a)^n > 1 + na$. Now, $P(1)$ is $1 + a > 1 + a$, which is *false*; so the original method of induction does not work. However, we use the adapted form above. We note that $P(2)$ is

$$(1+a)^2 > 1 + 2a.$$

Now, $(1+a)^2 = 1 + 2a + a^2 > 1 + 2a$, if $a \neq 0$, since a^2 is positive. Hence, $P(2)$ is true.
Next, let us suppose that

$$(1+a)^k > 1 + ka, \quad \text{where} \quad k \geqslant 2,$$

(that is, $P(k)$). Now

$$(1+a)^{k+1} = (1+a) \cdot (1+a)^k > (1+a)(1+ka),$$

using $P(k)$ and the fact that $1 + a > 0$,

$$= 1 + (k+1)a + ka^2 > 1 + (k+1)a, \qquad \text{because } a \neq 0.$$

But this is $P(k+1)$, so we have shown that $P(k) \Rightarrow P(k+1)$. Hence, by the adapted principle of induction, "$\forall \, n \geqslant 2, \, P(n)$" is true.

There is yet another principle of induction with which it is important to be familiar. Again we wish to show that a proposition of the form "$\forall \, n \in N, \, P(n)$" is true. However, it may happen that we cannot show that $P(k) \Rightarrow P(k+1)$ although we can show that $P(r) \Rightarrow P(k+1)$ where $r \leqslant k$. The following principle of induction covers this eventuality.
Suppose $P(n)$ is a condition on n.

Second Principle of Induction. If (i) $P(1)$ is true, and (ii) $P(1)$ & $P(2)$ & $\ldots$ & $P(k) \Rightarrow P(k+1)$, for each $k \in N$, then "$\forall \, n \in N, \, P(n)$" is true.

Note. This second principle also can be amended for use in proving the truth of propositions of the form "$\forall \, n \geqslant n_0, \, P(n)$". The proof is similar to that above. If "$\forall \, n \in N, \, P(n)$" is false, then by the well-ordering principle, there is a least number n_0 for which $P(n_0)$ is false. By (i), $n_0 \geqslant 2$. Also, $P(1), P(2), \ldots P(n_0 - 1)$ are all true, and so $P(1) \& P(2) \& \ldots \& P(n_0 - 1)$ is true. Hence by (ii) and the law of detachment, $P(n_0)$ is true, a contradiction.

Example 2.A.4. Show that every positive integer $n \geqslant 2$ can be expressed as a product of primes.

Proof. Let $P(n)$ be "n is expressible as a product of primes". We wish to show "$\forall\, n \geqslant 2, P(n)$" is true. (Note that this is the amended form.)

We first observe that if p is prime, then $P(p)$ is trivially true. Now (i) $P(2)$ is true, because 2 is prime. (ii) Suppose $2, 3, \ldots, k$ are expressible as products of primes, and consider $k + 1$. Either $k + 1$ is prime, in which case we are finished, by our first remark, or it is not prime. If $k + 1$ is not prime, then $k + 1 \geqslant 4$; moreover, $k + 1$ has factors, say $k + 1 = xy$, where $2 \leqslant x < k, 2 \leqslant y < k$. We observe that x and y may be anywhere between 2 and $k - 1$ inclusive. But, since we are taking $P(2), P(3), \ldots, P(k)$ as hypotheses, both $P(x)$ and $P(y)$ are true. Then, $k + 1$ is expressible as the product of the prime factors of x and the prime factors of y i.e. $P(2) \& P(3) \& \ldots \& P(k) \Rightarrow P(k + 1)$. By the induction principle, "$\forall\, n \geqslant 2, P(n)$" is true.

Remark. It is essential to verify the truth of $P(1)$, or $P(n_0)$ as the case may be. Consider the proposition, "$\forall\, n \in N, P(n)$" where

$$P(n) \quad \text{is "} n > 1 \text{"}.$$

Now, it is easy to see that $k > 1 \Rightarrow k + 1 > 1$, so that the induction step holds. But we cannot conclude that "$\forall\, n \in N, P(n)$" is now true. For $P(1)$: "$1 > 1$" is false. The omission of this part of the proof is therefore disastrous. [Note, though, that "$\forall\, n \geqslant 2, P(n)$" is true.]

The reader can think of induction as a principle of the following type. Suppose we have a lot of dominoes, each standing on its end, and such that if one falls over, it will strike the next. Then, it is plain that if we push over the first one, all the dominoes will fall down.

Exercises

1. If $x, y \in R$, prove that $(-x)y = -(xy)$.
2. Prove that $x^2 \geqslant 0$ for all $x \in R$.
3. Prove that if $x \geqslant y > 0$, then $1/x \leqslant 1/y$.
4. Prove that if $a > b > 0$, and $c > d > 0$, then $ac > bd$.
5. If a, b are positive real numbers, prove that

$$(a + b) \geqslant 2\sqrt{ab}.$$

6. If a is a positive real number, and n is a positive integer, use the relation $a^n - 1 = (a - 1)(a^{n-1} + a^{n-2} + \ldots + 1)$ to show that $a^n - 1 \geqslant n(a - 1)$.

7. If $a, b, c \in R$, prove that if $a > 0$,

$$at^2 + bt + c \geqslant 0 \quad \text{for all } t \in R$$

if and only if $b^2 \leqslant 4ac$.

8. If $a_1, a_2, \ldots, a_n$ and $b_1, b_2, \ldots, b_n$ are two sets of real numbers, prove that

$$\left(\sum_{i=1}^{i=n} a_i b_i \right)^2 \leqslant \left(\sum_{i=1}^{i=n} a_i^2 \right) \left(\sum_{i=1}^{i=n} b_i^2 \right).$$

This is called Cauchy's Inequality. [Consider the sum

$$\sum_{i=1}^{i=n} (a_i - b_i t)^2, \ t \in R, \text{ and use 7.}]$$

9. Prove that if $x \leqslant a$, for all $x \in E$, then sup $E \leqslant a$. Show, by an example, that if $x < a$, for all $x \in E$, then we cannot necessarily conclude that sup $E < a$.

10. Let A, B be sets in R. Let E be the set consisting of numbers of the form $a + b$, where $a \in A$, $b \in B$. Show that sup $E = $ sup $A +$ sup B.

11. Prove that, if $a > 0$, $\sup\{ax : x \in E\} = a \sup\{x : x \in E\}$. If $a < 0$, prove that $\sup\{ax : x \in E\} = a \inf\{x : x \in E\}$. Deduce similar relationships for $\inf\{ax : x \in E\}$.

CHAPTER 3

Functions

3.1 Introduction

Our purpose in this chapter is to examine and discuss the idea of a "function". The reader is no doubt familiar with functions described by such formulae as "$y = f(x)$" or more explicitly, "$y = x^3 - 2x + 4$" or "$y = e^x$".

We have deliberately used the words "functions described by such formulae as ..." above, because, as we shall see, a function is something more than a formula. It is, in fact, yet another kind of relation between sets. In the examples above, we have the set to which x belongs (i.e. a set X consisting of all numbers or elements that are allowed to replace x), and a second set Y, consisting of numbers y calculated from the formula for each possible value of $x \in X$. Usually, it is not the set Y which will be regarded as the set to be related with X, but some larger set S which contains Y. Our formulae, then, represent relations between the sets X and S, whereby each element of X has associated with it an element y in S.

We take this as our starting point for investigating functions; it seems reasonable that we should explore this idea in a more general way, and consider sets of any kind, rather than just sets of numbers. So, let us begin by making a tentative definition of a function.

Tentative Definition. Let A and B be two sets. A **function** (also called a **mapping**) *of* A *into* B is a relation which associates, with each element $a \in A$, an element $b \in B$. The relation may be given by a formula or rule as in the examples above, or by a complete account of the individual associations (we shall see an example of this later).

We now have a tentative definition, based on our experience. Let us now look at some examples of associations between sets, and consider whether our definition has any defects.

Example 3.1.1. Let A be the set $\{x \in R : -1 < x < 1\}$, B be the set R. Consider the relation between A and B given by associating, with each $x \in A$, the real number $1 + x^3$. We can express this symbolically by

$$x \to 1 + x^3$$

Here, each element of A has an associate in B. So this conforms to our tentative definition above.

Example 3.1.2.   Let A be the set of all names of countries, B the set of all names of cities. We can relate A to B by associating, with each name of a country, the name of its capital city; for instance,

$$\text{France} \rightarrow \text{Paris}$$

$$\text{England} \rightarrow \text{London}$$

$$\text{Kenya} \rightarrow \text{Nairobi}$$

and so on ...

Again, this conforms to our tentative definition; here A and B contain different kinds of element (which was not the case in Example 3.1.1.).

Example 3.1.3.   Let $A = \{x \in R : -1 \leqslant x \leqslant 1\}$, $B = R$. Suppose we relate A to B by associating with each $x \in A$, the real number whose sine is x. Thus,

$$0 \rightarrow 0, \quad \tfrac{1}{2} \rightarrow \pi/6, \quad -1/\sqrt{2} \rightarrow -\pi/4, \quad \text{and so on.}$$

This seems again to conform to our tentative definition. But let us look a little more closely. It is also the case that $\sin 2\pi = 0$ (indeed $\sin n\pi = 0$, $n \in Z$), $\sin 5\pi/6 = \tfrac{1}{2}$, $\sin 5\pi/4 = -1/\sqrt{2}$, so that 2π is a number whose sine is 0, $5\pi/6$ is a number whose sine is $\tfrac{1}{2}$, and so on ... If we say "associate with x the real number whose sine is x", what do we associate with 0? 0, or 2π, or 3π? What do we associate with $\tfrac{1}{2}$? $\pi/6$ or $5\pi/6$, or $13\pi/6, \ldots$? We begin to see that this association is useless, because the association with x of the real number whose sine is x is meaningless; given $x \in A$, there is no object which is **the** real number whose sine is x. One possible way out might be to say "associate with x **a** real number whose sine is x"; but this is equally unsatisfactory. If we are going to make use of relations between sets (especially those which are functions) in the course of logical arguments, then one requirement must be that there is no ambiguity. For, in that case, conclusions drawn from premises which are ambiguous in interpretation will depend on that interpretation and be themselves ambiguous; and different readers may well choose different interpretations. Many of the paradoxical "proofs" that $0 = 1$ depend on ambiguities of this sort; e.g. in taking square roots, one can choose positive or negative square roots.

If we look to Examples 3.1.1 and 3.1.2, we see that there, one finds no ambiguity. Each element $a \in A$ is associated with one and only one element in B. We therefore take this as an essential requisite in defining a function. So we have the following definition.

Definition.   Let A, B be sets. A **function** $f : A \rightarrow B$ is a relation which associates, with each element $a \in A$, one and only one element in B.

The function is usually denoted by lower case letters such as f, g, φ, $\psi, \ldots$ We write $f : A \rightarrow B$ to signify that f is a function of A into B.

This definition is fairly satisfactory. We shall see later how we can remove the problem of defining the meaning of the word "relation", by defining a function in terms of sets alone. First, we look at some more examples.

Example 3.1.4. Let $A = R$, $B = \{0, 1\}$. If $x \in A$ and x is rational, associate with x the number 1; if $x \in A$ and x is irrational, associate with x the number 0. Then, this relation between A and B is a function of A into B, in the sense of the definition above. We have

$$x \to \begin{cases} 1 & \text{if} \quad x \in Q \\ 0 & \text{if} \quad x \notin Q \end{cases}$$

so that the function is given by more than one formula.

Example 3.1.5. Let A be the set of all names of cities, B the set of all names of countries. Associate with each name of a city, the name of the country in which the city lies, e.g.

New York $\to$ U.S.A.

Leningrad $\to$ U.S.S.R.

Tokyo $\to$ Japan.

Is this relation a function? The answer in this case is no. For there may not be a unique name of a country in which a city of a given name lies; thus, if we consider the names Birmingham and Perth, we might find that readers in the U.S.A. would associate Birmingham with Alabama, U.S.A., and readers in the Far East would associate Perth with Australia, while those in Britain would be likely to associate the names with England and Scotland respectively. So this association is not meaningful; it does not satisfy the requirements of our definition; it is not a function.

Example 3.1.6. Let $A = \{a, b, c\}$, $B = \{1, 2, 3\}$. Consider the association between A and B given by

$$a \to 1, \qquad b \to 3, \qquad c \to 1.$$

This is a function of A into B. It satisfies the definition above. Here, we have a complete account of the relation. Every element of A and its associate in B is explicitly given. Again, A, B are different sets.

Finally, we have one more example to show that a function can be given by a simple rule or prescription, which is quite explicit, and yet there is no known algebraic formula for calculating the associate of an element in A.

Example 3.1.7. Let $A = B = N$ (the set of natural numbers). Associate, with each number k in A, the k-th prime number. Thus,

$$1 \to 2, \quad 2 \to 3, \quad 3 \to 5, \quad 4 \to 7, \dots, 8 \to 19, \dots$$

This is a function of N into N. Given any number k in N, there is one and only one number which is the k-th prime.

These examples illustrate some of the ways of defining a function. We point out that the function or relation is a one-way affair, emphasised by the arrow notation. A function or relation of A into B is not the same as one of B into A. We shall see that there are great difficulties in trying to do this reverse process.

The reader may also have observed that, in some of our examples of functions, not every element of B is associated with a member of A. This does not matter; in the first place, as we have just remarked, the function is a one-way operation, and secondly, we can always divide functions of A into B into two classes—one class for which every element of B is associated with a member of A, and the other when not every element of B has this property.

3.2 Second Definition of a Function

We begin by noting some of the terminology used in connection with functions. Suppose $f : A \to B$ is a function. Since the element of B associated with a particular element x of A depends only upon x itself and the function f, we usually denote this element of B by $f(x)$. It is called the **image of** x **under** f, or the **(function) value of** f **at** x.

Thus, $1 + x^3$ is the function value at x of the function which cubes x and adds 1. We sometimes write "the function given by $f(x) = 1 + x^3$". Here, $f(x)$ is not the function itself, but the value of the function; we comprehend the function by describing how it processes the element x. It is the most common method of identifying the function.

Definition. Let $f : A \to B$. The set A is called the **domain** of the function f. We write $\mathscr{D}(f) = A$. The set B is called the **image space** of f. We can also consider the subset of B consisting of all those elements of B which are images under f of elements of A. This subset is denoted by $f(A)$. Thus, $f(A) = \{y \in B : y = f(x), \text{ for at least one element } x \in A\}$. The set $f(A)$ is called the **range** of f, sometimes denoted by $\mathscr{R}(f)$. In general, if $f : A \to B$, $\mathscr{R}(f) \neq B$. Functions whose range is a subset of R are called **real-valued functions.**

Example 3.2.1. Let $A = B = R$, and let f be the squaring function; that is, if $x \in A$, $f(x) = x^2$. Then,

$$f(A) = \{y \in R : y \geqslant 0\}.$$

Example 3.2.2. Let A be the set N of natural numbers, B the set Q of rationals. Define a function $s : N \to Q$ by setting, for each element $n \in N$,

$$s(n) = 1/n.$$

(Again, we describe the function by showing how it works). Here, $s(N)$ is the set of positive harmonic fractions.

For the functions of Examples 3.1.1., 3.1.2., 3.1.4., 3.1.6. and 3.1.7., we have the following ranges:

Ex. 3.1.1. $\mathcal{R}(f) = \{y \in R : 0 < y < 2\}$

Ex. 3.1.2. $\mathcal{R}(f) = \{\text{set of names of capital cities}\}.$

Ex. 3.1.4. $\mathcal{R}(f) = \{0, 1\}.$

Ex. 3.1.6. $\mathcal{R}(f) = \{1, 3\}.$

Ex. 3.1.7. $\mathcal{R}(f) = \{\text{set of prime numbers}\}.$

One minor defect that we have encountered, and not yet cleared up, is that we have sometimes found ourselves unable to see the function in question as an object in itself. We can see how it processes the elements of its domain, but it, itself, remains somehow intangible. However, since it is a relation between sets, we ought surely to be able to expose the function for what it is, rather than merely to identify it by what it does.

If we look back to our definition in the last section, we see that the function is described by a procedure which "pairs off" an element of B with each element of A. If $x \in A$, the function f gives us the pair x, $f(x)$. We have written this previously as $x \to f(x)$, but we might equally well write it as $(x, f(x))$. This is, of course, an *ordered* pair; for we first have x, and then its "pair", namely the image of x under f. So if we take the whole collection of ordered pairs $(x, f(x))$, for all $x \in A$, we get a complete description of how the function f operates. Since $x \in A$, and $f(x) \in B$, Section 1.12 tells us that the collection $(x, f(x))$, for all $x \in A$ is a subset of $A \times B$, the product of the sets A, B. It is a special kind of subset, however; for there is one and only one ordered pair in the subset with first element x. To see this, suppose (a, y_1) and (a, y_2) were in the subset, with $y_1 \neq y_2$. This means $f(a) = y_1$ and $f(a) = y_2$, in contradiction of the definition of function.

We thus find ourselves led finally to a completely abstract definition of function as follows:

Definition. Let A and B be two sets, not necessarily distinct. A **function** (or **mapping**) f of A into B is a subset of the product set $A \times B$ with the property that, if $x \in A$, there is one and only one element $y \in B$ such that the pair (x, y) belongs to the subset f.

The element y is denoted by $f(x)$.

This set-theoretic definition of function may seem, to the reader, artificial and a long way away from ideas with which he is familiar. But this definition of function coincides with what he already thinks of as the "graph" of a function. To see this, let A and B each be the set R of real numbers, and consider the function $f : A \to B$ given by the

formula $f(x) = e^x$. The product set $A \times B$ becomes the real plane, and
the curve f shown in Fig. 3.2.1 is what the reader would think of as
the "graph" of f. According to our definition above, the curve *is* the
function f, if we regard the diagram as a pictorial representation of
the product set $A \times B$.

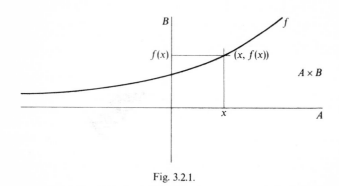

Fig. 3.2.1.

We may have other situations where A and B are not subsets of R,
and the graphical description of Fig. 3.2.1 is less convenient. We may
find it more useful, in these cases, to visualise the function f as an
associative relation between A and B, illustrated in Fig. 3.2.2, where A
and B are represented by disks, and f as an operation which connects
each element x of A with its image in B.

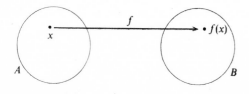

Fig. 3.2.2.

We shall take the definition on page 77 as our definition of function.
However, many of the functions which we shall consider will be described by a formula, or rule, and we shall not feel inhibited from
referring to the function, in these cases, by the rule, e.g. "the function
φ given by (the rule) $\varphi(x) = \alpha x^2 + \beta x + \gamma$, etc. . . ." Likewise, many of
the properties that functions possess are demonstrated by the behaviour
of the function values, and so the reader will find that we frequently
conduct our discussion in terms of function values, rather than of
ordered pairs.

3.3 Equality, Restriction and Extension

The definition of a function as a set allows us to use the ideas of set-equality and set-inclusion to develop similar ideas for functions.

Definition. Let f, g be functions. Then, the functions are **equal**, and we write $f = g$, if $\mathcal{D}(f) = \mathcal{D}(g)$ and $f(x) = g(x)$, for all $x \in \mathcal{D}(f)$.

Example 3.3.1. Let $A = \{x \in R : 0 \leqslant x \leqslant 1\}$. Let $f : A \to R$ be given by $f(x) = 2+x$, $g : A \to R$ by $g(x) = 4 - x^2/2 - x$. Then $f = g$. For $\mathcal{D}(f) = \mathcal{D}(g) = A$ and, for $x \in A$, $2+x = 4 - x^2/2 - x$.

Example 3.3.2. Let $A = \{x \in R : 0 \leqslant x \leqslant 1\}$. Let $f : A \to R$ be given by $f(x) = x+1$, g be given by $g(x) = (x^2-1)/(x-1)$. Then $f \neq g$. For $1 \notin \mathcal{D}(g)$; if we try to put 1 into the formula for $g(x)$, we get 0/0, which is meaningless. So, since $\mathcal{D}(f) \neq \mathcal{D}(g)$, f is not equal to g. Note, however, that for those members x for which f, g are both defined, $f(x) = g(x)$.

Example 3.3.3. Let $A = \{x \in R : 0 \leqslant x \leqslant 1\}$, $f : A \to R$ be given by

$$f(x) = \begin{cases} x & 0 < x < 1 \\ 0 & x = 0, 1 \end{cases},$$

$g : A \to R$ be given by

$$g(x) = \begin{cases} x & 0 < x < 1 \\ 1 & x = 0, 1 \end{cases},$$

Then $f \neq g$; for, although $\mathcal{D}(f) = \mathcal{D}(g)$, $f(0) \neq g(0)$ and $f(1) \neq g(1)$.

This definition uses Section 1.2 and Theorem 1.12–A, Corollary. We can likewise write down conditions for the set f to be a subset of the set g.

Theorem 3.3–A. Let f, g be functions. Then, f is contained in g if and only if $\mathcal{D}(f) \subset \mathcal{D}(g)$ and $f(x) = g(x)$, $\forall x \in \mathcal{D}(f)$.

Proof. Suppose $f \subset g$, and let $x \in \mathcal{D}(f)$. Then,

$$(x, f(x)) \in f \Rightarrow (x, f(x)) \in g$$
$$\Rightarrow x \in \mathcal{D}(g) \text{ and } g(x) = f(x).$$

Hence $\mathcal{D}(f) \subset \mathcal{D}(g)$ and $f(x) = g(x)$, $\forall x \in \mathcal{D}(f)$.
Conversely, if $\mathcal{D}(f) \subset \mathcal{D}(g)$ and $f(x) = g(x)$, $\forall x \in \mathcal{D}(f)$, then

$$\{(x, f(x)) : x \in \mathcal{D}(f)\} = \{(x, g(x)) : x \in \mathcal{D}(f)\}$$
$$\subset \{(x, g(x)) : x \in \mathcal{D}(g)\}$$
$$\Leftrightarrow f \subset g, \text{ by definition of function.} \qquad \blacklozenge$$

We use this result to introduce two new definitions.

Definition.   Let f, g be two functions. If $f \subset g$, we say that f is the **restriction** of g (to $\mathscr{D}(f)$); we say that g is an **extension** of f (to $\mathscr{D}(g)$).

For the purposes of reference, we note the following equivalent forms of the definitions.

Definition.   Let A, B be sets, $g : A \to B$. Suppose that X is a subset of A, and define a function $f : X \to B$ by setting $f(x) = g(x)$, $\forall\, x \in X$. Then, f is called the **restriction** of g to X (occasionally denoted by g/X).

Definition.   Let A, B be sets, $f : A \to B$. Suppose that g is a function such that (i) $A \subset \mathscr{D}(g)$ and (ii) $g(x) = f(x)$, for all x in A. Then, g is called an **extension** of f to $\mathscr{D}(g)$.

Example 3.3.4.   Let $A = B = R$, and consider the function sin (here, we are referring to the function by the rule—see page 78). We can restrict the function to the subset $[-\pi/2, \pi/2]$ of R. We call this restriction the function Sin (with upper case letter). Note that $\mathscr{R}(\sin) = \mathscr{R}(\mathrm{Sin})$.

Example 3.3.5.   Let $A = \{a, b, c\}$, $B = \{1, 2, 3\}$ and suppose f is the function $\{(a, 1), (b, 3), (c, 3)\}$. Let g be the function $\{(a, 1), (b, 3), (c, 3), (d, 2), (e, 4), (h, 1)\}$. Then g is an extension of f to $\{a, b, c, d, e, h\}$. Note that $\mathscr{R}(g) \neq \mathscr{R}(f)$.

3.4 Special Types of Function

In this section, we discuss some special types of general function. First, we have the special case when the domain of f is a subset of the image space, and f associates each element x with x itself.

Definition.   Let $A \subset E$, $f : A \to A$ given by $f(x) = x$, for every $x \in A$. This function is called the **identity** (**function**) on A, sometimes denoted by the special letter j. It associates the element x with itself: $x \to x$. The function $f : A \to E$ given by $f(x) = x$, $\forall\, x \in A$, is called the **inclusion** function.

Clearly, there can be an inclusion function of A into B only if $A \subset B$.

Example 3.4.1.   The function $f : R \to R$ given by $f(x) = x$, for every x in R, is the identity function on R. This function is illustrated in Fig. 3.4.1.

We may sometimes refer to this function as "the function x". Another special case is when the same element of B is associated with every element of A.

Definition.   Let A, B be sets, b an element of B. Suppose $f : A \to B$ is the function given by

$$f(x) = b, \quad \text{for every } x \in A.$$

Then f is called a **constant** function.

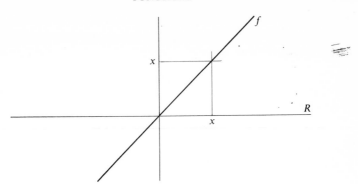

Fig. 3.4.1. Identity function in $R \times R$.

There are clearly as many constant functions of A into B as there are elements of B; for if y is a dummy with domain B, we can take y to be the image under f of every element of A, and this is a constant function.

Example 3.4.2. Let $A = \{a, b, c\}$, $B = \{1, 2, 3\}$, and f be given by $\{(a, 1), (b, 1), (c, 1)\}$. Then, f is a constant function (Fig. 3.4.2).

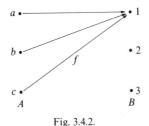

Fig. 3.4.2.

Example 3.4.3. Let A, B be the set R of real numbers, and suppose f is the function given by

$$f(x) = 2, \quad \text{for all } x \in R.$$

Again, f is a constant function (Fig. 3.4.3).

If $f: A \to B$, then, given two distinct elements x and y in A, the elements $f(x)$ and $f(y)$ in B may or may not be distinct. The constant function is an instance where *no* pair x, y in A have distinct images in

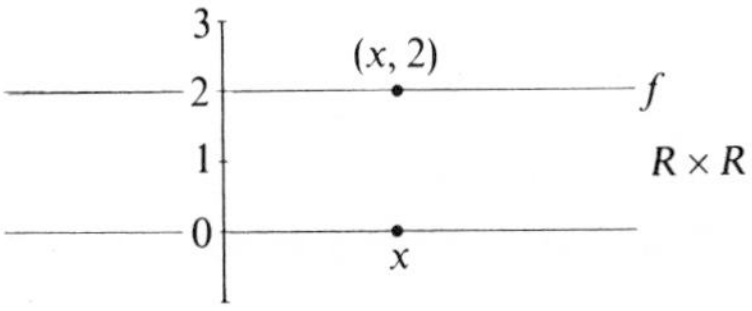

Fig. 3.4.3.

B. At the other extreme, a function may have the property that *every* pair x and y, with $x \neq y$, have distinct images in B. Such functions have a special name also.

Definition. Let A, B be sets, $f : A \to B$. Then, the function f is called $(1, 1)$,† or is a **one-to-one mapping**, if the images of distinct points of A, under f, are distinct points of B. That is, symbolically, if

$$x, y \in A \, \& \, x \neq y \Rightarrow f(x) \neq f(y).$$

This last statement is more frequently expressed in contrapositive form :

$$f \text{ is } (1, 1) \text{ if and only if } \forall \, x, y \in A, \, f(x) = f(y) \Rightarrow x = y.$$

Example 3.4.4. Let $A \subset B$. The identity function $j : A \to A$ is $(1, 1)$.

Example 3.4.5. Let A, B be two sets, $f : A \to B$ be a constant function. Then, f is not $(1, 1)$, *unless A consists of a single element.*

Proof. If f is constant, then there is an element $b \in B$ such that $f(x) = b$, for all $x \in A$. Thus, if a_1, a_2 are distinct points of A, $f(a_1) = f(a_2) = b$. But this means that f is not $(1, 1)$. If A consists of one element only, however, f is clearly $(1, 1)$.

Example 3.4.6. Let $A = B = R$. The function j_3, given by $j_3(x) = x^3$, for all $x \in R$, is $(1, 1)$. For, we have

$$x^3 = y^3 \Rightarrow x = y.$$

Example 3.4.7. Let $A = B = R$. The function φ given by setting $\varphi(x) = x^3 + 2x^2 - x - 2$, $\forall \, x \in R$ is not $(1, 1)$. For,

$$\varphi(1) = \varphi(-1) = 0, \text{ and } 1 \neq -1.$$

There is a simple method for testing whether a given function is $(1, 1)$, in the case when its graph is easy to depict. The graph of the function $f : A \to B$ is the subset $\{(x, f(x)) : x \in A\}$ of $A \times B$. Denote by $H(b)$ the subset $\{(x, b) : x \in A\}$ of $A \times B$. We have

Theorem 3.4–A. Let A, B be sets, $f : A \to B$. Then, f is $(1, 1)$ $\Leftrightarrow$ for each $b \in B$, $f \cap H(b)$ is empty or contains exactly one point.

Proof. We use the method of contradiction in each part, by assuming p and $\sim q$. See Section 1.10.

The proof is illustrated in Fig. 3.4.4. The subset $H(b)$ is a horizontal line, through the point b, in $A \times B$. If the graph of f cuts this line in at most one point, for *every* b, then f is $(1, 1)$. If the graph cuts the line $H(b)$ more than once, for *any* b, then f is not $(1, 1)$.

---

† *Note.* The word **injective** is often used instead of $(1, 1)$.

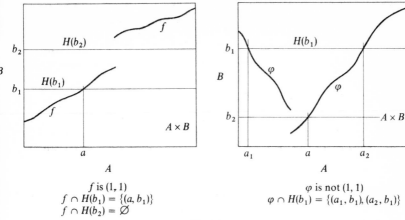

f is (1, 1)
$f \cap H(b_1) = \{(a, b_1)\}$
$f \cap H(b_2) = \varnothing$

φ is not (1, 1)
$\varphi \cap H(b_1) = \{(a_1, b_1), (a_2, b_1)\}$

Fig. 3.4.4.

(1) Suppose f is (1, 1). If $f \cap H(b_1)$ contains more than one point, for some b_1, then $\exists\, a_1, a_2$ in A, with $a_1 \neq a_2$ such that

$$(a_1, b_1) \quad \text{and} \quad (a_2, b_1) \in f \cap H(b_1).$$

Hence,

$$(a_1, b_1) \quad \text{and} \quad (a_2, b_1) \in f$$

which implies that $b_1 = f(a_1)$ and $b_1 = f(a_2)$. So, $f(a_1) = f(a_2)$ and $a_1 \neq a_2$, $\Rightarrow f$ is not (1, 1) $\Rightarrow\Leftarrow$. So, $f \cap H(b)$ contains at most one point, for every $b \in B$.

(2) Conversely, suppose $f \cap H(b)$ is empty or contains exactly one point, for every $b \in B$. We claim f is (1, 1). If not, $\exists\, a_1, a_2 \in A$ with $a_1 \neq a_2$, such that $f(a_1) = f(a_2)$. Write $f(a_1) = f(a_2) = b'$. Then $(a_1, b'), (a_2, b')$ belong to f, and to $H(b')$, by definition of the latter. So $f \cap H(b')$ contains at least two points $\Rightarrow\Leftarrow$. Hence, f is (1, 1).

3.5 Algebra of Functions

Suppose that B is a set in which operations of addition and multiplication are defined, A any set. (For example, we might take A, B to be subsets of R, and it is this context that we have in mind). Let f, g be functions of A into B.

Definition. We define the **sum function** of f and g to be the function φ given by

$$\varphi(x) = f(x) + g(x), \quad \text{for every } x \in A.$$

It is usual to denote the function φ by $f + g$.

Note that $f(x) \in B$, $g(x) \in B$, and so $f(x) + g(x)$ has meaning only if there is addition between elements of B.

Definition. The **difference function** of f and g is the function ψ given by

$$\psi(x) = f(x) - g(x), \quad \text{for every } x \in A.$$

We denote ψ by $f - g$. It exists only if subtraction is defined between elements of B.

Definition. The **product function** of f and g is the function θ given by

$$\theta(x) = f(x) \cdot g(x), \quad \text{for every } x \in A.$$

We usually denote θ by fg. It exists only if multiplication is defined between elements of B.

Definition. The **quotient function** of f and g is the function χ, defined for all elements x in A for which $g(x)$ is not the zero element of B, given by

$$\chi(x) = f(x)/g(x), \quad \text{for all } x \in A \text{ s.t. } g(x) \text{ is not zero in } B.$$

We denote χ by f/g. It exists only if division is defined between elements of B.

Note. If $f: A \to B$ and $g: C \to B$, then $f + g$, $f - g$, fg can only be defined on $A \cap C$, and f/g only on the subset of $A \cap C$ for which g does not take the value zero.

Example 3.5.1. Denote by j_n the function of R into R given by $j_n(x) = x^n$. If k is a number, the function kj_n is given by

$$kj_n(x) = kx^n.$$

Thus $4j_3$ is the function given by $4j_3(x) = 4x^3$.

Let $k_0, k_1, \ldots, k_r$ be real numbers, with $k_r \neq 0$. The function $f: R \to R$ given by

$$f(x) = k_0 + k_1 x + \ldots + k_r x^r$$

is called a **polynomial function**, of **degree** r. We have $f = k_0 + k_1 j + \ldots + k_r j_r$.

Example 3.5.2. By using the polynomial functions, we can construct the **rational functions.** This is a function ρ defined for all real numbers x for which $q(x) \neq 0$, given by

$$\rho(x) = p(x)/q(x),$$

where p and q are polynomial functions.

Example 3.5.3. The function $2 + j + j_3$ is a polynomial function of degree 3. Its value at x is $2 + x + x^3$. The function $(3 + j_2)/(1 + j_3)$, defined for all numbers except -1, is a rational function; its value at x is $(3 + x^2)/(1 + x^3)$.

Suppose now that B is an ordered set, $f: A \to B$.

Definition.   We say the function f is **bounded above** if there is an element k in B such that, for all $x \in A$, $f(x) \leqslant k$. f is **bounded below** if there is an element l in B such that, for all $x \in A$, $f(x) \geqslant l$. The function f is called **bounded** if it is both bounded above and bounded below.

This definition applies particularly to functions which map sets into subsets of R, although we have framed the definition in a slightly wider sense. The definition says that, if $f : A \to R$, then the *function* f is bounded, or bounded above, or below according as its *range* is a bounded subset (subset bounded above, or below) of R. We thus invest the function with the property that belongs to its range.

Suppose next that A and B are ordered sets, $f : A \to B$. Again, A and B might be subsets of R.

Definition.   The function f is called **increasing** if, for all $x, y \in A$, $x < y \Rightarrow f(x) < f(y)$. It is called **decreasing** if, for all $x, y \in A$, $x < y \Rightarrow f(x) > f(y)$.

There are two slightly weaker definitions associated with these.

Definition.   The function f is called **non-decreasing** if for all $x, y \in A$, $x < y \Rightarrow f(x) \leqslant f(y)$. It is called **non-increasing** if for all $x, y \in A$, $x < y \Rightarrow f(x) \geqslant f(y)$.

The word *monotonic* is often used to describe a function which belongs to one of these four types.

Note that, since we must compare both x, y and $f(x), f(y)$, the sets A, B must both be ordered sets.

Theorem 3.5–A.   Let A, B be ordered sets, $f : A \to B$. Then, if f is increasing (or decreasing), it is $(1, 1)$.

Proof.   Suppose f is increasing. Then for all $x < y$, $f(x) < f(y)$ i.e. $x \neq y \Rightarrow f(x) \neq f(y)$. So f is $(1, 1)$. ◆
The converse is false. Let $A = \{x \in R : -1 \leqslant x \leqslant 1\}$, $B = R$, and let f be the function given by

$$f(x) = \begin{cases} 2 - x & -1 \leqslant x < 0 \\ x & 0 \leqslant x \leqslant 1 \end{cases}$$

Then, $f(-1) = 3$, $f(-\tfrac{1}{2}) = \tfrac{5}{2}$, but $f(\tfrac{1}{2}) = \tfrac{1}{2}$, $f(1) = 1$. See Fig. 3.5.1.

Example 3.5.4.   Let $A = \{x \in R : -1 \leqslant x \leqslant 1\}$, $B = R$, and suppose f is the function given by

$$f(x) = (1 - x^2)^{\frac{1}{2}}$$

Then, f is a bounded function, since

$$0 \leqslant f(x) \leqslant 1, \qquad \forall\, x \in A.$$

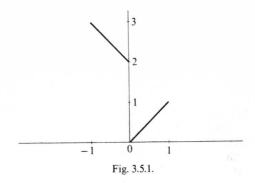

Fig. 3.5.1.

Example 3.5.5. Let s be the function with domain N and range in R given by

$$s(n) = 1/n^2, \qquad \forall \, n \in N.$$

Then, s is a decreasing function. For,

$$n_1 < n_2 \;\Rightarrow\; n_1^2 < n_2^2 \;\Rightarrow\; 1/n_1^2 > 1/n_2^2 \;\Rightarrow\; s(n_1) > s(n_2).$$

3.6 Composition of Functions

Suppose A, B, C are sets and $f:A \to B$, $g:B \to C$. There may be many possibilities for functions of A into C, but one obvious example sticks out. The functions f, g between them provide a transition from A to C (via the set B). For, if $x \in A$, then $f(x) \in B$; since $\mathscr{D}(g) = B$, $f(x) \in \mathscr{D}(g)$ and hence $g(f(x))$ is an element of C. Hence, from the point $x \in A$, we arrive at a point of C. Clearly, if f, g are functions, so is this relation between A and C. We therefore have the following definition.

Definition. Let A, B, C be sets, $f:A \to B$, $g:B \to C$. Then the mapping $\varphi:A \to C$ defined by

$$\varphi(x) = g(f(x)), \quad \text{for each } x \in A,$$

is called the **composition** of f and g. We denote φ by $g \circ f$.

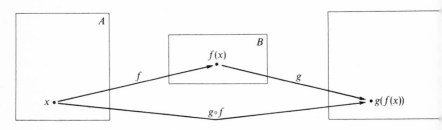

Fig. 3.6.1.

Example 3.6.1.   Let A be the subset of R given by $A = \{x \in R : -1 \leqslant x \leqslant 1\}$, B the subset given by $\{x \in R : x \geqslant 0\}$, $C = R$. Let $f : A \to B$ be given by

$$f(x) = 1 - x^2, \quad \text{for all } x \in A,$$

$g : B \to C$ be given by

$$g(y) = +\sqrt{y}, \quad \text{for all } y \in B.$$

Then the composition, $g \circ f$, is the function given by

$$g \circ f(x) = +\sqrt{1 - x^2}, \quad \text{for all } x \in A.$$

Example 3.6.2.   Let $A = B = C = R$, $f : A \to B$ be given by

$$f(x) = x^2, \quad \forall \, x \in A,$$

and $g : B \to C$ be given by

$$g(y) = y + 1, \quad \forall \, y \in B.$$

Then, $g \circ f : A \to C$ $(R \to R)$ is given by

$$g \circ f(x) = x^2 + 1, \quad \forall \, x \in R.$$

In the composition $g \circ f$, we have a function of A into C. If $x \in A$, we process x, first with f, and then the new element $f(x)$ in B with g. The order of processing is thus the **reverse** of the order in which f and g appear in print. Furthermore, the object $f \circ g$ is quite a different object from the function $g \circ f$; for, with $f \circ g$ we would process first *with g*, and so $f \circ g$ can be defined only on $\mathcal{D}(g)$, i.e. on B. If $y \in B$, then $g(y) \in C$; but of course $f \circ g(y) = f(g(y))$, and hence, for this to have any meaning, we must require $g(y)$ to belong to $\mathcal{D}(f)$ i.e. to A. Since $g(y) \in C$, this means that C must be a subset of A. Our conclusion, therefore, is: $f \circ g$ can be defined only if $C \subset A$, and if it is defined, it is a function of B into B. ($g : B \to A$ followed by $f : A \to B$).

This shows that it is highly unlikely that $f \circ g$ and $g \circ f$ will be the same even if both are defined; for $f \circ g$ maps B into B, while $g \circ f$ maps $A \to A$.

Example 3.6.3.   Let $A = \{1, 2, 3, 4\}$, $B = \{a, b, c\}$, $C = \{1, 2, 3\}$. Suppose $f : A \to B$ is given by $f(1) = c$, $f(2) = a$, $f(3) = b$, $f(4) = a$; suppose $g : B \to C$ is given by $g(a) = 3$, $g(b) = 1$, $g(c) = 2$.

Here, we have $C \subset A$, so $g \circ f$ and $f \circ g$ are both defined. $g \circ f$ is defined on A; it is given by

$$g \circ f(1) = 2, \quad g \circ f(2) = 3, \quad g \circ f(3) = 1, \quad g \circ f(4) = 3.$$

So $g \circ f$ is the subset

$$\{(1, 2), (2, 3), (3, 1), (4, 3)\}$$

of $A \times A$.

On the other hand, $f \circ g$ is defined, on B; it is given by

$$f \circ g(a) = b, \quad f \circ g(b) = c, \quad f \circ g(c) = a.$$

So $f \circ g$ is the subset

$$\{(a, b), (b, c), (c, a)\}$$

of $B \times B$, and clearly the two sets are completely different. The example is illustrated in Fig. 3.6.2.

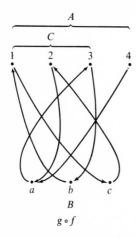 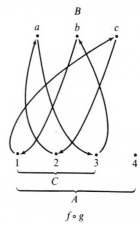

Fig. 3.6.2.

It can, of course, happen that A, B and C are all the same set, with the consequence that both $f \circ g$ and $g \circ f$ are defined, and both are functions of A into A. But even here, they are usually different functions. One need look no farther than Example 3.6.2. There, we have

$$f \circ g(x) = f(x+1) = (x+1)^2, \qquad \forall \, x \in R,$$

$$g \circ f(x) = g(x^2) = x^2 + 1, \qquad \forall \, x \in R,$$

and

$$(x+1)^2 \neq x^2 + 1 \text{ unless } x = 0.$$

We may ask what properties of f, g carry over to $g \circ f$, and conversely, what properties possessed by $g \circ f$ are possessed by f or g. We begin with the latter question.

Theorem 3.6–A.   Let A, B, C be sets, $f : A \to B$, $g : B \to C$. Then, $g \circ f$ is $(1, 1) \Rightarrow f$ is $(1, 1)$.

Proof.   Suppose $g \circ f$ is $(1, 1)$; then, $\forall \, a, b \in A$,

$$g \circ f(a) = g \circ f(b) \Rightarrow a = b \tag{1}$$

We now argue by contradiction, If f is not $(1, 1)$, $\exists\, a_1, b_1 \in A$ such that $a_1 \neq b_1$, and $f(a_1) = f(b_1)$. But

$$f(a_1) = f(b_1) \Rightarrow g(f(a_1)) = g(f(b_1)),$$

by definition of function. Thus,

$$g \circ f(a_1) = g \circ f(b_1) \quad \text{and } a_1 \neq b_1,$$

which contradicts (1). Hence f is $(1, 1)$. ◆

Let A, B, C be sets, $f : A \to B$, $g : B \to C$. Suppose $g \circ f$ is a constant function. Then, in this case, almost nothing can be deduced; f may be constant; g may be constant. Examples can be easily constructed to show f constant or non constant, and likewise for g. If $\mathscr{R}(f) = B$, however, then g must be constant.

Example 3.6.4.   Let $A = \{a, b, c\}$, $B = \{1, 2, 3, 4\}$, $C = \{\alpha, \beta, \gamma\}$.
(1) Let $f : A \to B$ be given by $f(x) = 1, \forall\, x \in A$, $g(1) = \alpha$. Then, $g \circ f$ is constant, and so is f. g may or may not be constant.
(2) Let $f : A \to B$ be given by $f(a) = 1$, $f(b) = 2$, $f(c) = 2$, $g : B \to C$ be given by $g(x) = \alpha, \forall\, x \in B$. Then $g \circ f$ is constant, g is constant and f is not.
(3) Let f be as in (2), g be given by $g(1) = \alpha$, $g(2) = \alpha$, $g(3) = \beta$, $g(4) = \gamma$. Then $g \circ f$ is constant, but neither f nor g is constant.

We next have the result that if two functions are $(1, 1)$, then so is their composition.

Theorem 3.6–B.   Let A, B, C be sets, $f : A \to B$, $g : B \to C$. Then,

$$f \text{ is } (1, 1) \text{ and } g \text{ is } (1, 1) \Rightarrow g \circ f \text{ is } (1, 1).$$

The proof is left to the reader, who should note that Theorems 3.6–A and 3.6–B are not converses of each other.

It is easy to show, in the context of constant functions, that if f or g is constant, then so is $g \circ f$. We mention at this point, two other results about composition functions.

Theorem 3.6–C.   Let A, B, C be sets, $f : A \to B$, $g : B \to C$.
  (a) if $\mathscr{R}(f) = B$ and $\mathscr{R}(g) = C$, then $\mathscr{R}(g \circ f) = C$.
  (b) if $\mathscr{R}(g \circ f) = C$, then $\mathscr{R}(g) = C$.
Proof of (b). Suppose $\mathscr{R}(g \circ f) = C$. Let c be any element of C. Then, there is an element $a \in A$ such that $c = g \circ f(a)$. That is, $c = g(f(a))$. Since $f(a) \in B$, we have $c = g(b)$, where $b = f(a) \in B$, i.e. $\mathscr{R}(g) = C$. *The proof of* (a) *is left to the reader.* ◆

Note.   A function $f : A \to B$ whose range is all of B is sometimes called **surjective**.

3.7 The Inverse Function

Suppose that A and B are sets, $f : A \to B$. We might ask what functions there are from B into A, based on the function f by a sort of reversing process. For example, if $b \in B$, we might think of associating b with the element $a \in A$ such that $b = f(a)$. However, there are two objections to this.

In the first place, there is no guarantee that there *is* any $a \in A$ such that $b = f(a)$. For this requires that $b \in f(A)$, and since we are supposing that $b \in B$, we must therefore have $B \subset f(A)$. But $f : A \to B$, so that $f(A) \subset B$; hence, in order to ensure that, given $b \in B$, there is an $a \in A$ such that $b = f(a)$, we must have $B = f(A)$; in other words, the range of f must be all of B.

There are two possible ways of overcoming this difficulty. One way is to accept the condition, restrict our attention to functions f whose range is all of B, and proceed from there. The other course, and the one which we shall adopt, is to alter the problem slightly, and turn our attention to finding a function, based on f, which maps the subset $f(A)$ of B into A. By considering $f(A)$ rather than B, we overcome the objection above; and of course, we include, as a special case, the situation when $f(A) = B$.

Nevertheless, even restricting our attention to $f(A)$, there is still a very serious difficulty; given an element $b \in f(A)$, there is absolutely no certainty that there is *only* one element $a \in A$ with $b = f(a)$. We know there is at least one, but there may be more. Suppose $b = f(a_1) = f(a_2)$ with $a_1 \neq a_2$. We can no longer associate with b the element in A such that b is the image of this under f. We are back in the ambiguous situation of Examples 3.1.3 and 3.1.5, and this association we are thinking up will not yield a function. So, we must ask that the situation $f(a_1) = f(a_2)$ and $a_1 \neq a_2$ should not arise. In other words, we demand that $f(a_1) = f(a_2) \Rightarrow a_1 = a_2$, or that f be $(1, 1)$.

So a solution of our problem depends on f being $(1, 1)$ (and considering $f(A)$ rather than B). Unfortunately, most functions are not $(1, 1)$, so our problem will not usually have a solution. However, let us define the function we are seeking when it does exist.

Definition. Let A, B be sets, $f : A \to B$ such that f is $(1, 1)$. Let a be a dummy with domain A, and write $b = f(a)$; then b is a dummy with domain $f(A)$.

Let φ be the function defined on $f(A)$ and taking values in A, given by setting, for each $b \in f(A)$,

$$\varphi(b) = a.$$

Then, φ is called the **inverse function** of f.

In consequence of the definition, if f is $(1, 1)$, then φ is defined by

$$\varphi \circ f(a) = a, \qquad \forall\, a \in A, \tag{1}$$

that is, $\varphi \circ f$ is the identity function.

Example 3.7.1.   Let A, B be the set of real numbers, $f : A \to B$ the function given by $f(x) = x^3$, for all x in A. In this case $\mathcal{R}(f) = R$, so the inverse function φ will also be a function of R into R. It is given by

$$\varphi(y) = y^{\frac{1}{3}},$$

for all y in R. We observe that, for all $x \in R$,

$$\varphi \circ f(x) = \varphi(x^3)$$
$$= (x^3)^{\frac{1}{3}}$$
$$= x$$

i.e. $\varphi \circ f$ is the identity (Fig. 3.7.1).

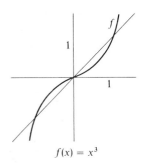

$$f(x) = x^3 \qquad\qquad\qquad \varphi(y) = y^{\frac{1}{3}}$$

Fig. 3.7.1.

Theorem 3.7–A.   Let f be a $(1, 1)$ function of A into B, φ the inverse function of f, mapping $f(A)$ into A. Then, φ is $(1, 1)$ and has range A. Consequently, φ has an inverse function of A into $f(A)$; the inverse function of φ is f.

Proof.   That $\mathcal{R}(\varphi) = A$ follows at once from the remark immediately preceding the theorem.

Next, suppose $\varphi(b_1) = \varphi(b_2)$; since $b_1, b_2 \in f(A)$, $\exists\, a_1, a_2 \in A$ such that $b_i = f(a_i)$, $i = 1, 2$. Hence

$$\varphi(f(a_1)) = \varphi(f(a_2))$$
$$\Rightarrow a_1 = a_2 \quad \text{by (1)}$$
$$\Rightarrow b_1 = b_2$$

so that φ is $(1, 1)$.

Finally, since $\varphi : f(A) \to A$ is $(1, 1)$, φ has an inverse function, ψ say, defined on $\mathcal{R}(\varphi) = A$, and given by

$$\psi \circ \varphi(b) = b, \qquad \forall\, b \in f(A).$$

Suppose $b = f(a)$, since f is (1, 1); then,

$$\psi \circ \varphi \circ f(a) = f(a), \qquad \forall\, a \in A.$$
$$\Rightarrow \psi(a) = f(a), \qquad \forall\, a \in A, \quad \text{by (1).}$$
$$\Rightarrow \quad \psi = f$$

by definition.   ◆

At this point, we shall digress to consider a more general situation, and show how the inverse function defined above is a special aspect of this.

We consider two sets A, B and a function $f : A \to B$, which is *not necessarily* (1, 1). If Y is a subset of B, we can consider the subset of A consisting of all elements of A whose images under f are in Y. It is convenient to have a name for this subset.

Definition.   Let A, B be sets, $f : A \to B$, Y a subset of B. Let X be the subset of A given by

$$X = \{x \in A : f(x) \in Y\}$$

Then, X is called the **inverse image** of Y under f. It is denoted by $f^{-1}(Y)$.

Y may be any subset of B; in particular, it may be a single-element subset b of B. The set $f^{-1}(\{b\})$, however, need not consist of a single element of A.

Example 3.7.2.   Let $A = B = R$, f be the function given by $f(x) = x^2$.
(1) if $Y_0 = \{y \in R : -1 \leqslant y \leqslant 9\}$, then $f^{-1}(Y_0) = \{x \in R : -3 \leqslant x \leqslant 3\}$;
(2) if $Y_1 = \{y \in R : y = 0\}$, then $f^{-1}(Y_1) = f^{-1}(\{0\}) = \{0\}$;
(3) if $Y_2 = \{1\}$, then $f^{-1}(Y_2) = \{-1, +1\}$;
(4) if $Y_3 = \{-1\}$, then $f^{-1}(Y_3) = \varnothing$.
(1) shows a general example of the inverse image of a set; (2), (3) and (4) show that if Y is a single-element subset of B, then $f^{-1}(Y)$ may contain several elements, one element, or even no elements at all.

The definition above shows us how to associate a subset of A with a given subset of B. It is clear that, given a subset Y of B, there is one and only one subset X of A such that $X = f^{-1}(Y)$. So we have set up a function which maps the *subsets* of B into the *subsets* of A. It is not a function of B into A, because Example 3.7.2. shows that more than one *element* of A may be associated with an *element* of B, or perhaps no element of A at all! So we have a function of the *subsets of B* into the *subsets of A*. This calls for a definition.

Definition.   Let A, B be sets, $f : A \to B$. Denote by f^{-1} the mapping of the subsets of B into the subsets of A defined by setting, for each subset Y of B,

$$f^{-1}(Y) = \{x \in A : f(x) \in Y\}.$$

This mapping or function is called the **inverse** of f.

Example 3.7.3.   Let $A = \{1, 2, 3\}$, $B = \{a, b, c\}$, and $f : A \to B$ be the function given by $f = \{(1, a), (2, c), (3, c)\}$. Consider the subsets of B and their inverse images under f:—

$$\varnothing \qquad\qquad f^{-1}(\varnothing) = \varnothing$$
$$\{a\} \qquad\qquad f^{-1}(\{a\}) = \{1\}$$
$$\{b\} \qquad\qquad f^{-1}(\{b\}) = \varnothing$$
$$\{c\} \qquad\qquad f^{-1}(\{c\}) = \{2, 3\}$$
$$\{a, b\} \qquad\qquad f^{-1}(\{a, b\}) = \{1\}$$
$$\{b, c\} \qquad\qquad f^{-1}(\{b, c\}) = \{2, 3\}$$
$$\{c, a\} \qquad\qquad f^{-1}(\{c, a\}) = \{1, 2, 3\} = A$$
$$\{a, b, c\} = B \qquad f^{-1}(B) = A.$$

This gives us a complete description of the inverse of f, viz. f^{-1}.

Note.   This function is called the *inverse* of f, and never the *inverse function* of f. The latter maps elements of $f(A)$ into the elements of A.

A glance at Example 3.7.3 will reveal interesting possibilities of set relations between $f^{-1}(Y_1)$, $f^{-1}(Y_2)$ as relations between Y_1 and Y_2 are set up. For instance, we note in Example 3.7.3, that $f^{-1}(\{a, c\}) = \{1, 2, 3\} = f^{-1}(\{a\}) \cup f^{-1}(\{c\})$. The next theorem elaborates this theme in more general terms.

Theorem 3.7–B.   Let A, B be sets, $f : A \to B$. Suppose Y_1, Y_2 are subsets of B. Then,

   (a) $Y_1 \subset Y_2 \Rightarrow f^{-1}(Y_1) \subset f^{-1}(Y_2)$;
   (b) $f^{-1}(Y_1 \cup Y_2) = f^{-1}(Y_1) \cup f^{-1}(Y_2)$;
   (c) $f^{-1}(Y_1 \cap Y_2) = f^{-1}(Y_1) \cap f^{-1}(Y_2)$;
   (d) $C_A(f^{-1}(Y_1)) = f^{-1}(C_B(Y_1))$.

Proof.   We shall prove (a) and (b), leaving (c) and (d) to the reader.
(a). Let x be an element of $f^{-1}(Y_1)$; then,

$$x \in f^{-1}(Y_1) \;\Leftrightarrow\; f(x) \in Y_1 \qquad \text{(definition)}$$
$$\Rightarrow\; f(x) \in Y_2 \qquad \text{(since } Y_1 \subset Y_2\text{)}$$
$$\Leftrightarrow\; x \in f^{-1}(Y_2) \qquad \text{(definition)}.$$

So

$$Y_1 \subset Y_2 \;\Rightarrow\; f^{-1}(Y_1) \subset f^{-1}(Y_2) \text{ by Theorem 1.8–A.}$$

(b). We have

$$x \in f^{-1}(Y_1 \cup Y_2) \Leftrightarrow f(x) \in Y_1 \cup Y_2$$
$$\Leftrightarrow f(x) \in Y_1 \quad \text{or} \quad f(x) \in Y_2$$
$$\Leftrightarrow x \in f^{-1}(Y_1) \quad \text{or} \quad x \in f^{-1}(Y_2)$$
$$\Leftrightarrow x \in f^{-1}(Y_1) \cup f^{-1}(Y_2)$$

whence the result by Theorem 1.8–B.   ◆

Suppose we now return to the problem of defining a function from $f(A)$ into A. Can we make use of the discussion we have just had? The answer is affirmative.

What we do is to consider all subsets of $f(A)$ which consist of a *single* element. If $\{b\}$ is such a subset, $f^{-1}(\{b\})$ will be a subset of A consisting of a single element, *provided that f is $(1, 1)$*; that is, $f^{-1}(\{b\}) = \{a\}$ for some $a \in A$. If we now identify the *subset* $\{b\}$ of $f(A)$ with the *element* b of $f(A)$, and the *subset* $\{a\}$ of A with the *element* a of A, we can think of f^{-1} (applied to single-element subsets of $f(A)$) as a function of $f(A)$ into A. It is not the inverse of f as defined on page 93; it is the *restriction* of this inverse f^{-1} to the collection of single-element subsets of $f(A)$.

It is easy to see that this restriction of f^{-1} is the same function as the inverse function φ, if we agree to identify single-element subsets with elements. So we introduce the following notation.

Definition.   Let A, B be sets, $f : A \to B$ a $(1, 1)$ function. The inverse function $\varphi : f(A) \to A$ will be denoted by f^{-1}.

Example 3.7.4.   Let $A = B = R$, and suppose f is the function sin. Its graph is shown in Fig. 3.7.2. Then, $f(A) = \{y \in R : -1 \leqslant y \leqslant 1\}$. The function, however, is not $(1, 1)$ [see Fig. 3.4.4]. It would therefore seem that the function sin does not have an inverse function, and this is indeed so.

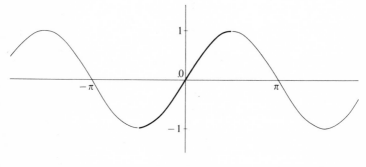

Graph of sin
Fig. 3.7.2.

However, we can construct an inverse function for a restriction of sin.

The function Sin (Example 3.3.1), whose domain is the subset $\{x \in R : -\pi/2 \leqslant x \leqslant \pi/2\}$ is a (1, 1) function. Hence, it has an inverse function, which maps the closed interval $[-1, 1]$ into the closed interval $[-\pi/2, \pi/2]$. This inverse function is usually called arcsin; we use a lower case "s" since no confusion can arise. Some textbooks use the notation $\sin^{-1}$, but we shall not adopt this. The function arcsin is discussed in detail in Section 9.8.

Example 3.7.5. Let $A = \{1, 2, 3\}$, $B = \{a, b, c\}$, and $f : A \to B$ be given by $\{(1, c), (2, a), (3, b)\}$. Then f is (1, 1), and $B = f(A)$. So f has an inverse function $f^{-1} : B \to A$, and

$$f^{-1} = \{(a, 2), (b, 3), (c, 1)\}.$$

Note that we merely reverse the order in the pairs of f.

3.8 Sequences

Most of our discussion so far has been about functions in general, whose domain has been an arbitrary set A. The present section is concerned with a particular kind of function whose domain is the set N of natural numbers. We have already seen examples of a function with domain N in Examples 3.1.7, 3.2.2 and 3.5.5.

One important property of the set N is that it has a *least element*, namely 1, and every non-empty subset of N also has a least element.* So we can "tabulate" or "enumerate" the elements of N, the least element, 1, being placed first, the next least, 2, being placed second, and so on... This gives us the *natural order* for $N : 1, 2, 3, 4, \ldots$ It follows also that every non-empty subset of N can also be enumerated in order of increasing magnitude. For example, the even natural numbers, being a subset of N, have a least element (namely 2); the set of all even natural numbers except 2 also has a least element, namely 4. Proceeding in this way, we obtain the tabulation $2, 4, 6, 8, \ldots$ for the even natural numbers.

Other sets besides N can be "enumerated", in the sense that we can produce a "list" which has a first element, a second element, a third, and so on, and each element of the given set occurs in a precise place in the list. For instance, $0, 1, -1, 2, -2, 3, -3, \ldots$ is a "list" of the integers Z. If n is a positive integer, then it occupies the $2n$-th place in this list. The reader can verify that 2 occupies fourth place, and 3 occupies sixth place. Likewise, if $-m$ denotes a negative integer (with $m > 0$), it occupies $(2m+1)$-th place; for example, -2 is in fifth place, which is $(2m+1)$-th with $m = 2$. However, the perceptive reader

---

* This is because N is "well-ordered" (Appendix to Chapter 2).

will have already observed that Z has no least element, and that Z is certainly not enumerated in order of increasing magnitude.

Of course, since N and Z are infinite sets, we cannot put the elements down in a "list" which has a *last* member; the "list" is unending. All we are saying is that some sets have the property that we can produce a tabulation of their elements, so that every element occupies a designated place, and we can say which element occurs in which place.

Not *all* sets can be "listed" in this way. The set R and many of its subsets do not have this property. Just why this is so is beyond our range of interest in this book, and so we will do no more than to assert it.

Now, suppose s is a function with domain N. We can certainly enumerate the elements of the range of s, irrespective of what sort of objects they may be. For, since $1 \to s(1)$, $2 \to s(2)$, and so on . . . , we merely superimpose, on $\mathcal{R}(s)$, the natural order of N. Thus, we have

$$
\begin{array}{cccc}
1, & 2, & 3, & 4, \dots \\
\downarrow & \downarrow & \downarrow & \downarrow \\
s(1), & s(2), & s(3), & s(4), \dots
\end{array}
$$

The *first* element of $\mathcal{R}(s)$ is defined to be the image of the first element in N, the *second* element of $\mathcal{R}(s)$ the image of the second element in N, . . . This special situation demands a new definition.

Definition.   Let s be a function with domain N and range in some set B. Then, the set

$$\{s(1), s(2), s(3), s(4), \dots\}$$

of elements of the range of s, listed in corresponding order to N, is called a **sequence**. It may be written with or without the braces.

If the range of s is in R, then the set $\{s(1), s(2), s(3), s(4), \dots\}$ is called a **real** sequence.

The element $s(n)$ of $\mathcal{R}(s)$, the image of n, is called the **n-th term** of the sequence.

A special notation is used for sequences, to indicate that it is not just an ordinary set. We write s_n for the n-th term, instead of $s(n)$. The sequence is thus written as

$$\{s_1, s_2, s_3, s_4, \dots\},$$

with or without the braces. Another more concise notation is $\{s_n\}$. Thus, $\{a_n\}$, $\{b_n\}$ denote sequences derived from functions a, b of N into R.

A sequence contains infinitely many terms, and for this reason, the terminology "infinite sequence" used to be common in textbooks. We shall not adopt it. Note, however, that although the sequence $\{s_n\}$ contains infinitely many terms, the range of the associated function s need not (see Example 3.8.2).

Example 3.8.1. Let $s: N \to R$ be given by writing, for each $n \in N$, $s(n) = (-1)^n/n^2$. Then, s determines the sequence

$$-1, \tfrac{1}{4}, -\tfrac{1}{9}, \tfrac{1}{16}, \ldots$$

For, $s(1) = -1$, $s(2) = \tfrac{1}{4}$, $s(3) = -\tfrac{1}{9}$, etc. This sequence is also written as $\{(-1)^n/n^2\}$.

Example 3.8.2. Let $s: N \to R$ be given by writing, for each $n \in N$,

$$s(n) = (-1)^n \text{ i.e. } s(n) = \begin{cases} 1 \text{ if } n \text{ is even} \\ -1 \text{ if } n \text{ is odd.} \end{cases}$$

Then, s determines the sequence

$$-1, 1, -1, 1, \ldots$$

or $\{(-1)^n\}$. In this case, $\mathscr{R}(s)$ contains only two distinct elements, namely $+1$ and -1.

Example 3.8.3. Let s be the function with domain N and image space $R \times R$ given by setting, for each $n \in N$,

$$s_n = (1/n, n^2 - 1).$$

Then, s determines the sequence

$$(1, 0), (\tfrac{1}{2}, 3), (\tfrac{1}{3}, 8), (\tfrac{1}{4}, 15), \ldots$$

Here, each function value is an ordered pair; nevertheless, the first ordered pair is $s(1)$, the second is $s(2)$ etc.; the sequence is a *sequence of ordered pairs*, in this case.

In general, the function s associated with a sequence $\{s_n\}$ is described by giving a rule or formula for calculating s_n.

We can talk about special kinds of sequence, as we talked about special kinds of function. Most important, from our point of view, are the ideas of increasing sequences and bounded sequences. In view of our earlier remark about investing functions with properties that belong to their range, this is particularly easy for sequences.

Definition. Let $\{s_n\}$ be a real sequence. Then, we say $\{s_n\}$ is **increasing** if $s_n < s_m$ for all $n < m$.

An alternative form, which is easily shown to be equivalent, is to say that, for all $n \in N$, $s_n < s_{n+1}$.

Definition. If $\{s_n\}$ is a real sequence, we say that $\{s_n\}$ is **non-decreasing** if $n < m$ implies that $s_n \leqslant s_m$. (Alternatively, if $s_n \leqslant s_{n+1}$, for all n.)

We leave the reader to write out the definitions of decreasing and non-increasing real sequences.

Definition. If $\{s_n\}$ is a real sequence, we say that $\{s_n\}$ is **bounded above** if there is a constant K such that for all n, $s_n \leqslant K$. It is **bounded below** if there is a constant M such that, for all n, $s_n \geqslant M$. A real sequence which is bounded above and bounded below is called **bounded**.

Example 3.8.4. An increasing real sequence is bounded below.

Proof. Let $\{s_n\}$ be increasing. Then, if $n < m$, $s_n < s_m$. In particular, taking $n = 1$,

$$s_1 < s_m, \qquad \text{for all } m > 1.$$

Let $M = s_1$; then

$$s_m \geqslant M, \qquad \text{for all } m \in N.$$

i.e. $\{s_n\}$ is bounded below. ◆

Suppose now that $\{s_n\}$ is a sequence, determined by a function s of N into some set B, say. Let $\{v_k\}$ be an increasing sequence of natural numbers. Then, $\{v_k\}$ is determined by an increasing function v with domain N and *range in N*. (Furthermore, by Theorem 3.5–A, v is $(1, 1)$.) We can therefore consider the composition σ of v and s; σ has domain N and range in B, and so determines a sequence $\sigma_1, \sigma_2, \sigma_3, \sigma_4, \ldots$ Since $\sigma_k = \sigma(k) = s \circ v(k) = s(v_k)$, it follows that the sequence determined by σ is

$$s_{v_1}, s_{v_2}, s_{v_3}, s_{v_4}, \ldots$$

This new sequence is a subset of the set $s_1, s_2, s_3, s_4, \ldots$, for we have $s \circ v(N) \subset s(N)$. It is called a *subsequence* of $\{s_n\}$. Since v is any increasing function on N into N, it is clear that a sequence $\{s_n\}$ will have many subsequences.

In view of the fact that $v(N)$ is a subset of N we can also think of σ above as the restriction of s to $v(N)$. Since v_k is the kth term of the sequence $\{v_k\}$, the restriction of s to $v(N)$ determines the sequence

$$s_{v_1}, s_{v_2}, s_{v_3}, s_{v_4}, \ldots,$$

as above.

So, we have the following definition.

Definition. Let $\{s_n\}$ be a sequence, determined by the function $s : N \to B$, and let $\{v_k\}$ be an increasing sequence of *natural numbers*, determined by $v : N \to N$. Then the sequence determined by the composition $s \circ v : N \to B$,

$$s_{v_1}, s_{v_2}, s_{v_3}, s_{v_4}, \ldots$$

is called a **subsequence** of $\{s_n\}$, and is written briefly as $\{s_{v_k}\}$.

The notation indicates that the k-th term of the subsequence is the same as the v_k-th term of the original sequence.

Example 3.8.5. Let $s : N \to R$ be the function given by

$$s(n) = (-1)^n / n^2.$$

It determines the sequence $-1, \frac{1}{4}, -\frac{1}{9}, \frac{1}{16}, \ldots$ The set of even natural numbers forms an increasing sequence, which is determined by the function $v: N \to N$ given by $v(k) = 2k$. The restriction of s to $\{v_k\}$ thus determines the sequence $s_2, s_4, s_6, s_8, \ldots$; using the composition approach, $s \circ v(k) = s(v_k) = s(2k) = s_{2k}$, as before. Hence we obtain for the general term of the subsequence

$$s_{2k} = (-1)^{2k}/(2k)^2$$
$$= 1/4k^2;$$

it is therefore the sequence $\frac{1}{4}, \frac{1}{16}, \frac{1}{36}, \frac{1}{64}, \ldots$ The third term $(k = 3)$ of this, for instance, is $\frac{1}{36}$, which is the sixth $(v_k = 2k = 6)$ term of the original.

Example 3.8.6. Let s be the function given by $s(n) = 2^n/n!$. It determines the sequence

$$2, 2, \tfrac{4}{3}, \tfrac{2}{3}, \tfrac{4}{15}, \ldots$$

The set of all prime numbers is an increasing sequence of natural numbers, given by the function v where

$$v(k) = k\text{-th prime number};$$

thus $v(1) = 2, v(2) = 3, v(3) = 5, v(4) = 7, \ldots$ (see Example 3.1.7).

The restriction of s to the set $\{v_k\} = \{2, 3, 5, 7, \ldots\}$ determines the subsequence

$$2, \tfrac{4}{3}, \tfrac{4}{15}, \tfrac{8}{315}, \ldots$$

with k-th term s_{v_k}, to be calculated from the given information.

Once again, $s \circ v(k) = s(v_k) = s_{v_k}$; thus,

$$s_{v_1} = s \circ v(1) = s(2) = 2,$$
$$s_{v_2} = s \circ v(2) = s(3) = \tfrac{4}{3},$$
$$s_{v_3} = s \circ v(3) = s(5) = \tfrac{4}{15}(= 2^5/5!)$$
$$s_{v_4} = s \circ v(4) = s(7) = \tfrac{8}{315}(= 2^7/7!).$$

So we see how to calculate the subsequence as a composition, and as a restriction.

The study of sequences is a subject of importance in Analysis, and so we shall devote the whole of the next chapter to a detailed account of sequences. Many of the results have analogues for real valued functions also; these we shall see when we discuss real valued functions in Chapter 6.

Exercises

Which of the following are functions?

1. $A = \{x \in R : x \geqslant 0\}$, $B = R$, f given by $f(x) = \sqrt{x}, \forall\, x \in A$.

2. A = set of all married men, B the set of all women, f given by $f(a)$ = wife of a, $\forall\ a \in A$.
3. A and B as in Exercise 2, and g given by $g(b)$ = husband of b, $\forall\ b \in B$.

   In the following six exercises, $A = \{1, 2, 3\}$, $B = \{a, b, c\}$. Which of the following sets are functions of A into B?
4. $f_1 = \{(1, a), (2, a), (3, a)\}$.
5. $f_2 = \{(1, b), (3, c)\}$.
6. $f_3 = \{(3, c), (1, b), (2, b)\}$.
7. $f_4 = \{(a, 1), (b, 1), (c, 2)\}$.
8. $f_5 = \{(1, a), (2, b), (3, d)\}$.
9. $f_6 = \{(1, c), (3, a), (2, b)\}$.
10. Let A be the set $\{x \in R : -2 \leqslant x \leqslant 6\}$; let f be the function on A given by $f(x) = x^2$. Find $f(4)$, $f(-4)$, $f(y-2)$.
11. Let $f : R \to R$ be given by

$$f(x) = \begin{cases} 2x + 3 & x \geqslant 5; \\ 4 - x^2 & -1 \leqslant x < 5; \\ -(9x + 10) & x < -1; \end{cases}$$

   find $f(6)$, $f(-1)$, $f(-4)$, $f(3)$, $f(5)$.
12. Let $A = \{\alpha, \beta, \gamma, \delta\}$, $B = R$, $f : A \to B$ be given by $f = \{(\alpha, 0), (\beta, 1), (\gamma, 1), (\delta, 0)\}$. What is $\mathcal{R}(f)$?
13. Let A, B be sets. Denote by $V(a)$ the subset of $A \times B$ given by

$$V(a) = \{(a, y) : y \in B\}.$$

   Prove that a subset G of $A \times B$ is a function of A into B if and only if, for each $a \in A$, $G \cap V(a)$ consists of a single point.
   [Hint: $V(a)$ represents a vertical line through a. If $G \cap V(a)$ contains more than one point, then G contains two ordered pairs with first element a. If $G \cap V(a)$ is empty, then G cannot be a function with domain A. Conversely, if G is a function of A into B, G contains precisely one ordered pair with first element a.]
14. Let A, B be sets, and let $H(b)$ be defined as in Section 3.4. Let f be a function of A into B. Show that the range of f is all of B if and only if, for all $b \in B$, $f \cap H(b)$ is not empty.
   [$H(b)$ is a horizontal line through b. If $f \cap H(b)$ is empty, f does not contain an ordered pair with second element b. Converse similar.]
15. Let $f : A \to B$ be a constant function. If f is also $(1, 1)$, show that A must consist of a single element.
16. If $f : A \to B$ is a constant function, and the range of f is all of B, show that B consists of a single element.
17. Which of the functions occurring in Exercises 1–8 are $(1, 1)$? Which have range all of B? [For example, in Exercise 9, f_6 is $(1, 1)$, because distinct elements of A have distinct images;

$\mathscr{R}(f) = B$, because each element of B appears as a second element in the ordered pairs of f_6.]

18. Let A = set of all human beings, $B = N$. Let $\varphi : A \to B$ be given by

$$\varphi(x) = \text{age in years, of } x, \ \forall \ x \in A.$$

Is $\varphi(1, 1)$? Is $\mathscr{R}(\varphi) = B$?

19. Let $A = \{1, 2, 3\}$, $B = \{a, b\}$. Define all possible functions of A into B, and say which are $(1, 1)$.

20. If A, B are as in Exercise 19, define all possible functions of B into A, and say which are $(1, 1)$.

21. Show by constructing suitable examples, that in Theorem 3.6–A, g need not be $(1, 1)$, while in Theorem 3.6–C(b), $\mathscr{R}(f)$ need not be all of B.

22. Prove Theorem 3.6–B.

23. Show, by examples, that the condition "g is $(1, 1)$" is necessary in Theorem 3.6–B, and the condition "$\mathscr{R}(f) = B$" is necessary in Theorem 3.6–C(a).

24. Prove Theorem 3.7–B(c) and (d).

25. A certain mapping f of A into B is also a mapping of B into A. Show that (a) $A = B$, (b) f need not be $(1, 1)$.

26. f and g are functions on R into R given by

$$f(x) = 2x - 3, \quad g(x) = x^2 + 5, \quad \forall \ x \in R.$$

Find $f(5)$, $g(-2)$, $g \circ f(0)$, $f \circ g(7)$, $g(x - 1)$, $f \circ g(x - 1)$, $g \circ g(x)$, $f \circ g(0)$.

27. Show, by an example, that the statement

$$f^{-1}(Y_1) \subset f^{-1}(Y_2) \ \Rightarrow \ Y_1 \subset Y_2$$

is false.

28. Let A, B be sets, $f : A \to B$. Let X be any subset of A. Show that $f^{-1} \circ f(X) \supset X$. Show also that $f^{-1} \circ f(X) = X \ \Leftrightarrow \ f$ is $(1, 1)$. [Hint for second part: suppose for all X, $X = f^{-1} \circ f(X)$ and f is not $(1, 1)$; then there exist x_1, x_2 with $x_1 \neq x_2$ but $f(x_1) = f(x_2)$. Consider $X' = \{x_1\}$ and show $X' \neq f^{-1} \circ f(X')$. Conversely, suppose f is $(1, 1)$, X any subset of A. Show that if $x \in f^{-1} \circ f(X)$, then $x \in X$ (using the $(1, 1)$ property). Hence, by the first part of the exercise, $f^{-1} \circ f(X) = X$.]

29. Let A, B be sets, $f : A \to B$. Suppose Y is any subset of B. Prove that $f \circ f^{-1}(Y) \subset Y$, and that the inclusion may be strict; and that

$$f \circ f^{-1}(Y) = Y \ \Leftrightarrow \ \mathscr{R}(f) = B.$$

[If $x \in f \circ f^{-1}(Y)$, then we can write $x = f(z)$, where $z \in f^{-1}(Y)$. Hence, $x \in Y$.

Let Y be any subset of B, y any element of Y. Then, if $\mathscr{R}(f) = B(\supset Y)$, there is an element $x \in A$ such that $y = f(x)$.

Show that this implies $y \in f \circ f^{-1}(Y)$ and use the first part for equality.

Conversely, if $\mathscr{R}(f) \neq B$, there is a point $y \in B$ such that $y \neq f(x)$, for any $x \in A$. Take $Y = \{y\}$.]

30. Suppose that A, B are sets, $f : A \to B$, $g : B \to A$, and $g \circ f$ is the identity function on A. Which of the following assertions are true and which are false;
    (a) $g = f^{-1}$;
    (b) the range of f is all of B;
    (c) the range of g is all of A;
    (d) g is $(1, 1)$;
    (e) f is $(1, 1)$?

31. Let $A = \{1, 2, 3, 4\}$, $B = \{a, b, c\}$, $f : A \to B$ be given by $f = \{(1, c), (2, a), (3, b), (4, c)\}$. Find $f^{-1}(\{a\})$, $f^{-1}(B)$, $f^{-1}(\{b, c\})$, $f^{-1}(\{c\})$. Is there an inverse function of f?

32. Let $f : R \to R$ be the function given by

$$f(x) = x^2 - 5x + 6, \qquad \forall \, x \in R.$$

What is $f^{-1}(\{0\})$? What is $f^{-1}(\{2\})$? If $B = \{y \in R : 0 \leqslant y \leqslant 2\}$, find $f^{-1}(B)$. Has f got an inverse function?

33. Let A, B, C be sets, $f : A \to B$, $g : B \to C$ such that inverse functions f^{-1}, g^{-1} exist. Show that $g \circ f$ has an inverse function, and find the connection between $(g \circ f)^{-1}$, f^{-1} and g^{-1}.

34. Prove that if f is increasing, then so is f^{-1}.

35. Let $\{s_n\}$ be a real sequence. Suppose v is the sequence given by setting, for each $p \in N$,

$$v(p) = p + k,$$

where k is a fixed positive integer. v is called a **shift** sequence. What is the subsequence $s \circ v$?

Work out this example for the particular case when $s_n = n^2$, and $k = 6$.

Part Three: The Limit Process (Convergence)

Quite the most fundamental concept in Analysis is that of the *limit of a function*. It underlies the idea of the sum of a series, and it also underlies the ideas of differentiation and integration. In Part Three, we therefore give a systematic introduction to this important concept. We begin, in Chapter 4, by discussing the convergence of sequences, for this provides the easiest introduction to limits. Next, in Chapter 5, we consider the closely related problem of convergence of infinite series. Chapter 6 is then concerned with expanding the idea of limit to general real valued functions (of which a real sequence is a special type), and to developing the idea and properties of a continuous function. Although Chapters 7, 8 and 9, on The Derivative, Integration and Elementary Functions, are also aspects of the limit process, they are considered separately, under the title of The Calculus, in Part Four.

CHAPTER 4

Sequences

4.1 Convergence of Sequences

We have defined a sequence already in Section 3.8, and our purpose in this chapter is to explore the properties of real sequences, especially the property of convergence.† This is not a property which all sequences possess, however. Consider the following examples of sequences.

Examples 4.1.

1. $\{1/n\}$ is the sequence $1, \frac{1}{2}, \frac{1}{3}, \frac{1}{4}, \ldots$
2. $\{(-1)^n\}$ is the sequence $-1, 1, -1, 1, \ldots$
3. $\{2^n\}$ is the sequence $2, 4, 8, 16, \ldots$
4. $\{1+(-1)^n/n^3\}$ is the sequence $0, \frac{9}{8}, \frac{26}{27}, \frac{65}{64}, \frac{124}{125}, \ldots$

What can we say about these particular sequences? Let us make the obvious remarks; in the first, the terms get progressively smaller; in the second, the terms alternate between 1 and -1; in the third, the terms increase in size very rapidly—notice that the seventh term exceeds 100, the tenth exceeds 1,000, while the seventeenth is over 100,000; in the last, the terms are all getting closer to 1, as we progress down the list. Thus, we may conclude that different sequences exhibit different sorts of behaviour. Not a very original thought, the reader will agree. However, if we look a little more closely at the behaviour of sequences, we see that there are not so very many really different possibilities; for instance, Examples 4.1.1 and 4.1.4 above reveal the same *kind* of behaviour. A pattern emerges in each, and this pattern is a trend of successive terms to approximate more closely a particular number. In Example 4.1.1, the number is 0, in Example 4.1.4 it is 1. On the other hand, Examples 4.1.2 and 4.1.3 certainly do not exhibit such behaviour. They belong to different categories. Hence, we might begin our investigation of sequences by trying to classify them, gathering together in one class all sequences which exhibit the same kind of behaviour.

The examples above provide us with a beginning. We divide the collection of all sequences into two classes—those sequences (like Examples 4.1.1 and 4.1.4) which show an overall trend towards some single particular real number, and on the other hand, those which do not (like Examples 4.1.2 and 4.1.3). We have said an "overall trend",

---

† Henceforth, in this chapter, by "sequence" we shall mean *real* sequence.

because such a sequence as

$$\frac{1}{3}, \frac{1}{2}, \frac{1}{9}, \frac{1}{4}, \frac{1}{27}, \frac{1}{16}, \cdots$$

showing an overall trend towards the real number 0, surely belongs with Examples 4.1.1 and 4.1.4, although every term is not closer to 0 than its predecessor. The single particular number mentioned above is called a "limit". The concepts of limits and limiting processes are fundamental in analysis, and, as we shall see, they appear in many disguises.

Basically, the limiting process expresses the intuition underlying Examples 4.1.1 and 4.1.4, that if we look at a large number of terms of the sequence, we can discern a real number towards which the numbers in the sequence are inexorably drawn. Now, of course, since by definition a sequence has infinitely many terms, we cannot depend on the terms of the sequence actually attaining this goal. In the first example above, no term in the sequence attains the value 0, and similarly, in the last, there is no term whose value is exactly 1. However, if we consider the sequence $1, 1, 1, 1, \ldots$ where every term has the value 1, then this value *is* the same as the "limit".

Nonetheless, we can sum up our intuitive feeling about the matter by saying that if the sequence s_n has a "limit", say the number α, then, as long as we choose k large enough, we can make all the terms from s_k on as close as we please to α. Now this is still not nearly precise enough; we are left with subjective phrases like "as close as we please" and "large enough", which are obviously all too prone to misinterpretation. To overcome this lack of precision, we specify what "large enough" means in terms of k, for any prescribed margin of difference from α, and this we do by playing a game, in which we are the defenders, and our opponents are the challengers. The game is played as follows. The challenger plays first, and he is allowed to pick any positive number as the margin of difference which will be permitted from the value α. He then challenges us to find an integer k such that all terms of the sequence after the k-th are within his chosen margin of difference. If we succeed in doing this, we win that game. If we always win, whatever margin of difference is named by the challenger, then the sequence has "limit" α. If, however, the challenger wins, *even once*, then the number α is not a "limit".

The game has a traditional symbolism. The margin of difference allowed is denoted by the letter ε (similar to the sign for membership of a set); the integer which the defender claims will give him victory is denoted by the symbol n_0. However, this integer n_0 will depend on how large or small ε is; the defender always plays second, and hence, if he wins a game and the challenger then selects a smaller margin ε, the defender will also alter his choice of integer n_0. For this reason, the integer n_0 is often written as $n_0(\varepsilon)$ to indicate that it is chosen dependently on ε.

We thus come to the following definition, which is, in essence, a summary of the last two paragraphs.

Definition.   Let $\{s_n\}$ be a sequence, α a real number. Then, we say that $\{s_n\}$ has **limit** α, or that $\{s_n\}$ **converges** to α, if given any number $\varepsilon > 0$, there exists an integer $n_0(\varepsilon)$ such that, for all integers $n > n_0(\varepsilon)$, we have

$$|s_n - \alpha| < \varepsilon.$$

We write $\lim s_n = \alpha$, or $s_n \to \alpha$.

The inequality $|s_n - \alpha| < \varepsilon$ above is just the formal expression of the phrase "s_n differs from α by less than ε." The whole definition can be expressed in terms of the symbolism of Chapter 1; thus,

$$\lim s_n = \alpha \Leftrightarrow \forall \, \varepsilon > 0, \ \exists \, n_0(\varepsilon) \in N \quad \text{such that}$$
$$\forall \, n > n_0(\varepsilon), \quad |s_n - \alpha| < \varepsilon.$$

Before we look at some examples on the calculation of limits, the following pictorial illustration may help to cement the idea of convergence. We plot the points $P_1 \, (1, s_1)$, $P_2 \, (2, s_2)$, $P_3 \, (3, s_3)$, and so on, in the co-ordinate plane. For a point to have ordinate within distance ε of α, the point must lie in the strip, of width 2ε, with centre line $y = \alpha$. To say that $\lim s_n = \alpha$ is to assert that, no matter how narrow a strip we take, we can always find a line $x = n_0(\varepsilon)$ such that all the points P_n to the right of this line lie within the strip (Fig. 4.1.1).

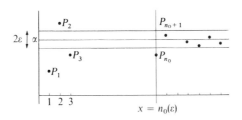

Fig. 4.1.1.

Example 4.1.5.   The sequence $\{1/n\}$ converges to 0.

This result is an obvious one; so obvious, indeed, that we have already, in the discussion above, assumed it to be true. We now justify this by demonstrating that it conforms to the definition. Thus, if ε is any positive real number, we must show there is an integer $n_0(\varepsilon)$ such that, for all $n > n_0, |1/n - 0| < \varepsilon$. We work backwards, in effect;

$$|1/n - 0| < \varepsilon \ \Leftrightarrow \ 1/n < \varepsilon \quad \text{(removing modulus signs since $1/n - 0$ is positive)}$$
$$\Leftrightarrow \ n > 1/\varepsilon \quad \text{(Exercise 3 of Chapter 2).}$$

Therefore, if $n_0(\varepsilon)$ is a positive integer greater than $1/\varepsilon$ (indeed, greater than $1/\varepsilon - 1$ is sufficient), then,

$$n > n_0(\varepsilon) \Rightarrow n > 1/\varepsilon$$
$$\Rightarrow 1/n < \varepsilon$$

that is, for all $n > n_0(\varepsilon)$, we have $|1/n - 0| < \varepsilon$, as required by the definition. So $\{1/n\}$ has limit zero.

The existence of a positive integer greater than $1/\varepsilon$ is assured by the Archimedean property of R (Theorem 2.6–B).   ◆

The technique of this proof, and of many proofs in convergence, is to show how the defender can always win, no matter what the challenger does. Thus, we see above that the defender is saying "I choose the integer $n_0(\varepsilon)$ to be any integer greater than $1/\varepsilon$". This is a winning play, whatever ε the challenger may choose. Instead of a collection of particular statements like "If the challenger chooses the margin of difference to be $\frac{1}{100}$, I (the defender) say that all terms in the sequence after the hundred-and-first are closer to 0 than $\frac{1}{100}$", we use dummies. ε represents any margin of difference, and $n_0(\varepsilon)$, or in the example above, $1/\varepsilon$, represents the "winning" integer.

Example 4.1.6. Let x be a real number with $|x| < 1$. Then, $\lim x^n = 0$.

Proof. If $x = 0$, then the result is certainly true. Suppose, then, $x \neq 0$. Since $|x| < 1$, we have $1/|x| > 1$ (Exercise 3, Chapter 2). Write $1/|x| = 1 + h$; then $h > 0$.

Now, let $\varepsilon > 0$; we examine what happens if $|x^n|$ is to be less than ε. Again, we are working backwards from the answer. First, we estimate how big $|x^n|$ can possibly be;

$$|x^n - 0| = |x|^n$$
$$= 1/(1 + h)^n$$
$$= \frac{1}{1 + nh + \binom{n}{2}h^2 + \ldots + h^n}$$
$$< 1/nh \quad \text{(because all terms in the denominator above are positive).}$$

Therefore, if we can ensure that $1/nh < \varepsilon$, it will be even more sure that $|x^n| < \varepsilon$. But

$$1/nh < \varepsilon \Leftrightarrow n > 1/\varepsilon h.$$

Hence, if we choose $n_0(\varepsilon) = 1/\varepsilon h$, it is certainly true that, for all integers $n > n_0(\varepsilon)$, we have

$$|x^n - 0| < \varepsilon.$$

Thus, $\lim x^n = 0$, as required.   ◆

Note. In this example, the number $n_0(\varepsilon)$ is, of course, not necessarily the *least* integer such that for $n > n_0$, $|x^n| < \varepsilon$. For we have estimated $|x^n|$ rather crudely; we are using $1/nh$ as a measure of the size of $|x^n|$, and to get this, we replace $(1 + h)^n$ by nh. To see just how uneconomical this is, take for example, $h = \frac{1}{2}$ and $n = 10$; then $(1 + \frac{1}{2})^{10}$, is approximately 50, while $10 \cdot \frac{1}{2}$ is 5. So, the corresponding $|x^{10}|$ is approximately 0·02, while $1/10h$ is 0·2. Therefore, $|x^n|$ may be very much smaller than $1/nh$, and so, $|x^n|$ may be less than ε for all integers $n > n(\varepsilon)$ for a smaller $n(\varepsilon)$ than $n_0(\varepsilon)$. *This does not matter.* If the reader will look again at the definition of limit, he will see that what is required is that, "given any $\varepsilon > 0$, there exists *an* integer $n_0(\varepsilon)$ such that . . .". It does not *have* to be the least such integer. Furthermore, if given $\varepsilon > 0$, there is a number $n_0(\varepsilon)$ such that, for all $n > n_0(\varepsilon)$, we have $|s_n - \alpha| < \varepsilon$, then it is also true that, if n_1 is an integer greater than $n_0(\varepsilon)$, we have $|s_n - \alpha| < \varepsilon$ for all $n > n_1$. So n_1 could equally well play the role of $n_0(\varepsilon)$.

The examples above show how we go about proving statements of the form "s_n converges to α". It is equally important that we should know how to disprove statements of this kind. To do this, we note that the statements

"It is true that s_n does not converge to α"

and

" It is false that s_n converges to α"

are equivalent. Hence, by the symbolic definition on page 107,

$$\sim [\lim s_n = \alpha] \Leftrightarrow \sim [\forall\, \varepsilon > 0,\, \exists\, n_0 \in N \text{ s.t. } \forall\, n > n_0(\varepsilon),\, |s_n - \alpha| < \varepsilon]$$

$$\Leftrightarrow \exists\, \varepsilon > 0 \text{ s.t. } \sim [\exists\, n_0 \in N \text{ s.t. } \forall\, n > n_0(\varepsilon),\, |s_n - \alpha| < \varepsilon]$$
(by Rule 1 of Section 1.9)

$$\Leftrightarrow \exists\, \varepsilon > 0 \text{ s.t. } \forall\, n_0 \in N,\, \sim [\forall\, n > n_0,\, |s_n - \alpha| < \varepsilon]$$
(by Rule 2 of Section 1.9)

$$\Leftrightarrow \exists\, \varepsilon > 0 \text{ s.t. } \forall\, n_0 \in N,\, \exists\, n > n_0 \text{ s.t. } \sim [|s_n - \alpha| < \varepsilon]$$
(by Rule 1 of Section 1.9)

$$\Leftrightarrow \exists\, \varepsilon > 0 \text{ s.t. } \forall\, n_0 \in N,\, \exists\, n > n_0 \text{ s.t. } |s_n - \alpha| \geqslant \varepsilon.$$

Therefore, to show that the sequence $\{s_n\}$ does not converge to α, we must demonstrate that for some value of $\varepsilon > 0$, we can find an integer n greater than any prescribed integer n_0, for which the difference between s_n and α is *not* less than ε.

Example 4.1.7. The sequence $\{(-1)^n\}$ does not converge to 1.

Proof. In view of the fact that every other term of the sequence is -1, the result seems obvious. However, we show how the recipe above works. If n is odd, $(-1)^n = -1$, and so $|(-1)^n - 1| = 2$. Moreover, if n_0 is any prescribed integer, the integer $2n_0 + 1$ is odd, and it is greater than

n_0. Hence, if we take $\varepsilon = 1$, and $n = 2n_0 + 1$, we have

$$|(-1)^n - 1| = 2$$

So $\{(-1)^n\}$ does not converge to 1.   ◆

Note.   In fact, we could have chosen ε to be any number satisfying $0 < \varepsilon \leqslant 2$.

It seems clear that a sequence $\{s_n\}$ cannot converge to two different numbers α and β. Convergence means that the terms s_n get closer and closer to the limit; so we must somewhere commit ourselves to either α or β. We cannot, as it were, have our loyalties divided. However, we must justify this piece of perception.

Theorem 4.1–A.   If the sequence $\{s_n\}$ converges to α, and to β, then $\alpha = \beta$.

Proof.   We argue by contradiction, using method (c) of Section 1.10. Suppose that $\lim s_n = \alpha$, and $\lim s_n = \beta$, with $\alpha \neq \beta$. We may assume that $\alpha < \beta$. (This is "$\sim q$" of Theorem 1.10–H.) By definition of limit, if ε is *any* positive number, ∃ an integer $n_0(\varepsilon) \in N$ such that for all $n > n_0(\varepsilon)$,

$$|s_n - \alpha| < \varepsilon$$

i.e.

$$-\varepsilon < s_n - \alpha < \varepsilon.$$

We can therefore take ε to be $\frac{1}{2}(\beta - \alpha)$, by Theorem 1.10-B. For the particular case when $\varepsilon = \frac{1}{2}(\beta - \alpha)$, denote the integer $n_0(\varepsilon)$ by n_1, for typographical convenience. So, for all $n > n_1$, we have

$$-\tfrac{1}{2}(\beta - \alpha) < s_n - \alpha < \tfrac{1}{2}(\beta - \alpha).$$

The right-hand inequality can be written as

$$s_n < \tfrac{1}{2}(\beta + \alpha), \quad \text{for all } n > n_1. \tag{1}$$

Similarly, if we take ε again to be $\frac{1}{2}(\beta - \alpha)$, we can find a positive integer n_2 such that, for all $n > n_2$,

$$-\tfrac{1}{2}(\beta - \alpha) < s_n - \beta < \tfrac{1}{2}(\beta - \alpha),$$

since $\lim s_n = \beta$. The left-hand inequality here may be written as

$$\tfrac{1}{2}(\beta + \alpha) < s_n, \quad \text{for all } n > n_2. \tag{2}$$

Therefore, if n is greater than both n_1 and n_2 (e.g. if $n = n_1 + n_2$), both (1) and (2) hold simultaneously; that is, $s_n < \frac{1}{2}(\beta + \alpha)$ and $\frac{1}{2}(\beta + \alpha) < s_n$, which is a self-contradiction. So, by Theorem 1.10–H(c), we have $\alpha = \beta$.   ◆

The technique of proof is illustrated in Fig. 4.1.2. If $\alpha \neq \beta$, then the distance between α and β is $\beta - \alpha$. We now use the fact that the sequence $\{s_n\}$ converges. On the one hand, s_n must eventually be closer to α than $\frac{1}{2}(\beta - \alpha)$ i.e. it must lie to the left of the midpoint of the line joining α and

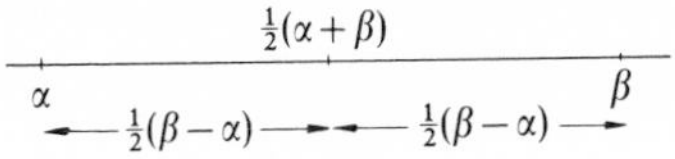

Fig. 4.1.2.

β. On the other, s_n must also eventually be closer to β than $\frac{1}{2}(\beta - \alpha)$ i.e. s_n must lie to the right of the point $\frac{1}{2}(\alpha + \beta)$. These are, of course, incompatible, and so give us the required contradiction.

Before proceeding further, we observe the following: if K is a positive real number, then, in order to show that $\lim s_n = \alpha$, it is sufficient to prove that, given any $\varepsilon > 0$, $\exists n_0(\varepsilon) \in N$ such that, for all $n > n_0(\varepsilon)$,

$$|s_n - \alpha| < K\varepsilon.$$

To see this, let $\eta = \varepsilon/K$; then $\eta > 0$, and so we can regard η as an example of an "ε" above. Therefore, there is a positive integer $n_0(\eta)$ such that, for all $n > n_0(\eta)$, we have

$$|s_n - \alpha| < K\eta$$

i.e.

$$|s_n - \alpha| < K\varepsilon/K = \varepsilon$$

which means, by definition, that $\{s_n\}$ converges to α. We make use of this equivalent definition of convergence frequently.

Definition.   A sequence $\{s_n\}$ is said to be **convergent** if there is a number α such that $\lim s_n = \alpha$. If there is no such number, the sequence is called **divergent**.

The sequences of Examples 4.1.2 and 4.1.3 are therefore divergent. Thus, we have divided the collection of all real sequences into two classes—the class of *convergent sequences*, and that of *divergent sequences*. Within the latter class are several subclasses of special interest. We notice that although Examples 4.1.2 and 4.1.3 are both examples of divergent sequences, the behaviour they exhibit is quite different. It is behaviour of the type exemplified in the latter that we now examine more closely.

The terms of the sequence $\{2^n\}$ get very large as n gets very large, and the larger n becomes, the larger 2^n becomes. To put this another way, we can find a point, after which, all the terms of the sequence are larger than any prescribed number. For instance, suppose we think of the number "one billion" (i.e. 10^{12}). Then, all terms of the sequence $\{2^n\}$ after the fortieth term are certainly greater than one billion. From this beginning, we formulate the following precise definition of the situation described above.

Definition.   Let $\{s_n\}$ be a sequence. Suppose that, for every real number $A > 0$, there is a positive integer n_0 such that, for all $n > n_0$,

$$s_n > A.$$

Then, we say that $\{s_n\}$ **diverges to** $+\infty$ (or diverges to ∞) and write $\lim s_n = \infty$, or $s_n \to \infty$.

This definition has a similar form to the definition of $\lim s_n = \alpha$, when α is a real number. We merely have replaced the phrase "s_n is closer to α than ε" by the phrase "s_n is greater than A" (since we cannot write "s_n is closer to $+\infty$ than A"!). We can depict the situation diagrammatically, as in Fig. 4.1.3. As before, we plot the points P_1 $(1, s_1)$, P_2 $(2, s_2)$, and so on. Then $\lim s_n = \infty$ means that if $y = A$ represents any horizontal line, there is a positive integer n_0 such that, for $n > n_0$, all the points P_n lie above the line $y = A$. As in the case of convergence, the choice of n_0 usually depends on A, and so, we often write $n_0(A)$ to indicate this.

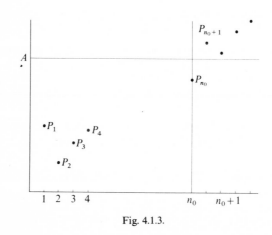

Fig. 4.1.3.

Example 4.1.8.   The sequence $\{2^n\}$ diverges to ∞.

Proof.   We use a technique similar to that of Example 4.1.5, and show how to choose a suitable n_0 for a given value of A. Again, we work backwards, and look for a *sufficient* condition to make s_n exceed A. Thus,

$$2^n > A \Leftrightarrow n \ln 2 > \ln A$$

$$\Leftrightarrow n > \ln A / \ln 2.$$

Therefore, take $n_0(A)$ to be the integer nearest $\ln A / \ln 2$; it follows that $n > n_0(A) \Rightarrow 2^n > A$. So, $\lim 2^n = \infty$.   ◆

A very similar subclass is that of sequences which diverge to $-\infty$. By analogy with the case above, this definition is easily formulated.

Definition.   The sequence $\{s_n\}$ is said to **diverge to** $-\infty$ if, given any real number B, there is a positive integer $n_0(B)$ such that, for all

$n > n_0(B)$, we have

$$s_n < B.$$

We write $\lim s_n = -\infty$, or $s_n \to -\infty$.

Example 4.1.9. The sequence $\{-e^n\}$ diverges to $-\infty$.

Proof. Let $B < 0$: then,

$$-e^n < B \Leftrightarrow e^n > -B \Leftrightarrow n > \ln(-B).$$

So, choose $n_0(B)$ to be the integer nearest $\ln(-B)$.   ◆

4.2 Monotonic Sequences

So far, we have not fully used the fact that the sequences with which we are dealing are real sequences, so that the values $\{s_n\}$ belong to an ordered set. Hence, we have, at our disposal, the ideas of bounded sequences and increasing sequences. See Section 3.8 for the definitions of these. In order to establish convergence of a sequence we have, up to now, had to guess at a limit α, and attempt to prove that $\lim s_n = \alpha$. For certain kinds of sequence, we shall see that guesswork is unnecessary.

Example 4.2.1. The sequences $\{(-1)^n\}$, $\{1-1/n\}$, $\{\sin n\pi/2 + (-1)^n/n\}$ are all bounded.

For, if $a_n = (-1)^n$, then, $\forall\, n$, $-1 \leqslant a_n \leqslant 1$. Likewise, if $b_n = 1-1/n$, then, $0 \leqslant b_n < 1$; and if $c_n = \sin(n\pi/2)+(-1)^n/n$, then, $-\frac{4}{3} \leqslant c_n < 1$.

Example 4.2.2. The sequences $\{1-1/n\}$, $\{n^2\}$, $\{1\}$ are non-decreasing; the first two are increasing.

For, we have

$$1-1/n < 1-1/(n+1), \quad \text{for all } n,$$
$$n^2 < (n+1)^2, \quad \text{for all } n,$$
$$1(=s_n) \leqslant 1(=s_{n+1}), \quad \text{for all } n.$$

We note that the sequence $\{s_n\}$ is non-decreasing if and only if $s_m \leqslant s_n$ whenever m, n are integers with $m < n$. It follows that a non-decreasing sequence $\{s_n\}$ is bounded below (by s_1) (Example 3.8.4), a non-increasing sequence $\{s_n\}$ is bounded above (also, for example, by s_1).

We next consider non-decreasing sequences. We have just said that such a sequence is necessarily bounded below; but it may be bounded above, or it may not. We next prove that these alternatives completely determine the behaviour of the sequence.

Theorem 4.2–A. Let $\{s_n\}$ be a non-decreasing sequence. If $\{s_n\}$ is bounded above, then it is convergent; if it is not bounded above, then it diverges to ∞.

Proof. (1). Suppose $\{s_n\}$ is bounded above. Then, by Theorem 2.5–A, the set $\{s_n\}$ has a least upper bound; call this α. Then

$$s_n \leqslant \alpha, \quad \text{for all } n. \tag{1}$$

Further, if $\varepsilon > 0$, there is a positive integer n_0, such that

$$s_{n_0} > \alpha - \varepsilon \quad \text{(definition of least upper bound)}.$$

Next,

$$\{s_n\} \text{ non-decreasing} \Leftrightarrow s_n \geqslant s_{n_0}, \forall \, n > n_0$$
$$\Rightarrow s_n > \alpha - \varepsilon \, \forall \, n > n_0.$$

By (1), we have that, given $\varepsilon > 0$, $\exists \, n_0 \in N$ such that, for all $n > n_0$,

$$\alpha - \varepsilon < s_n \leqslant \alpha$$

i.e.

$$|s_n - \alpha| < \varepsilon.$$

Hence, $\lim s_n = \alpha$, and $\{s_n\}$ is convergent.

Before going on to the second situation, let us look at this proof pictorially (Fig. 4.2.1). To say $\{s_n\}$ is bounded above means there is a line $y = K$, below which all the points $P_n \, (n, s_n)$ in the co-ordinate plane lie. By Theorem 2.5–A, there is a lowest such line $y = \alpha$. If n_0 is any positive integer, the fact that $\{s_n\}$ is non-decreasing means that all points P_n with $n > n_0$ lie on or above the line $y = s_{n_0}$. So, because we can find a line $y = s_{n_0}$ as close as we please to $y = \alpha$, (definition of supremum), all the points P_n with $n > n_0$ are squeezed into a strip of width ε, and this is the situation of Fig. 4.1.1. The reader should observe how and where the hypotheses "non-decreasing" and "bounded above" are used in the proof.

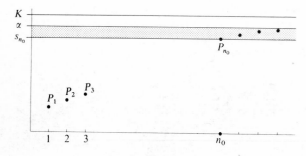

Fig. 4.2.1.

(2). Suppose on the other hand, that $\{s_n\}$ is not bounded above. This means that, if A is any positive number, there is a positive integer n_0 with $s_{n_0} > A$. But now, since $\{s_n\}$ is non-decreasing,

$$n > n_0 \Rightarrow s_n \geqslant s_{n_0},$$
$$\Rightarrow s_n > A.$$

By definition, this means that $\{s_n\}$ diverges to ∞. ◆

This part of the theorem can be illustrated pictorially also. We note the following analogous theorem:

Theorem 4.2–B. Let $\{s_n\}$ be a non-increasing sequence. If $\{s_n\}$ is bounded below, then it is convergent; if it is not bounded below, then it diverges to $-\infty$.

A sequence which is non-decreasing, or non-increasing, is called **monotonic**. Notice that an increasing sequence is, of course, non-decreasing. We can thus sum up the conclusions of the first parts of the two theorems of this section in the following way.

Theorem 4.2–C. Every bounded monotonic sequence is convergent.

We use Theorem 4.2–A to prove the proposition in the following exercise.

Example 4.2.3. The sequence $\{(1 + 1/n)^n\}$ is convergent.

Proof. We show that this sequence is increasing and bounded above. The first few terms of the sequence are

$$2, (\tfrac{3}{2})^2, (\tfrac{4}{3})^3, (\tfrac{5}{4})^4, (\tfrac{6}{5})^5, \ldots$$

i.e.

$$2, \tfrac{9}{4}, \tfrac{64}{27}, \tfrac{625}{256}, \tfrac{7776}{3125}, \ldots$$

Now, it is plain that

$$2 < \tfrac{9}{4} < \tfrac{64}{27}$$

and easy to verify that

$$\tfrac{64}{27} < \tfrac{625}{256} < \tfrac{7776}{3125}.$$

So we conclude that the sequence is almost certainly increasing. However, we cannot rely on "conclusions" formed by examining five special cases; we must therefore prove that the sequence is increasing.

By the binomial theorem,

$$(1 + 1/n)^n = \sum_{r=0}^{r=n} \binom{n}{r} \frac{1}{n^r}$$

$$= 2 + \sum_{r=2}^{r=n} \frac{n(n-1)\ldots(n-r+1)}{1\,2\ldots r} \frac{1}{n^r}$$

$$= 2 + \sum_{r=2}^{r=n} \frac{1}{r!}\left(1 - \frac{1}{n}\right)\left(1 - \frac{2}{n}\right)\dots\left(1 - \frac{r-1}{n}\right),$$

since there are r terms in the numerator, and we divide each of them by n. For $k = 1, 2, \dots, r-1$,

$$\frac{1}{n} > \frac{1}{n+1} \Rightarrow -k/n < -k/(n+1)$$

$$\Rightarrow 1 - k/n < 1 - k/(n+1)$$

$$\Rightarrow (1 - 1/n)(1 - 2/n)\dots\left(1 - \frac{r-1}{n}\right)$$

$$< \left(1 - \frac{1}{n+1}\right)\left(1 - \frac{2}{n+1}\right)\dots\left(1 - \frac{r-1}{n+1}\right)$$

(Exercise 4, Chapter 2).

So, this being the case for $r = 2, 3, \dots, n$, we have

$$(1 + 1/n)^n < 2 + \sum_{r=2}^{r=n} \frac{1}{r!}\left(1 - \frac{1}{n+1}\right)\dots\left(1 - \frac{r-1}{n+1}\right)$$

$$< 2 + \sum_{r=2}^{r=n+1} \frac{1}{r!}\left(1 - \frac{1}{n+1}\right)\dots\left(-1\frac{r-1}{n+1}\right)$$

$$= \left(1 + \frac{1}{n+1}\right)^{n+1}.$$

Hence, for any positive integer n, we have $s_n < s_{n+1}$ i.e. $\{s_n\}$ is increasing.

It only remains to prove that the sequence is bounded above. To begin with, $(1 + 1/n)^n > 0$, for all $n \in N$, so, it is bounded below. Next,

$$(1 + 1/n)^n = 2 + \frac{n(n-1)}{2!} \cdot \frac{1}{n^2} + \frac{n(n-1)(n-2)}{3!} \cdot \frac{1}{n^3} + \dots + \frac{1}{n^n}$$

$$< 2 + 1/2! + 1/3! + \dots + 1/n!$$

$$< 2 + \tfrac{1}{2} + \tfrac{1}{4} + \dots + 1/2^{n-1}$$

$$= 2 + (1 - \tfrac{1}{2}^n)$$

$$< 3.$$

Thus, $0 < (1 + 1/n)^n < 3$, for all n, and so $\{(1 + 1/n)^n\}$ is increasing and bounded. By Theorem 4.2–A, it is therefore convergent.†   ◆

---

† This proof tells us nothing about the actual value of the limit. However, by applying Example 4.3.3, Corollary 3, it can be shown that the limit of $(1 + 1/n)^n$ lies between 2.5 and 3. It is denoted by the symbol e, and has a value of 2·71828 to five decimal places. See also Chapter 9.

4.3 The Algebra of Limits

Since we are discussing real sequences, we can define the sum, difference, product and quotient of two sequences after the manner of Section 3.5. In this section, we investigate the limits of these new sequences, which of course we will expect to depend on the original sequences. We have

Theorem 4.3–A. Let $\{s_n\}$, $\{t_n\}$ be sequences, which converge to α and β respectively. Then,

    (i) $\lim(s_n + t_n) = \alpha + \beta$;

    (ii) $\lim(s_n t_n) = \alpha\beta$

    (iii) if $\beta \neq 0$, $\lim s_n/t_n = \alpha/\beta$.

Proof of (i). We begin by writing down our hypotheses. Let $\varepsilon > 0$. Since $\lim s_n = \alpha$, there is a number $n_1 \in N$ such that for all $n > n_1$, $|s_n - \alpha| < \varepsilon$. Since $\lim t_n = \beta$, there is a number $n_2 \in N$ such that for all $n > n_2$, $|t_n - \beta| < \varepsilon$.

We observe that if n exceeds both n_1 and n_2, the inequalities above are simultaneously true.

To show that $s_n + t_n$ has limit $\alpha + \beta$, we must show that for all n large enough, the difference between $s_n + t_n$ and $\alpha + \beta$ can be made as small as we please. Therefore, we try to estimate this difference; we have

$$|s_n + t_n - (\alpha + \beta)| = |(s_n - \alpha) + (t_n - \beta)|$$

$$\leqslant |s_n - \alpha| + |t_n - \beta| \quad \text{(by Theorem 2.4–B).}$$

If now, $n > \max(n_1, n_2)$, then each of these terms is less than ε, by our hypothesis. So, we have, for all $n > \max(n_1, n_2)$,

$$|(s_n + t_n) - (\alpha + \beta)| < 2\varepsilon,$$

and so, in view of the remark following Theorem 4.1–A,

$$\lim(s_n + t_n) = \alpha + \beta.$$

Proof of (ii). We again try to proceed in a similar way, and estimate the difference $s_n t_n - \alpha\beta$. Now, this cannot be written as the product $(s_n - \alpha)(t_n - \beta)$; but we try to write $s_n t_n - \alpha\beta$ in terms of the factors $(s_n - \alpha)$ and $(t_n - \beta)$. We find that

$$|s_n t_n - \alpha\beta| = |s_n t_n - \alpha t_n + \alpha t_n - \alpha\beta| \quad \text{(adding and subtracting } \alpha t_n)$$

$$\leqslant |s_n t_n - \alpha t_n| + |\alpha t_n - \alpha\beta|$$

$$= |t_n||s_n - \alpha| + |\alpha||t_n - \beta|.$$

If we can now show that $|t_n| \leqslant K$, for all n, then, using our hypotheses, we have $|s_n t_n - \alpha\beta| < (K+|\alpha|)\varepsilon$ for all $n > \max(n_1, n_2)$ and the result will follow by the remark after Theorem 4.1.–A.

Since $\lim t_n = \beta$, there is an integer $n_3 \in N$ such that, for all $n > n_3$, $|t_n - \beta| < 1$ (i.e. we take $\varepsilon = 1$ in the definition). So, we have, for all $n > n_3$,

$$|t_n| \leqslant 1 + |\beta|.$$

Take $K = \max(|t_1|, |t_2|, \ldots, |t_{n_3}|, 1 + |\beta|)$; then certainly, for all n, we have $|t_n| \leqslant K$. Thus, (ii) is proved.

Proof of (iii). Supposing that $\beta \neq 0$, we try to estimate the difference between s_n/t_n and α/β:

$$\begin{aligned}
|s_n/t_n - \alpha/\beta| &= \frac{|s_n\beta - t_n\alpha|}{|\beta t_n|} \\
&= \frac{|s_n\beta - \alpha\beta + \alpha\beta - t_n\alpha|}{|\beta t_n|} \\
&\leqslant \frac{|s_n - \alpha|}{|t_n|} + \frac{|\alpha||t_n - \beta|}{|\beta||t_n|}.
\end{aligned}$$

We see then that the proof devolves around showing that $1/|t_n|$ is not too large, i.e. $|t_n|$ is not too small.

Now, if $\beta \neq 0$, then eventually, t_n will be closer to β than $\frac{1}{2}|\beta|$. That is, taking $\varepsilon = \frac{1}{2}|\beta|$, there is an integer n_4 such that, for all $n > n_4$,

$$|t_n - \beta| < \tfrac{1}{2}|\beta|$$

which means

$$|t_n| > \tfrac{1}{2}|\beta|.$$

Hence, if $n > \max(n_1, n_2, n_4)$, we have

$$|s_n/t_n - \alpha/\beta| < (2/|\beta| + 2|\alpha|/|\beta|^2)\varepsilon,$$

and, again by the remark following Theorem 4.1–A, the proof is complete.   ◆

We note the following important corollaries.

Corollary 1.   By taking $t_n = k$, for all n, in (ii), we have $\lim(ks_n) = k\alpha$. This result is true for any real k.

Corollary 2. $\lim(s_n - t_n) = \alpha - \beta$.

For, in consequence of Corollary 1, $\lim(-t_n) = -\beta$ (put $s_n = t_n$, and $k = -1$ in Corollary 1). Hence, by (i) of the theorem,

$$\lim(s_n - t_n) = \lim(s_n + (-t_n)) = \alpha - \beta.$$

Example 4.3.1. Prove that

$$\lim \frac{n^3 + 3n^2 + 5}{2n^3 + 7n + 1} = \frac{1}{2}.$$

Proof. For each $n \in N$,

$$\frac{n^3 + 3n^2 + 5}{2n^3 + 7n + 1} = \frac{1 + 3/n + 5/n^3}{2 + 7/n^2 + 1/n^3}.$$

By Theorem 4.3–A (i), $\lim(1 + 3/n + 5/n^3) = 1 + \lim 3/n + \lim 5/n^3$; by Corollary 1,

$$\lim 3/n = 3 \lim 1/n = 0,$$

and

$$\lim 5/n^3 = 5 \lim 1/n^3;$$

by Theorem 4.3–A (ii) applied twice, $\lim 1/n^3 = (\lim 1/n)^3 = 0$. Hence, $\lim(1 + 3/n + 5/n^3) = 1$. Similarly, $\lim(2 + 7/n^2 + 1/n^3) = 2$; so, by Theorem 4.3–A (iii),

$$\lim \frac{1 + 3/n + 5/n^3}{2 + 7/n^2 + 1/n^3} = \frac{1}{2}. \qquad \blacklozenge$$

Example 4.3.2. Let $\{s_n\}$ be the sequence given by $s_1 = 1$, and for $n \geq 1$, $s_{n+1} = \sqrt{(6 + s_n)}$. Then, $\lim s_n = 3$.

Proof. We have $s_1 = 1$, $s_2 = \sqrt{7}$. Now $s_3 = \sqrt{(6 + \sqrt{7})}$, and so, since $\sqrt{7} > 1$, $\sqrt{(6 + \sqrt{7})} > \sqrt{(6 + 1)} = s_2$. Similarly, $s_4 = \sqrt{[6 + \sqrt{(6 + \sqrt{7})}]}$; but $s_3 > s_2 \Rightarrow \sqrt{(6 + \sqrt{7})} > \sqrt{7} \Rightarrow s_4 > \sqrt{(6 + \sqrt{7})} = s_3$. Hence, we may conjecture that $\{s_n\}$ is increasing. The method by which we showed $s_4 > s_3$ suggests that induction might be the easiest method to use.

So, suppose that $s_k > s_{k-1}$; then,

$$s_{k+1}^2 = 6 + s_k > 6 + s_{k-1}.$$

Hence,

$$s_{k+1} > \sqrt{(6 + s_{k-1})} = s_k.$$

Also, $s_1 < s_2$, and so, by the principle of induction, $s_n < s_{n+1}$ for all n. Next, we try to show that $\{s_n\}$ is bounded above. It will then be convergent, by Theorem 4.2–A.

Suppose $s_1, s_2, \ldots, s_k$ satisfy $s_r \leq K$, $r = 1, 2, \ldots, k$. Now,

$$s_{k+1}^2 = 6 + s_k \leq 6 + K \Rightarrow s_{k+1} \leq \sqrt{(6 + K)}$$

$$\Rightarrow s_{k+1} \leq K \quad \text{if} \quad \sqrt{(6 + K)} \leq K,$$

$$\text{i.e. if} \quad 6 + K \leq K^2$$

$$\text{i.e. if} \quad K^2 - K - 6 \geq 0$$

$$\text{i.e. if} \quad (K - 3)(K + 2) \geq 0.$$

So, if we take $K \geqslant 3$, the induction step holds. Now, $s_1 = 1$ which is less than 3. Hence, by the principle of induction, $s_n \leqslant K$, for all n.

The sequence $\{s_n\}$ is therefore convergent; write $\lim s_n = x$. Since $s_{n+1}^2 = 6 + s_n$, it follows from Theorem 4.3–A that

$$(\lim s_{n+1})^2 = 6 + \lim s_n,$$

i.e.

$$x^2 = 6 + x,$$

whence

$$x = 3 \text{ or } -2.$$

Since s_n is clearly greater than zero for all n, the limit cannot be -2. Hence, $\lim s_n = 3$, as required.   ◆

Example 4.3.3.   Let $\{s_n\}, \{t_n\}$ be sequences with limits α and β respectively. Suppose that, for all $n, s_n \geqslant t_n$. Prove that $\alpha \geqslant \beta$.

Proof. We use the method (A) of contradiction of Section 1.10. Suppose $\alpha < \beta$. (This is the "$\sim q$" of Theorem 1.10–H). Write $\eta = \frac{1}{2}(\beta - \alpha)$. Since $\lim s_n = \alpha$, there is an integer n_1 such that, for all $n > n_1$,

$$|s_n - \alpha| < \eta \qquad \text{(we take } \varepsilon = \eta \text{ using Theorem 1.10–B).}$$

Since $\lim t_n = \beta$, there is a number n_2 such that, for all $n > n_2$,

$$|t_n - \beta| < \eta.$$

Hence, for all $n > \max(n_1, n_2)$ we have

$$\alpha - \eta < s_n < \alpha + \eta,$$
$$\beta - \eta < t_n < \beta + \eta.$$

Since $\alpha + \eta = \beta - \eta = \frac{1}{2}(\beta + \alpha)$, this means that, for all $n > \max(n_1, n_2)$,

$$s_n < \tfrac{1}{2}(\beta + \alpha) < t_n,$$

which contradicts the hypothesis that $s_n \geqslant t_n$, for all n (i.e. we have deduced "$\sim P$"). Thus $\alpha \geqslant \beta$, by Theorem 1.10–H (a).   ◆

The reader should note the similarity in pattern between this proof and that of Theorem 4.1–A.

Corollary 1.   The result above is true if we replace the phrase "$s_n \geqslant t_n$, for all n" by "$s_n \geqslant t_n$, for all n exceeding some integer n_0". The details are left to the reader.

Corollary 2.   The result of Example 4.3.3 is false if we replace "$\geqslant$" by "$>$". However, the following result is true: if $s_n > t_n$, for all n, then $\lim s_n \geqslant \lim t_n$.

For, let $s_n = 2/n$, $t_n = 1/n$; then, for all n, $s_n > t_n$, but $\lim s_n = \lim t_n = 0$.

Corollary 3. As special cases we have the following results:
(i) if, for all $n > n_0$, $s_n \geqslant K$, a constant, then $\lim s_n \geqslant K$;
(ii) if, for all $n > n_0$, $s_n > K$, a constant, then $\lim s_n \geqslant K$.

4.4 Limit Superior and Limit Inferior

Up to now, we have discussed convergent sequences, and sequences which diverge to $+\infty$ or $-\infty$. There are sequences which belong to none of these categories; for example, $\{(-2)^n\}$ and $\{\sin(n\pi/2)\}$. We have also discussed bounded sequences, and unbounded sequences. A sequence which is not bounded is unbounded above or unbounded below, or both. We have deduced relationships between membership of these classes; for instance, we have shown that a convergent sequence is bounded (this comes in the proof of Theorem 4.3–A (ii)), and a sequence which diverges to ∞ or $-\infty$ is, by definition, unbounded. Examples 4.1.2 and 4.1.7 show that a bounded sequence is not necessarily convergent. The sequence $\{(-2)^n\}$ shows that an unbounded sequence does not necessarily diverge to ∞ or to $-\infty$. We can summarise our findings in the following diagram (Fig. 4.4.1); thus, for instance, the set of sequences which diverge to $-\infty$ is a subset of those which are bounded above, but not bounded below. Our purpose in this section is to investigate the top left hand square, especially the part which does not contain convergent sequences.

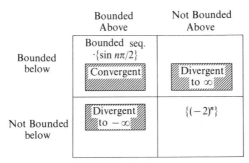

Fig. 4.4.1.

So, throughout this section, *we shall suppose that $\{s_n\}$ is a* **bounded** *sequence.* Consider the sequences $\{(-1)^n\}$ and $\{\sin n\pi/2 + (-1)^n/n\}$ They are bounded (Example 4.2.1). If we plot the points of these sequences, on a co-ordinate system, for large values of n, we detect an interesting phenomenon (Figs. 4.4.2, 4.4.3). In the first case, the odd terms are all -1, the even terms are all $+1$, and so the subsequence $\{s_{2n+1}\}$, consisting of just the odd terms, converges to -1, while the subsequence $\{s_{2n}\}$, consisting of just the even terms, converges to $+1$. In the second case, the sequence $\{t_{4n+1}\}$ (that is, every other odd term)

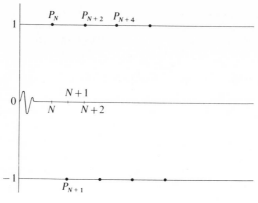

Fig. 4.4.2.

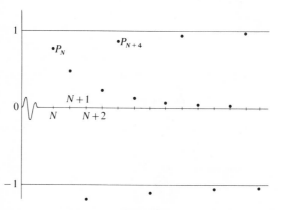

Fig. 4.4.3.

converges to 1, for $t_{4n+1} = 1 - 1/(4n+1)$; the sequence $\{t_{4n+3}\}$ converges to -1, for $t_{4n+3} = -1 - 1/(4n+3)$. Thus, in both cases, the bounded sequences contain convergent *sub*sequences. Now, we try to develop a theory to explain this.

Consider the subsequence $s_k, s_{k+1}, s_{k+2}, \ldots$ of $\{s_n\}$. We can denote this by $\{s_{n+k-1}\}$. (See Exercise 35 of Chapter 3.) Since $\{s_n\}$ is bounded, it is bounded above, and so, we have $s_n \leqslant K$ for all n. Hence $s_{n+k-1} \leqslant K$, for all n, i.e. $\{s_{n+k-1}\}$ is bounded above. Denote the supremum of $\{s_{n+k-1}\}$ by m_k. m_k exists, by Theorem 2.5–A. Then, $s_{n+k-1} \leqslant m_k$, for all n. In particular, the terms $s_{k+1}, s_{k+2}, s_{k+3}, \ldots$ do not exceed m_k, so that m_k is an upper bound of the subsequence $\{s_{n+k}\}$. It follows that the supremum of $\{s_{n+k}\}$, namely m_{k+1}, does not exceed m_k. (m_{k+1} is the *least* upper bound of $\{s_{n+k}\}$.) Hence, $m_{k+1} \leqslant m_k$.

If we now turn our attention to the sequence $m_1, m_2, m_3, \ldots$ defined by writing, for each $n \in N$,

$$m_n = \sup\{s_n, s_{n+1}, s_{n+2}, \ldots\},$$

we observe that $\{m_n\}$ is a non-increasing sequence. In particular, $m_n \leqslant m_1$, for all $n \in N$.

In a similar way, the sequence $\{l_n\}$, defined by writing, for all $n \in N$,

$$l_n = \inf\{s_n, s_{n+1}, s_{n+2}, \ldots\},$$

is non-decreasing. In particular, $l_1 \leqslant l_n$, for all $n \in N$.

Furthermore, for any $n \in N$, $l_n \leqslant s_n \leqslant m_n$, so that we have the chain of inequalities,

$$l_1 \leqslant l_n \leqslant m_n \leqslant m_1,$$

for every $n \in N$. The sequence $\{m_n\}$ is therefore bounded below, by l_1, and since it is non-increasing, it is therefore convergent, by Theorem 4.2–B. Write $\lim m_n = \mu$. The number μ is called the **limit superior** (or the **upper limit**) of the sequence $\{s_n\}$. We write

$$\mu = \lim \sup s_n$$

or

$$\mu = \overline{\lim} \, s_n$$

The sequence $\{l_n\}$ is bounded above, by m_1, and hence, by Theorem 4.2–A, is also convergent. Write $\lim l_n = \lambda$. Then, λ is called the **limit inferior** (or **lower limit**) of $\{s_n\}$, and we write

$$\lambda = \lim \inf s_n$$

or

$$\lambda = \underline{\lim} \, s_n.$$

By definition of sup and inf, $m_n - l_n \geqslant 0$ for all n; by Theorem 4.3–A, Corollary 2, $\lim(m_n - l_n) = \mu - \lambda$; hence, by Corollary 3 of Example 4.3.3, $\mu - \lambda \geqslant 0$ i.e. $\lambda \leqslant \mu$.

Example 4.4.1.   Find the limits superior and inferior of $\{(-1)^n\}$.

The sequence $\{(-1)^n\}$ is $-1, 1, -1, 1, -1, 1, \ldots$; it is clear that $m_n = 1$, $l_n = -1$, for all n. Hence, $\lim m_n = 1$, $\lim l_n = -1$. So $\lim \sup(-1)^n = 1$, $\lim \inf(-1)^n = -1$.

Example 4.4.2.   Find the limits superior and inferior of

$$\left\{\sin \frac{n\pi}{2} + \frac{(-1)^n}{n}\right\}.$$

The terms of the sequence are given by

$$s_{2n} = 1/2n \qquad \text{for all } n,$$
$$s_{4n+1} = 1 - 1/(4n+1) \qquad \text{for all } n,$$
$$s_{4n+3} = -1 - 1/(4n+3) \quad \text{for all } n.$$

Hence, m_n is given by

$$m_n = 1, \quad \text{for all } n,$$

while l_n is given by

$$l_{4n} = -1 - 1/(4n+3)$$
$$l_{4n+1} = -1 - 1/(4n+3)$$
$$l_{4n+2} = -1 - 1/(4n+3)$$
$$l_{4n+3} = -1 - 1/(4n+3).$$

(The reader should note that the number m_n, the supremum of $\{s_k : k \geqslant n\}$, is never attained, while the number l_n, the infimum of $\{s_k : k \geqslant n\}$ is always attained, and is attained by the first term of the form s_{4k+3} on or after s_n).

We have $\lim m_n = 1$, $\lim l_n = -1$, as before. So,

$$\lim \sup (\sin n\pi/2 + (-1)^n/n) = 1, \ \lim \inf (\sin n\pi/2 + (-1)^n/n) = -1.$$

Example 4.4.3.   Find the limits superior and inferior of $\{(-1)^n/n^2\}$. The sequence is $-1, \frac{1}{4}, -\frac{1}{9}, \frac{1}{16}, \ldots$ We have

$$m_n = \begin{cases} 1/n^2 & \text{if } n \text{ is even} \\ 1/(n+1)^2 & \text{if } n \text{ is odd.} \end{cases}$$

Since the even terms form a positive decreasing sequence, and the odd terms are negative, the supremum of $s_n, s_{n+1}, s_{n+2}, \ldots$ will therefore be the first even term in this sequence i.e. s_n if n is even, s_{n+1} if n is odd. Likewise,

$$l_n = \begin{cases} -1/n^2 & \text{if } n \text{ is odd} \\ -1/(n+1)^2 & \text{if } n \text{ is even,} \end{cases}$$

for similar reasons.

It follows easily that $\lim m_n = 0$ and $\lim l_n = 0$. Hence,

$$\lim \sup (-1)^n/n^2 = \lim \inf (-1)^n/n^2 = 0.$$

In this particular case, the limits superior and inferior coincide; the sequence $\{(-1)^n/n^2\}$ is, of course, convergent (to zero). We shall see later that this is no accident (Theorem 4.4–E).

We now go on to investigate the properties of the numbers μ and λ. The following result is a consequence of the definition.

Theorem 4.4–A. Let $\{s_n\}$ be a bounded sequence, with

$$\limsup s_n = \mu.$$

Then,
  (i) for every $\varepsilon > 0$, there is a number $n_0 \in N$ such that, for all $n > n_0$,

$$s_n < \mu + \varepsilon;$$

  (ii) if ε is any positive number, and r is any positive integer, there is a positive integer $n > r$ such that

$$s_n > \mu - \varepsilon.$$

Proof (i). Let m_n have the significance described earlier in this section, so that $\mu = \lim m_n$. If $\varepsilon > 0$, there is an integer $n_0 \in N$ such that, for all $n > n_0$,

$$|m_n - \mu| < \varepsilon$$

i.e. such that

$$\mu - \varepsilon < m_n < \mu + \varepsilon.$$

Since $s_n \leqslant m_n$, for all n, it follows that

$$s_n < \mu + \varepsilon, \quad \text{for all } n > n_0.$$

Proof (ii). Let r be any positive integer, $\varepsilon > 0$, and suppose that $q > r$. Now,

$$m_q = \sup(s_q, s_{q+1}, s_{q+2}, \ldots);$$

hence, by definition of sup, $m_q - \varepsilon$ is not an upper bound of the set $s_q, s_{q+1}, s_{q+2}, \ldots$. Thus, there is a positive integer $n \geqslant q > r$ such that

$$s_n > m_q - \varepsilon.$$

But $m_q \geqslant \mu$, since $\{m_n\}$ is non-increasing; hence,

$$s_n > \mu - \varepsilon$$

and $n > r$.   ◆

Remark. Given a positive integer r, there are infinitely many positive integers $n > r$ for which $s_n > \mu - \varepsilon$. For, if $n_1 > r$ and $s_{n_1} > \mu - \varepsilon$, then we can appeal to (ii) with r replaced by n_1: there is a number $n_2 \in N$ with $n_2 > n_1$ and $s_{n_2} > \mu - \varepsilon$, and so on . . . .

   The conditions (i) and (ii) of Theorem 4.4–A are not only necessary to say that $\mu = \limsup s_n$; they are, in fact, also sufficient. Theorem 4.4–A shows that if $\mu = \limsup s_n$, then (i) and (ii) follow. Theorem 4.4–B, which follows, shows that $\limsup s_n$ is the only number which satisfies (i) and (ii).

Theorem 4.4–B. Let $\{s_n\}$ be a bounded sequence. Suppose that M is a number such that

(a) for every $\varepsilon > 0$, $\exists\, n_0 \in N$ such that, for all $n > n_0$,

$$s_n < M + \varepsilon;$$

(b) if ε is any positive number and r is any positive integer, there is a positive integer $n > r$ such that

$$s_n > M - \varepsilon.$$

Then, $M = \lim \sup s_n = \mu$.

Proof. Suppose $M > \mu$; then, taking $\varepsilon = (M - \mu)/2$ in (i) of Theorem 4.4–A, we see that there is a number $n_0 \in N$ such that, for all $n > n_0$,

$$s_n < \mu + \tfrac{1}{2}(M - \mu) = \tfrac{1}{2}(M + \mu).$$

But then, there is no positive integer $n > n_0$ with

$$s_n > M - \tfrac{1}{2}(M - \mu) = \tfrac{1}{2}(M + \mu),$$

which contradicts (b). Hence, $M \leqslant \mu$.

Similarly, using (ii) of Theorem 4.4–A and (a), we find that $M \geqslant \mu$. Hence, $M = \mu$. ◆

At this point, we state the corresponding results for $\lim \inf s_n$.

Theorem 4.4–C. Let $\{s_n\}$ be a bounded sequence, with $\lim \inf s_n = \lambda$. Then,

(i) for every $\varepsilon > 0$, there is a number $n_0 \in N$ such that, for all $n > n_0$,

$$s_n > \lambda - \varepsilon.$$

(ii) if $\varepsilon > 0$, and r is any positive integer, there is a positive integer $n > r$ such that

$$s_n < \lambda + \varepsilon.$$

Conversely, if λ is a number which satisfies (i) and (ii), then

$$\lambda = \lim \inf s_n.$$

Details are left to the reader as an exercise.

An important consequence of the ideas of limits superior and inferior is contained in the following theorem.

Theorem 4.4–D. Let $\{s_n\}$ be a bounded sequence. Then, there is an increasing sequence $\{t_n\}$ of positive integers such that the subsequence $\{s_{t_n}\}$ converges. That is, every bounded sequence contains a convergent subsequence.

Proof. We begin by illustrating the result. In Example 4.4.1, define $t_n = 2n$; then $\{s_{2n}\}$ converges to 1 (the limit superior). In Example 4.4.2, take $t_n = 4n + 3$; then $\{s_{4n+3}\}$ converges to -1 (the limit inferior). Likewise, in Example 4.4.3, we can find subsequences which converge to the limit superior and the limit inferior.

In view of this, we try to find a constructive proof, and show that there is a subsequence which converges to the limit superior. (We could also do the same with the limit inferior).

So, let $\lim \sup s_n = \mu$. In consequence of Theorem 4.4–A, there are infinitely many positive integers k such that

$$\mu - \varepsilon < s_k < \mu + \varepsilon.$$

In particular, this is so if we take $\varepsilon = 1/n$, for any $n \in N$. Take $\varepsilon = 1$; the set $\{k \in N : \mu - 1 < s_k < \mu + 1\}$ is infinite. Write $t_1 =$ smallest positive integer in this set. We now define $\{t_n\}$ by induction. Suppose t_1 has been defined. Then write

$$t_{i+1} = \text{least positive integer in the set}$$
$$\{k \in N : \mu - 1/(i+1) < s_k < \mu + 1/(i+1), \ \& \ k > t_i\}.$$

Clearly $t_i < t_{i+1}$, for all i, so $\{t_n\}$ is an increasing sequence of positive integers. Further,

$$|s_{t_n} - \mu| < 1/n, \quad \text{for every } n,$$

which implies that $\lim s_{t_n} = \mu$.   ◆

Theorem 4.4–D is a special case of a general result in Analysis known as the **Bolzano–Weierstrass Theorem**. In the context of the set R, this theorem states that if E is a bounded infinite subset of R, then E has at least one limit point. [Limit point is defined in Section 6.1.] If E is a bounded **closed** infinite subset of R, then there is a limit point *in E* (see Exercise 22 of Chapter 6 for definition of "*closed set*"). We now take up the remark at the conclusion of Example 4.4.3. If the limits superior and inferior coincide, the sequence converges. The converse is also true.

Theorem 4.4–E.   Let $\{s_n\}$ be a bounded sequence. Then, $\{s_n\}$ is convergent if and only if

$$\lim \sup s_n = \lim \inf s_n.$$

The common value is $\lim s_n$.

Proof (a).   Let $\mu = \lim \sup s_n$, $\lambda = \lim \inf s_n$ and suppose $\mu = \lambda$. Let $\varepsilon > 0$. By Theorem 4.4–A (i), there is a number $n_0 \in N$ such that, for all $n > n_0$,

$$s_n < \mu + \varepsilon.$$

By Theorem 4.4–C (i), there is a number $n_1 \in N$ such that, for all $n > n_1$,

$$s_n > \lambda - \varepsilon = \mu - \varepsilon.$$

Therefore, if $n_2 > \max(n_0, n_1)$, we have, for all $n > n_2$,

$$|s_n - \mu| < \varepsilon,$$

that is, $\lim s_n = \mu$.

Proof (b). Conversely, suppose $\lim s_n = \alpha$. We already know that $\mu \geqslant \lambda$. Let $\varepsilon > 0$; then, there is a number n_0 in N such that, for all $n > n_0$,

$$\alpha - \varepsilon < s_n < \alpha + \varepsilon.$$

Hence, for $n > n_0$, $\alpha + \varepsilon$ is an upper bound of $\{s_n\}$; therefore,

$$\alpha + \varepsilon \geqslant m_n$$

$$\Rightarrow \alpha + \varepsilon \geqslant \mu \quad \text{(by Example 4.3.3, Corollary 3).}$$

Also, for $n > n_0$, we have, similarly,

$$\alpha - \varepsilon \leqslant l_n$$

$$\Rightarrow \alpha - \varepsilon \leqslant \lambda.$$

Hence, we have

$$\alpha - \varepsilon \leqslant \lambda \leqslant \mu \leqslant \alpha + \varepsilon.$$

Since this is true for any $\varepsilon > 0$, we have $\alpha \leqslant \lambda \leqslant \mu \leqslant \alpha$ i.e. $\lambda = \mu = \alpha$. ◆

4.5 The General Principle of Convergence

Theorem 4.4–E gives a test for the convergence of a bounded sequence. It can, however, be cumbersome, if the limits superior and inferior are difficult to calculate. In this section, we shall prove another test for the convergence of a sequence, which is sometimes simpler. Let us begin by asking: what should we expect of a convergent sequence? Suppose $\lim s_n = \alpha$. Then, since all the terms are getting progressively closer to α, we should expect that if p and q are large, $|s_p - s_q|$ should be small, and getting smaller. We shall see, indeed, that this is necessary. Is it also sufficient? To try to prove this, we naturally fall back on the only test we have, at present, for general sequences, *viz.* Theorem 4.4–E.

First, however, we introduce a definition of what we mean by the "smallness" of $|s_p - s_q|$.

Definition. The sequence $\{s_n\}$ is said to be **fundamental** or **Cauchy**,[†] if, for each $\varepsilon > 0$, there is a number $n_0 \in N$ such that, for every pair of positive integers $p, q > n_0$, we have

$$|s_p - s_q| < K\varepsilon, \quad K \text{ a constant.}$$

We now come to the theorem which is called the *General Principle of Convergence*, or *Cauchy's criterion*.

Theorem 4.5–A (Cauchy). The sequence $\{s_n\}$ is convergent if and only if it is fundamental.

[†]After A-L. Cauchy (1789–1857), a French mathematician who made great contributions to the development of Analysis.

Proof (*Necessity*).   Suppose $\lim s_n = \alpha$. If $\varepsilon > 0$, there is a number $n_0 \in N$ such that, for all $n > n_0$,

$$|s_n - \alpha| < \varepsilon.$$

Hence, if $p, q > n_0$, we have

$$\begin{aligned} |s_p - s_q| &= |s_p - \alpha + \alpha - s_q| \\ &\leqslant |s_p - \alpha| + |s_q - \alpha| \\ &< 2\varepsilon. \end{aligned}$$

Thus, $\{s_n\}$ is fundamental.

(*Sufficiency*).   Suppose that, given $\varepsilon > 0$, there is a number $n_0 \in N$ such that, for all $q > p > n_0$,

$$s_p - \varepsilon < s_q < s_p + \varepsilon.$$

Then, the sequence $\{s_q, s_{q+1}, s_{q+2}, \ldots\}$ is bounded, for $q = p+1$, $p+2, \ldots$. Hence,

$$s_p - \varepsilon \leqslant l_q, \qquad m_q \leqslant s_p + \varepsilon,$$

and so

$$s_p - \varepsilon \leqslant \lambda, \qquad \mu \leqslant s_p + \varepsilon,$$

where λ, μ are $\liminf s_n$, $\limsup s_n$ respectively. That these exist follows from the boundedness of $\{s_{p+1}, s_{p+2}, \ldots\}$. Hence,

$$s_p - \varepsilon \leqslant \lambda \leqslant \mu \leqslant s_p + \varepsilon$$
$$\Rightarrow 0 \leqslant \mu - \lambda \leqslant 2\varepsilon.$$

This being true for any ε, it follows that $\mu = \lambda$. Hence, by Theorem 4.4–E, $\{s_n\}$ is convergent. ◆

Although we have said that the General Principle of Convergence provides a test for the convergence of sequences, we must not get carried away by this. Like Theorem 4.4–E, it is often difficult to apply positively. However, since the condition $|s_p - s_q| < K\varepsilon$, for all pairs p, q exceeding n_0, is *necessary*, as well as sufficient, it follows that if this condition is *not* satisfied, then the sequence is *not* convergent. So Theorem 4.5–A is of great value as a provider of the criterion for non-convergence by counterexample; that is, if $\{s_n\}$ is a sequence, and we can find an $\varepsilon > 0$ such that, for all integers $n_0 \in N$, there is a pair of integers p_0, q_0 each exceeding n_0 with $|s_{p_0} - s_{q_0}| \geqslant \varepsilon$, then $\{s_n\}$ is not convergent.

This is easily established using Theorem 4.5–A and Rule 3 of Chapter 1, Section 9. We have

$$\{s_n\} \text{ is convergent} \Leftrightarrow \forall\, \varepsilon > 0, \exists\, n_0 \in N \text{ s.t. } \forall\, p, q > n_0, |s_p - s_q| < \varepsilon,$$

so that

$\{s_n\}$ is not convergent

$$\Leftrightarrow \; \sim [\forall \, \varepsilon > 0, \, \exists \, n_0 \in N \text{ s.t. } \forall \, p, q > n_0, |s_p - s_q| < \varepsilon]$$

$$\Leftrightarrow \; \exists \, \varepsilon > 0 \text{ s.t. } \forall \, n_0 \in N, \, \exists \, p, q > n_0 \text{ s.t. } |s_p - s_q| \geqslant \varepsilon,$$

by Rule 3 of Section 1.9, which is precisely what we have said in words above.

Example 4.5.1. $\{(-1)^n\}$ is not convergent.

We know this already from a previous example. But, using Theorem 4.5–A, we proceed as follows:

if n_0 is any positive integer, then for any integer $m > n_0$, we have

$$|s_m - s_{m+1}| = 2.$$

For, successive terms are ± 1 alternately. So, if we take $\varepsilon < 2$, say $\varepsilon = 1$, we can take $n_0 = $ any positive integer, $p = m > n_0$, $q = m+1$, and then $|s_p - s_q| > \varepsilon$. So $\{s_n\}$ is not fundamental, and hence, not convergent.   ◆

Exercises

1. Show that, if $\{s_n\}$ is a sequence such that

$$|s_{n+1}/s_n| < r,$$

   for $n = 1, 2, 3, \ldots$, where $0 < r < 1$, then $\lim s_n = 0$. (Use Example 4.1.6.)

2. Prove that, if $\lim |s_{n+1}/s_n| = \lambda$, where $0 \leqslant \lambda < 1$, then $\lim s_n = 0$.

3. If x is any real number, then $\{x^n/n!\}$ has limit zero.

4. If k is a positive integer and $|x| < 1$, $\{n^k x^n\}$ has limit zero.

5. Find $\inf s_n$ where (a) $s_n = (n^2 + 3)/(n^2 + 1)$, (b) $s_n = n! e^{-n}$.

6. Let x_1, x_2 be numbers, with $x_1 < x_2$. Write $x_{n+2} = \frac{1}{2}(x_{n+1} + x_n)$, for $n = 1, 2, \ldots$. Show that $x_1, x_3, x_5, \ldots$ is an increasing sequence, $x_2, x_4, x_6, \ldots$ is decreasing, and that $\lim x_n$ exists and has the value $\frac{1}{3}(x_1 + 2x_2)$.

7. If $2xy = x^2 + 1$, show that $y \geqslant 1$ when $x \geqslant 0$, and also that $y - 1 \leqslant \frac{1}{2}(x - 1)$ when $x \geqslant 1$. Use this to prove that the sequence $\{a_n\}$ defined by

$$a_1 > 0, \; 2a_{n+1} = \frac{1}{a_n} + a_n \qquad (n \geqslant 1)$$

   is convergent, and find the number to which it converges.

8. $\{a_n\}, \{b_n\}$ are sequences such that

$$a_1 > b_1 > 0,$$

$$2a_{n+1} = a_n + b_n,$$

$$2/b_{n+1} = 1/a_n + 1/b_n.$$

Prove that

$$b_n < b_{n+1} < a_{n+1} < a_n$$

for all n, and that

$$a_n - b_n < \tfrac{1}{2}(a_{n-1} - b_{n-1});$$

deduce that $\{a_n\}, \{b_n\}$ have the same limit k, where $k^2 = a_1 b_1$.
(**Hint**: consider the difference $a_{n+1} - b_{n+1}$.)

9. Find lim sup s_n where (a) $s_n = 1/n + (-1)^n$, (b) $s_n = (1 - 1/n) \sin \tfrac{1}{2} n\pi$.

10. Prove that, if $\{s_n\}$ is bounded, and lim $t_n = t$, then

$$\lim \sup\{s_n + t_n\} = t + \lim \sup s_n.$$

[**Hint**: let $\mu = \lim \sup\{s_n + t_n\}$. Write down conditions on $s_n + t_n$ by Theorem 4.4–A. Also, lim $t_n = t$ means $t - \varepsilon < t_n < t + \varepsilon$ if $n > n_2$. Use this in conjunction with inequalities just found to obtain inequalities for s_n (e.g. $s_n < \mu - t + 2\varepsilon, \forall n > n_3$) and apply Theorem 4.4–B.]

11. Prove that if $\{s_n\}, \{t_n\}$ are bounded sequences, then
   (a) $\lim \inf s_n + \lim \inf t_n \leqslant \lim \inf(s_n + t_n)$.
   (b) $\lim \inf(s_n + t_n) \leqslant \lim \inf s_n + \lim \sup t_n$.
   (c) $\lim \inf s_n + \lim \sup t_n \leqslant \lim \sup(s_n + t_n)$.
   (d) $\lim \sup(s_n + t_n) \leqslant \lim \sup s_n + \lim \sup t_n$.

12. Discuss the behaviour of the following sequences.
   (a) $\{(1 + n^{-\frac{1}{2}} \ln n)^n\}$ (d) $\{2/n(n + \sqrt{n})\}$
   (b) $\{(1 + \sin \pi/n)^n\}$ (e) $\{3^n/e^{n+1}\}$
   (c) $\{(n/n + 1)^{n^2}\}$ (f) $\{(e^{1/n} - 1)^n\}$.

13. Prove that if $\{s_n\}$ converges to α, then every subsequence of $\{s_n\}$ also converges to α. Is it the case that if lim $s_{v_k} = \alpha$, for every subsequence $\{s_{v_k}\}$ of $\{s_n\}$, then lim $s_n = \alpha$?

CHAPTER 5

Series

5.1 Introduction

Let $\{a_n\}$ be a real sequence. In the last chapter, we were concerned with the long term development of a pattern of behaviour in the individual terms a_n. On the other hand, if we are presented with a succession of numbers, it is always tempting to add them together; if we take the successive terms of the sequence $\{a_n\}$, then we can add these together, and keep a running total, as in the table below:—

Sequence	Running Total	
a_1	a_1	$= "A_1"$
a_2	$a_1 + a_2$	$= "A_2"$
a_3	$a_1 + a_2 + a_3$	$= "A_3"$
$\vdots$		$\vdots$
a_n	$a_1 + a_2 + \ldots + a_n$	$= "A_n"$
$\vdots$		$\vdots$

We see that by this means we have constructed a new sequence $\{A_n\}$, where A_n is the running total after n terms of the sequence.

Since $\{A_n\}$ is a sequence, we can ask questions about its behaviour; does $\lim A_n$ exist as a real number? Is $\lim A_n = \infty$? This is the sort of problem that we are going to discuss in this chapter—the behaviour of the sequence $\{A_n\}$, and more importantly, how this behaviour is related to the original numbers $\{a_n\}$.

In order to emphasise this relationship with the numbers of the sequence $\{a_n\}$, we express the limit of the sequence $\{A_n\}$ in terms of these numbers. We do this *formally*; that is, we invent a symbolism that indicates we are concerned with the numbers $\{a_n\}$ although we discuss $\{A_n\}$. *This symbolism has no algebraic meaning.* We write, for $\lim A_n$, the formal expression

$$a_1 + a_2 + a_3 + \ldots; \tag{1}$$

we call the formal expression (1) an **infinite series**. Sometimes the terminology "the infinite series associated with the sequence $\{a_n\}$" is used, but we will avoid this.

At this point, we introduce some of the jargon which will be used in this chapter;

I. The series $a_1 + a_2 + a_3 + \ldots$ is usually written as

$$\sum_{n=1}^{\infty} a_n;$$

this is pronounced "sigma, $n = 1$ to infinity, a_n". Sigma (Σ) is the Greek upper case "S", and stands here for "sum", since we are "adding" the terms together. If no confusion is likely to arise, we also write Σa_n.

II. The real number a_n is called the **n-th term** of the series.

III. The real number $A_n = a_1 + a_2 + \ldots + a_n$ is called the **sum to n terms**, or the **n-th partial sum**.

IV. The sequence $\{A_n\}$ is called the **sequence of partial sums**. Now the behaviour of the series $\sum\limits_{n=1}^{\infty} a_n$ is the behaviour of the sequence $\{A_n\}$, and so we can at once formulate ideas of convergence and divergence of series. Moreover, we shall see in many of the theorems how we use the sequence of partial sums to determine the behaviour of the series.

5.2 Convergence of a Series

We begin at once with the definition, which is evident from the preceding remarks.

Definition. The series $\sum\limits_{n=1}^{\infty} a_n$ is said to be **convergent** if the sequence $\{A_n\}$ is convergent.

If $\lim A_n = s$, then we call s the **sum of the series** $\sum\limits_{n=1}^{\infty} a_n$, and write $\sum\limits_{n=1}^{\infty} a_n = s$.

So, to find the sum of a series, we need only find the limit of a sequence. Often, however, we are interested only in knowing that the series converges i.e. that $\lim A_n$ exists. For this, we can if necessary adapt the Cauchy Theorem 4.5–A; (*Cauchy Condition*): the series $\sum\limits_{n=1}^{\infty} a_n$ converges if and only if, given $\varepsilon > 0$, there is an integer $n_0 \in N$ such that, for all pairs of integers $p > q > n_0$, we have

$$|a_{q+1} + a_{q+2} + \ldots + a_p| < K\varepsilon$$

for some constant K.

To see this, we need only observe that

$$a_{q+1} + a_{q+2} + \ldots + a_p = A_p - A_q.$$

Definition.   The series $\sum\limits_{n=1}^{\infty} a_n$ is said to be **divergent** if it is not convergent i.e. if the sequence $\{A_n\}$ is divergent.

We mention one other device which is often used.

V. The symbols $\sum\limits_{n=1}^{\infty} a_{k+n}$, $\sum\limits_{m=k+1}^{\infty} a_m$, and $a_{k+1}+a_{k+2}+a_{k+3}+\ldots$ all mean the series whose first term is a_{k+1}, and whose n-th term is a_{k+n}.

It is easy to verify that the q-th term of $\sum\limits_{n=1}^{\infty} a_{p+n}$ is the $(p+q)$-th term of $\sum\limits_{n=1}^{\infty} a_n$.

So far, we have stressed the similarity between sequences and series. However, there is one important distinction between them. In the sequence $\{a_n\}$, it is essentially the behaviour of the terms a_n for large values of n which is significant; to see this, we need only observe that if k is some fixed integer, then $\lim a_{n+k} = \lim a_n$ (if this exists). But in a convergent series every single term is significant. For if we omit a_1, then the sum of the series will surely change by the amount a_1. This is the subject of our first theorem. Before we prove it, we note again explicitly that the *sequence* $\{a_n\}$ and the *series* Σa_n are *not* the same.

Theorem 5.2–A.   If $\sum\limits_{n=1}^{\infty} a_n$ is convergent, with sum s, then for any positive integer k, $\sum\limits_{n=1}^{\infty} a_{n+k}$ is convergent, and its sum is $s-a_1-a_2-\ldots-a_k$.

The technique of the proof is to make use of the sequence $\{A_n\}$, so that we can appeal to the results of Chapter 4. Therefore, in the proof, we immediately relate the partial sums of the two series. Since we are told the behaviour of $\{A_n\}$, this will allow us to deduce the behaviour of the sequence of partial sums of $\sum\limits_{n=1}^{\infty} a_{n+k}$.

Proof.   We prove the case $k = 1$. Any other case can be proved similarly.

Let A_n^* be the n-th partial sum of $\sum\limits_{n=1}^{\infty} a_{n+1}$; then, by definition of partial sum,

$$A_n^* = a_2+a_3+\ldots+a_{n+1}.$$

(N.B. the first term of $\sum\limits_{n=1}^{\infty} a_{n+1}$ is a_2); now,

$$A_{n+1} = a_1+a_2+\ldots+a_{n+1},$$

where A_n is the n-th partial sum of $\sum_{n=1}^{\infty} a_n$; hence,

$$A_n^* = A_{n+1} - a_1$$

$$\Rightarrow \lim A_n^* = \lim A_{n+1} - \lim a_1 \quad \text{(by Theorem 4.3–A, Corollary 2)}$$

$$= s - a_1$$

since by hypothesis, $\lim A_n = s$. Thus, $\sum_{n=1}^{\infty} a_{n+1}$ converges, with sum $s - a_1$. ◆

What does the theorem *prove*? It proves that if we chop off a term (a_1) or a block of terms $(a_1 + a_2 + \ldots + a_k)$ from the front of a convergent series, then we alter the value of the sum by this amount, but we do not destroy the convergence of the series. The next theorem is a reverse argument; if we *add on* a term or a block of terms to the front of a convergent series, then we do not destroy the convergence, though we will, in general, alter the sum. The proof is patterned after Theorem 5.2–A.

Theorem 5.2–B. If $\sum_{n=1}^{\infty} a_{n+k} = s^*$, then $\sum_{n=1}^{\infty} a_n$ converges, with sum $s^* + a_1 + a_2 + \ldots + a_k$ (k is a positive integer).

Proof. We again consider the case $k = 1$. Let A_n, A_n^* be as in Theorem 5.2–A. Then, by hypothesis, $\lim A_n^* = s^*$. But, by direct computation,

$$A_{n+1} = a_1 + A_n^*$$

$$\Rightarrow \lim A_{n+1} = \lim a_1 + \lim A_n^* \text{ (by Theorem 4.3–A(i))}$$

$$= a_1 + s^*.$$

So, by definition, $\sum_{n=1}^{\infty} a_n$ converges, with sum $s^* + a_1$. ◆

The next theorem gives the algebraic rules for manipulating convergent series.

Theorem 5.2–C. If $\sum_{n=1}^{\infty} a_n = s$, $\sum_{n=1}^{\infty} b_n = t$, then

(i) $\sum_{n=1}^{\infty} (a_n \pm b_n) = s \pm t$;

(ii) $\sum_{n=1}^{\infty} (ka_n) = ks$, k being a constant.

Proof. Let A_n, B_n be the n-th partial sums of Σa_n, Σb_n respectively. Then, $\lim A_n = s$, $\lim B_n = t$. Let C_n, D_n be the n-th partial sums of

$\Sigma(a_n \pm b_n)$, $\Sigma(ka_n)$; by elementary algebra,

$$C_n = (a_1 \pm b_1) + (a_2 \pm b_2) + \ldots + (a_n \pm b_n)$$
$$= (a_1 + a_2 + \ldots + a_n) \pm (b_1 + b_2 + \ldots + b_n)$$
$$= A_n \pm B_n$$
$$\Rightarrow \lim C_n = \lim(A_n \pm B_n)$$
$$= \lim A_n \pm \lim B_n \quad \text{(by Theorem 4.3–A(i) and Corollary 2)}$$
$$= s \pm t.$$

This proves (i). To prove (ii), we have

$$D_n = ka_1 + \ldots + ka_n$$
$$= kA_n$$
$$\Rightarrow \lim D_n = k \lim A_n \quad \text{(Theorem 4.3–A, Corollary 1)}$$
$$= ks. \qquad \blacklozenge$$

If we think about the convergence of a series, even in vague terms of "adding up" a sum, then it seems clear that if the series Σa_n converges with sum s, the absolute size of the later terms of the series must diminish. This is the message of the next theorem, one of the most fundamental in the study of series. In it, we establish a relationship between the series Σa_n and the sequence $\{a_n\}$.

Theorem 5.2–D. If Σa_n is convergent, then $\lim a_n = 0$.

Proof. Let A_n denote the n-th partial sum, and suppose that $\lim A_n = s$. Then,

$$a_n = A_n - A_{n-1}$$
$$\Rightarrow \lim a_n = \lim A_n - \lim A_{n-1} \quad \text{(Theorem 4.3–A, Corollary 2)}$$
$$= s - s$$
$$= 0. \qquad \blacklozenge$$

We use the symbol Σa_n here, as no confusion is likely. The proof again depends on the sequence $\{A_n\}$. We know the behaviour of this; we want to deduce the behaviour of $\{a_n\}$. Accordingly, we try to express a_n in terms of $\{A_n\}$ i.e. to write down what we want to know in terms of what we already do know. Once we have a_n in terms of $\{A_n\}$ the rest of the proof is easy, using the results of Chapter 4 again.

Theorem 5.2–D is of course a necessary condition for convergence. We shall see in Section 5.3 that the series $\Sigma(1/n)$ does not converge, although by Example 4.1.5 $\lim 1/n = 0$. So the theorem is not sufficient. The necessity of the condition, however, allows us to establish a useful test for suspected non-convergence; by using the contrapositive form (see Theorem 1.7–C) of Theorem 5.2–D, we have

Corollary. If $\lim a_n \neq 0$, then Σa_n is not convergent.

We must, however, be careful not to make the mistake of confusing contrapositive with converse (Section 1.7). We have already remarked that Theorem 5.2–D does not contain a sufficient condition for the convergence of Σa_n; hence its converse ("if $\lim a_n = 0$, then Σa_n is convergent") is *false*. Lim $a_n = 0$ does not guarantee convergence of Σa_n; it merely makes it a possibility.

Before going on to look at some specific series, we note the following result about grouping terms of a series in parentheses.

Theorem 5.2–E. If $\displaystyle\sum_{n=1}^{\infty} a_n = s$, then any series obtained from this by grouping terms in parentheses, but *without altering the order of the terms*, is also convergent with sum s. That is, if

$(a_1 + a_2 + \ldots + a_{k_1})$ is the first parenthesis, with sum b_1,

$(a_{k_1+1} + a_{k_1+2} + \ldots + a_{k_2})$ is the second, with sum b_2,

$(a_{k_{n-1}+1} + a_{k_{n-1}+2} + \ldots + a_{k_n})$ is the n-th, with sum b_n,

then $b_1 + b_2 + b_3 + \ldots$ converges, with sum s.

The proof is left as an exercise. Note that the converse is not valid. A series containing groups of terms in parentheses may converge; if the parentheses are removed, the series obtained may not converge, e.g. the series $(1-1)+(2-2)+(3-3)+\ldots$ is convergent, with sum zero. The series $1-1+2-2+3-3+\ldots$ does not converge; its partial sums are given by

$$A_n = \begin{cases} 0 & \text{if } n \text{ is even} \\ \dfrac{n+1}{2} & \text{if } n \text{ is odd} \end{cases}$$

and this sequence does not have a limit.

5.3 Some Special Series

5.3.1   The Geometric Series

One of the simplest series is that in which every term is a fixed multiple of that preceding. To take the simplest case, when the first term is unity, the series is

$$1 + r + r^2 + r^3 + \ldots \quad (r \text{ a real number}).$$

The n-th term is r^{n-1}, the n-th partial sum, A_n, is given by

$$A_n = 1 + r + r^2 + \ldots + r^{n-1} = \begin{cases} n & \text{if } r = 1 \\ \dfrac{1-r^n}{1-r} & \text{if } r \neq 1 \end{cases}$$

If $|r| < 1$, then $\lim r^n = 0$, (Example 4.1.6), whence

$$\lim \frac{r^n}{1-r} = 0;$$

it follows that $\sum\limits_{n=1}^{\infty} r^{n-1}$ is convergent, with sum $1/(1-r)$. If $|r| \geqslant 1$, then $|r^{n-1}| \geqslant 1$, and so, by the corollary to Theorem 5.2–D, the series does not converge.

5.3.2.   The Harmonic Series $[\sum\limits_{n=1}^{\infty} (1/n)]$

The series $1 + \frac{1}{2} + \frac{1}{3} + \frac{1}{4} + \ldots$ diverges. For, by Theorem 5.2–E, if it were convergent, so would any grouping in parentheses of this series. We shall exhibit such a grouping which diverges. (The counterexample method again!) We write

$$\sum \frac{1}{n} = 1 + (\tfrac{1}{2}) + (\tfrac{1}{3} + \tfrac{1}{4}) + (\tfrac{1}{5} + \ldots + \tfrac{1}{8}) + \ldots;$$

in general, terms in the k-th parenthesis satisfy

$$\frac{1}{2^{k-1}+1} + \ldots + \frac{1}{2^k} > \frac{1}{2^k} + \frac{1}{2^k} + \ldots + \frac{1}{2^k} \quad (2^{k-1} \text{ terms})$$

i.e. $> \frac{1}{2}$. Hence,

$$A_{2^{k+1}} > 1 + \tfrac{1}{2} + \tfrac{1}{2} + \ldots + \tfrac{1}{2}$$
$$= 1 + \tfrac{1}{2}(k+1).$$

So $\lim A_{2^{k+1}} = \infty$, and therefore $\Sigma(1/n)$ does not converge.

This is an important result, since the series $\Sigma(1/n)$ is one of the standard series used for testing convergence of other series. Note, too, that for this series $\lim a_n = 0$, illustrating the falsehood of a converse to Theorem 5.2–D.

5.3.3.   The Series $\sum\limits_{n=1}^{\infty} (1/n^2)$

The series $1 + \frac{1}{4} + \frac{1}{9} + \frac{1}{16} + \ldots$ is convergent. To prove this, we must show that the sequence of partial sums converges. The calculation of the partial sums is difficult, so precision is out of the question. However, if we can show, by more crude approximations, that the sequence of partial sums converges, this will do equally well. We accomplish this in two stages. First, it is not too difficult to find a particular subsequence of partial sums which converges, and which has the advantage of being easy to calculate approximately. This, however, is not sufficient to prove our result. We must show that *any* subsequence of partial sums converges. The second stage then consists in showing, again by rough estimates, that any partial sum does not differ significantly from one of the partial sums of the subsequence in stage (i). How to choose the subsequence of the first stage is a matter of intuition and experience. Remember, though, that the only series we know to be convergent is the geometric series with $|r| < 1$. Our aim must therefore be to try to relate $\Sigma(1/n^2)$ with such a series.

Denote the n-th partial sum by A_n as usual; consider this bracketed as follows:

$$A_n = 1 + (\tfrac{1}{4} + \tfrac{1}{9}) + (\tfrac{1}{16} + \ldots + \tfrac{1}{49}) + \ldots$$
$$+ \left[\frac{1}{2^{2k}} + \ldots + \left(\frac{1}{2^{k+1} - 1} \right)^2 \right] + \ldots + \frac{1}{n^2}.$$

(i) Let us first suppose that we have a number of complete parentheses. Then, n is of the form $2^{m+1} - 1$, where m is a positive integer. In the parenthesis

$$\left(\frac{1}{2^k} \right)^2 + \ldots + \left(\frac{1}{2^{k+1} - 1} \right)^2 \qquad (1)$$

there are 2^k terms, none of which exceeds the first term, namely $(1/2^k)^2$. So the contribution of the k-th parenthesis is less than $2^k(1/2^k)^2$ i.e. less than 2^{-k}. Hence, if $n = 2^{m+1} - 1$,

$$A_n < 1 + \tfrac{1}{2} + \tfrac{1}{4} + \ldots + \frac{1}{2^m}$$
$$< \sum_{k=0}^{\infty} \frac{1}{2^k} \quad \text{(geometric series with } r = \tfrac{1}{2}\text{)}$$
$$= 2.$$

So $A_n < 2$ for all n of the form $2^{m+1} - 1$. Furthermore, the subsequence $A_3, A_7, A_{15}, \ldots$ is increasing, since all the terms are positive. Hence, by Theorem 4.2–A, this subsequence is convergent. This completes the first stage.

(ii) Now, let n be any integer. We can find an integer m such that $2^m - 1 < n \leqslant 2^{m+1} - 1$. Using (1), the value of the m-th parenthesis is less than 2^{-m}. Since $2^m \leqslant n \leqslant 2^{m+1} - 1$, we have

$$A_n - A_{2^m - 1} \leqslant A_{2^{m+1} - 1} - A_{2^m - 1} < 2^{-m} \qquad (2)$$

i.e. $A_n < 2 + 2^{-m}$ (by stage (i)).

Hence, A_n is bounded above; since it is also increasing, the sequence $\{A_n\}$ converges. Hence the series $\Sigma(1/n^2)$ converges. Observe that the sum of the series satisfies the inequality $s \leqslant 2$.

In stage (ii), we suppose that there are not necessarily a number of complete brackets. However, the last term of the n-th partial sum will clearly occur between the ends of successive brackets; we show that the contribution of the incomplete bracket tends to zero, and appeal to stage (i).

5.4 Series with Non-negative Terms

We now restrict our attention to a particular class of series, in which all the terms are of the same sign. We assume without loss that the sign is positive. Such series are amenable to treatment by general techniques, and we shall see that principles can be laid down for dealing with them. What we are interested in, primarily, at this stage, is whether or not they converge; the precise value of the sum is not important.

So, let $\sum\limits_{n=1}^{\infty} a_n$ be a series with non-negative terms, that is, $a_n \geqslant 0$ for all values of n. We begin by proving a fundamental result which gives a necessary and sufficient condition for the convergence of such a series.

Theorem 5.4–A. The series $\sum\limits_{n=1}^{\infty} a_n$, where $a_n \geqslant 0$ for all n, converges if and only if there is a positive constant K such that

$$A_n \leqslant K \quad \text{for all } n.$$

Proof. Sufficiency: by hypothesis, $a_n \geqslant 0$. Hence,

$$A_{n+1} = A_n + a_{n+1}$$
$$\geqslant A_n.$$

Thus $\{A_n\}$ is a non-decreasing sequence. Hence, if $\{A_n\}$ is bounded above by the positive constant K, the sequence $\{A_n\}$ converges, by Theorem 4.2–A i.e. Σa_n is convergent.

Necessity: Suppose the series Σa_n converges; then the sequence $\{A_n\}$ is convergent. Since $a_n \geqslant 0$, $\{A_n\}$ is non-decreasing and so, by Theorem 4.2–A, converges to its supremum. Thus,

$$A_n \leqslant s \quad \text{for all } n.$$

Now, for K, choose any real number greater than s; then,

$$A_n \leqslant K \quad \text{for all } n. \qquad \blacklozenge$$

The theorem shows that a series with non-negative terms is convergent if and only if its partial sums are bounded above. This theorem, however, is not easily applicable in practice. We have already encountered difficulty in calculating partial sums in 5.3.3. We therefore pass on to tests of convergence which are easy to apply in specific examples. The first of these, the Comparison Test, is the most simple, and it will prepare the way for more refined tests.

Theorem 5.4–B (Comparison Test, first form). If $\sum\limits_{n=1}^{\infty} a_n$ converges with sum s, and there is a constant $k > 0$ such that, for every

value of n, $0 \leqslant b_n \leqslant ka_n$, then $\sum\limits_{n=1}^{\infty} b_n$ is also convergent, and

$$\sum_{n=1}^{\infty} b_n \leqslant ks.$$

Proof. Let A_n, B_n denote the n-th partial sums of the two series; then clearly, $B_n \leqslant kA_n$; since, by Theorem 5.4–A, $A_n \leqslant s$, we have

$$B_n \leqslant ks \quad \text{for all } n,$$
$$\Rightarrow \lim B_n \leqslant ks.$$

So, by Theorem 5.4–A, $\sum\limits_{n=1}^{\infty} b_n$ is convergent, with sum not exceeding ks. ◆

If we look at the contrapositive form of this result, we obtain a theorem on divergent series.

Theorem 5.4–C. If $\sum\limits_{n=1}^{\infty} a_n$ diverges, and $0 \leqslant ka_n \leqslant b_n$, where k is a positive constant, for all n, then $\sum\limits_{n=1}^{\infty} b_n$ diverges.

The proof is left to the reader (suppose $\sum\limits_{n=1}^{\infty} b_n$ converges, and apply Theorem 5.4–B).

We now come to another form of the Comparison Test. In consequence of Theorems 5.2–A and 5.2–B, it is the long range behaviour of the series which determines its convergence or divergence, so that the strict requirements of Theorem 5.4–B are not necessary. For instance, if $0 \leqslant b_n \leqslant ka_n$ for all $n \geqslant 200$, say, the result of Theorem 5.4–B is still valid, even though $b_n > ka_n$ for $1 \leqslant n \leqslant 199$. To see this, we apply Theorem 5.4–B to the series $\sum\limits_{n=200}^{\infty} a_n$ and $\sum\limits_{n=200}^{\infty} b_n$. The first converges by Theorem 5.2–A, so the latter converges by Theorem 5.4–B. But then, $\sum\limits_{n=1}^{\infty} b_n$ converges, by Theorem 5.2–B. Therefore, it is the long term comparison which is important, and this leads naturally to a limit form of the Comparison Test. This is better than Theorems 5.4–B, 5.4–C in two ways; it is usually more easily and more widely applicable (but see Example 5.4.2!).

Theorem 5.4–D (Comparison Test, Limit form). If $a_n \geqslant 0$, $b_n \geqslant 0$ for all values of n, and $\lim a_n/b_n = \lambda$, where λ is a *nonzero* real number, then Σa_n, Σb_n are either *both* convergent or *both* divergent.

Proof. Since $\lim a_n/b_n = \lambda$, there is (taking $\varepsilon = \frac{1}{2}\lambda$ in the formal definition of limit by Theorem 1.10–B) an integer n_0 in N such that

$$\left|\frac{a_n}{b_n} - \lambda\right| < \frac{\lambda}{2} \quad \text{if } n \geqslant n_0$$

i.e.

$$\frac{\lambda}{2} < \frac{a_n}{b_n} < \frac{3\lambda}{2} \quad \text{if } n \geqslant n_0.$$

Hence, for $n \geqslant n_0$, we have

$$0 \leqslant \tfrac{1}{2}\lambda b_n \leqslant a_n \tag{4}$$

$$0 \leqslant a_n \leqslant \frac{3\lambda}{2} b_n. \tag{5}$$

Suppose $\sum\limits_{n=1}^{\infty} a_n$ is convergent. Then, by Theorem 5.2–A, so is $\sum\limits_{n=n_0}^{\infty} a_n$, and hence by (4) and Theorem 5.4–B, so is $\sum\limits_{n=n_0}^{\infty} b_n$. But then, by Theorem 5.2–B, $\sum\limits_{n=1}^{\infty} b_n$ converges.

If, on the other hand, $\sum\limits_{n=1}^{\infty} a_n$ diverges, so does $\sum\limits_{n=n_0}^{\infty} a_n$ and so, by (5) and Theorem 5.4–C, so does $\sum\limits_{n=n_0}^{\infty} b_n$ (we take $k = 2/3\lambda$ in Theorem 5.4–C). It follows that $\sum\limits_{n=1}^{\infty} b_n$ diverges.   ◆

Example 5.4.1. Prove that $\Sigma[n/(3n+2)^3]$ is convergent.

Proof. Let $b_n = n/(3n+2)^3$. The magnitude of b_n, for large n, is "about" $n/27n^3$ or $1/27n^2$ (i.e. if n is large, $1/27n^2$ is a good approximation to b_n). This suggests that we try to apply Theorem 5.4–D with $a_n = 1/n^2$, since we know the behaviour of $\Sigma(1/n^2)$. Now,

$$\frac{a_n}{b_n} = \frac{(3n+2)^3}{n^3} = 27 + \frac{54}{n} + \frac{36}{n^2} + \frac{8}{n^3},$$

and hence $\lim a_n/b_n = 27$, which is a nonzero number. By Theorem 5.4–D, Σa_n, Σb_n converge or diverge together. Since we know from 5.3.3 that Σa_n converges, so does Σb_n.   ◆

Example 5.4.2. Discuss $\Sigma(1/n^s)$, where s is a positive real number. We have already investigated the cases $s = 1$ (divergent) and $s = 2$ (convergent). Suppose that $s \neq 1, 2$ and let us see what happens if we apply Theorem 5.4–D.

Let $a_n = 1/n$, $b_n = 1/n^s$. Then,

$$\frac{a_n}{b_n} = n^{s-1}$$

so that

$$\lim a_n/b_n = \begin{cases} \infty & \text{if } s > 1 \\ 0 & \text{if } s < 1 \end{cases}.$$

Similarly, if $a_n = 1/n^2$, we obtain similar results for $s < 2$, and $s > 2$. Hence, Theorem 5.4–D is of no use in this case. Far from being a panacea, it has strict limitations. We therefore try the less sophisticated versions, namely Theorems 5.4–B, 5.4–C.

Suppose, to begin with, we use as our comparison the divergent series $\Sigma(1/n)$. This means we have in mind an application of Theorem 5.4–C; so we should look for series in which $b_n \geqslant 1/n$. Now clearly, if $s < 1$, then $n^s \leqslant n$, and so $1/n \leqslant 1/n^s$. Hence, by Theorem 5.4–C, $\Sigma(1/n^s)$ diverges if $s < 1$. If $s > 1$, $n^s \geqslant n$, and nothing further can be said, since the inequality of Theorem 5.4–C is now reversed. Therefore, let us turn our attention to the known convergent series $\Sigma(1/n^2)$. In a similar way, we want to find series for which b_n satisfies $b_n \leqslant 1/n^2$, i.e. numbers s such that $1/n^s \leqslant 1/n^2$. But this is equivalent to having $n^2 \leqslant n^s$, which is certainly the case if $s > 2$. So, by Theorem 5.4–B, $\Sigma(1/n^s)$ converges if $s > 2$. This method again fails if $s < 2$, since the inequality of Theorem 5.4–B is reversed.

We are thus left with the range $1 < s < 2$. It can be shown, using the method of 5.3.3 that $\Sigma(1/n^s)$ converges if $s > 1$, and we shall leave this as an exercise. An alternative method of proof is to use the Integral Test, but we can justify this only when we come to Chapter 8. ◆

Example 5.4.3. Discuss

$$\Sigma \left(\frac{n^2 + n - 1}{n^3 + 2} \right)^{\frac{1}{2}}.$$

Here, let $b_n = [(n^2 + n - 1)/(n^3 + 2)]^{\frac{1}{2}}$. If n is large, the size of the numerator is *about* n, that of the denominator *about* $n^{\frac{3}{2}}$. So the magnitude of b_n is *about* $1/\sqrt{n}$. This suggests an application of Theorem 5.4–D with $a_n = 1/\sqrt{n}$. We therefore have

$$\frac{a_n}{b_n} = \left(\frac{n^3 + 2}{n^3 + n^2 - n} \right)^{\frac{1}{2}}$$

$$= \{(1 + 2/n^3)/(1 + 1/n - 1/n^2)\}^{\frac{1}{2}}.$$

By the usual methods, we find that $\lim a_n/b_n = 1$. But, by Example 5.4.2, $\Sigma(1/\sqrt{n})$ diverges ($s = \frac{1}{2}$); hence by Theorem 5.4–D so does $\Sigma[(n^2 + n - 1)/(n^3 + 2)]^{\frac{1}{2}}$. ◆

We now give a special form of the Comparison Test. It is this form which will be used subsequently, to prove the validity of two further tests. This special case uses the geometric series as the series Σa_n.

Theorem 5.4–E (Comparison Test, Special case). If $0 < r < 1$, and $0 \leqslant b_n \leqslant kr^n$, where $k > 0$ is a constant, for all sufficiently large values of n, then Σb_n converges.

Proof. For all $n \geqslant n_0$, $0 \leqslant b_n \leqslant kr^n$. Now, $\sum\limits_{n=n_0}^{\infty} kr^n$ converges, by 5.3.1, Theorem 5.2–A and Theorem 5.2–C (ii). Hence, Σb_n converges, by Theorems 5.4–B and 5.2–B.   ◆

Again, the inequality $0 \leqslant b_n < kr^n$ need hold only for all $n \geqslant n_0$, in view of Theorems 5.2–A and 5.2–B. This inequality at once suggests the pattern of the proof. Note that in all tests of convergence, the value of the sum is not under consideration; we are interested only in whether or not the series converges. So we use Theorems 5.2–A and 5.2–B quite freely.

In Theorems 5.4–B, 5.4–C, and 5.4–D we have required knowledge of a specific series in order to deduce the behaviour of the series we are interested in. However, such a series may not be directly or easily available. We must therefore seek to find other ways of determining whether or not a given series converges. We have already met a necessary condition for convergence, namely, that the n-th term should tend to zero. This, though, is far from sufficient. But clearly, from observation of the behaviour of the series $\Sigma(1/n^s)$, the degree of rapidity with which $b_n \to 0$ has a vital bearing on the convergence or divergence of Σb_n. The Comparison Test is really a test of this nature; if $b_n \to 0$ as rapidly as a_n (which happens if $b_n \leqslant ka_n$), then, should Σa_n be convergent, Σb_n will be convergent also. In the absence of a second series for comparison, we must therefore try to devise some means of testing the rapidity of decay of b_n, in terms of the sequence $\{b_n\}$ itself. An obvious, though crude, way of accomplishing this is to look at the *ratio* of successive terms (b_{n+1}/b_n). In order that b_n should tend to zero, we might expect such a condition as $(b_{n+1}/b_n) < 1$; we shall see shortly that this is not quite sufficient to ensure convergence. However, we now show that if we strengthen the condition to read $b_{n+1}/b_n < r < 1$, then this *is* sufficient (though not necessary) to guarantee convergence. This criterion is embodied in the following test, due to the French mathematician J. B. D'Alembert (1717–1783).

Theorem 5.4–F (Ratio Test, first form).   Let $b_n \geqslant 0$. If
 (i) there is a positive real number $r < 1$, and a positive integer n_0 such that, for all $n \geqslant n_0$, $b_{n+1}/b_n < r$, then Σb_n is convergent;
 (ii) there is a number $R > 1$ and a positive integer n_1 such that, for $n \geqslant n_1$, $b_{n+1}/b_n > R$, then Σb_n diverges.

Proof. For $n \geqslant n_0$, $b_n < rb_{n-1}$; repetition of this inequality yields the final inequality

$$b_n < r^n(b_{n_0}r^{-n_0}) = kr^n, \quad \text{say.}$$

We now apply Theorem 5.4–E. Since $r < 1$, Σb_n converges.

(ii) For $n \geqslant n_1$, $b_n > Rb_{n-1}$; repetition of this yields

$$b_n > R^n(b_{n_1}R^{-n_1}).$$

Now, $b_{n_1}R^{-n_1}$ is a nonzero constant. Since $R > 1$, $R^n \to \infty$, and so $b_n \nrightarrow 0$. By the Corollary to Theorem 5.2–D, Σb_n diverges. ◆

As with the Comparison Test, the Ratio Test can be expressed in terms of a limit. This is often easy to apply, although we lose some of the precision of the last test (see (iii) below).

Theorem 5.4–G (Ratio Test, limit form). Let $b_n \geqslant 0$. If

(i) $\lim (b_{n+1}/b_n) = \lambda < 1$, then Σb_n converges;
(ii) $\lim (b_{n+1}/b_n) = \mu > 1$, then Σb_n diverges;
(iii) $\lim (b_{n+1}/b_n) = 1$, then the test is **inconclusive** and fails.

Proof. (i) Since $\lim (b_{n+1}/b_n) = \lambda$, there is an integer n_0 such that, for $n \geqslant n_0$, we have

$$\left| \frac{b_{n+1}}{b_n} - \lambda \right| < \tfrac{1}{2}(1 - \lambda).$$

Here, we take $\varepsilon = \tfrac{1}{2}(1 - \lambda)$ again using Theorem 1.10–B. This yields

$$\frac{b_{n+1}}{b_n} < \tfrac{1}{2}(1 + \lambda) \quad \text{if } n \geqslant n_0.$$

Since $\lambda < 1$, we have $\tfrac{1}{2}(1 + \lambda) = r < 1$. So, by Theorem 5.4–F(i), Σb_n converges.

(ii) is proved similarly.

(iii) This case stands apart. If $\lim (b_{n+1}/b_n) = 1$, then we cannot draw *any* conclusion. To see this, we exhibit two series, one convergent, the other divergent, for which the limit of the ratio is 1. We do not need to look far; let $b_n = 1/n^2$, $a_n = 1/n$. Then,

$$\frac{a_{n+1}}{a_n} = \frac{n}{n+1} \to 1 \quad \text{as } n \to \infty$$

(Σa_n diverges). But

$$\frac{b_{n+1}}{b_n} = \frac{n^2}{(n+1)^2} = \left(\frac{n}{n+1} \right)^2 \to 1$$

(Σb_n converges). Hence, if $\lim (b_{n+1}/b_n) = 1$, no inferences can be made. ◆

We observe again that the proof of this result depends on reformulating the definition of limit in terms of the preceding theorem. Theorem

5.4–F(i) will be satisfied if ε (in the definition of limit) satisfies $\lambda + \varepsilon = r < 1$ i.e. if $\lambda + \varepsilon < 1$. So we choose $\varepsilon < 1 - \lambda$.

Note, however, that the ratio test is a *one-way* test. As we remarked in the discussion prior to Theorem 5.4–F, the condition $b_{n+1}/b_n < r < 1$ is sufficient, but not necessary. In other words, there are convergent series which do not satisfy this condition. Therefore we *cannot* conclude that if Σb_n converges, then $b_{n+1}/b_n < r < 1$ for large n. For example, the series

$$\frac{1}{3} + \frac{1}{2} + \frac{1}{3^2} + \frac{1}{2^2} + \frac{1}{3^3} + \frac{1}{2^3} + \cdots$$

converges. It is the sum of two convergent geometric series of positive terms, namely $\Sigma 1/2^k$, $\Sigma 1/3^k$. The ratio of successive terms of the series above is $\frac{1}{3}(\frac{2}{3})^k$ if n is even (of the form $2k$), and is $(\frac{3}{2})^k$ if n is odd (of the form $2k - 1$). But $(\frac{3}{2})^k \to \infty$ as $k \to \infty$; so the ratio test is not satisfied. Therefore, let us remember:

(1)
$$\left.\begin{array}{l} \lim \dfrac{b_{n+1}}{b_n} = \lambda < 1 \\[2ex] \dfrac{b_{n+1}}{b_n} < r < 1 \quad \text{if } n \geqslant n_0 \end{array}\right\} \Rightarrow \Sigma b_n \text{ convergent}$$

(2) $\quad \Sigma b_n$ convergent $\not\Rightarrow$
$$\left\{\begin{array}{l} \lim \dfrac{b_{n+1}}{b_n} = \lambda < 1 \\[2ex] \dfrac{b_{n+1}}{b_n} < r < 1 \quad \text{if } n \geqslant n_0 \end{array}\right.$$

The Ratio Test is especially useful in dealing with series involving a dummy, x. Here, an application of the test, in its limit form, yields an inequality for x. This is perhaps best illustrated by an example.

Example 5.4.4. Show that if k is a positive integer, then $\Sigma n^k x^n$ converges for all positive x satisfying $x < 1$.

Proof. The n-th term is $n^k x^n = b_n$. Work out the ratio of successive terms:

$$\frac{b_{n+1}}{b_n} = \left(\frac{n+1}{n}\right)^k x$$

$$= \left(1 + \frac{1}{n}\right)^k x;$$

now look at limits:

$$\lim \frac{b_{n+1}}{b_n} = \lim \left(1 + \frac{1}{n}\right)^k x$$

$$= x,$$

since $\lim(1 + 1/n)^k = 1$, if k is a positive integer. Now apply the Ratio Test. $\Sigma n^k x^n$ therefore converges if $x < 1$.   ◆

Corollary. Note also by the Ratio Test that $\Sigma n^k x^n$ diverges if $x > 1$, while if $x = 1$ the test fails. To decide the case $x = 1$, we put $x = 1$ in the series, which becomes Σn^k. Clearly, if $k > 0$, $n^k \nrightarrow 0$. So, the series is divergent for $x = 1$.

There are many other tests for the convergence of series of positive terms. These have been devised to fill the gap left by case (iii) above, or to cover situations where the Ratio Test fails in other ways, like the dovetailed geometric series above. We shall prove one other test, and mention a second. The test we shall prove is called the Root Test. It, too, is an easy consequence of Theorem 5.4–E, and is due to A. L. Cauchy (France, 1789–1857).

Theorem 5.4–H (Root Test, first form). Let $b_n \geqslant 0$. If
  (i) there is a real number r such that $0 < r < 1$, and an integer n_0 such that for all $n \geqslant n_0$, $b_n^{1/n} < r$, Σb_n converges;
  (ii) there is a real number $R > 1$ and an integer n_1 such that for all $n \geqslant n_1$, we have $b_n^{1/n} > R$, then Σb_n diverges.

Proof. (i) $b_n^{1/n} < r \Rightarrow b_n < r^n$.
This holds for all $n \geqslant n_0$. Hence, by Theorem 5.4–E with $k = 1$, Σb_n converges.
  (ii) $b_n^{1/n} > R \Rightarrow b_n > R^n$. Since $R > 1$, $R^n \to \infty$. Thus, $b_n \nrightarrow 0$, and Σb_n diverges (Corollary to Theorem 5.2–D).   ◆

The result can be stated in a limit form in this case also. The proof is left as an exercise. See also Exercises 11 and 12.

Theorem 5.4–I (Root Test, limit form). Let $b_n \geqslant 0$. If
  (i) $\lim b_n^{1/n} = \lambda < 1$, then Σb_n converges;
  (ii) $\lim b_n^{1/n} = \mu > 1$, then Σb_n diverges;
  (iii) $\lim b_n^{1/n} = 1$, the test is inconclusive, and fails.

The test we now state without proof, the Gauss Test, is sharper than both the Ratio and the Root Tests, in that it distinguishes cases when these tests are inconclusive.

Theorem 5.4–J (Gauss's Test). Let $b_n \geqslant 0$. If

$$\frac{b_{n+1}}{b_n} = 1 - \frac{k}{n} + \frac{R_n}{n^2},$$

where $|R_n|$ is bounded, then
  (i) Σb_n converges if $k > 1$,
  (ii) Σb_n diverges if $k \leqslant 1$.

5.5 Alternating Series

Having looked at series whose terms are all of one sign, we now go on to consider series which are not subject to this restriction. One such class of series which yields easily to analysis is the particular case when the successive terms are of opposite sign; thus, if $a_n \geqslant 0$ for all n, we shall consider the series

$$a_1 - a_2 + a_3 - a_4 + \ldots$$

Here, as always, we shall require $\lim a_n = 0$ for convergence, in consequence of Theorem 5.2–D. We shall see that this is almost all we do require; the fundamental theorem which follows is sometimes ascribed to the German mathematician G. W. Leibniz (1646–1716).

Theorem 5.5–A (Alternating Series Test). Let $\{a_n\}$ be a non-increasing sequence of positive terms, converging with limit zero. Then, the alternating series

$$a_1 - a_2 + a_3 - a_4 + \ldots$$

converges.

Proof. Let $A_n = a_1 - a_2 + a_3 - \ldots + (-1)^{n+1} a_n$.

We consider $A_{2n+3} - A_{2n+1}$; these are successive partial sums which end with a *positive* term.

$$A_{2n+3} - A_{2n+1} = a_{2n+3} - a_{2n+2} \leqslant 0$$

since $\{a_n\}$ is non-increasing. Hence, for $n = 0, 1, 2, \ldots$

$$A_{2n+3} \leqslant A_{2n+1}$$

and so the odd partial sums therefore form a non-increasing sequence. A similar analysis shows that $A_{2m+2} \geqslant A_{2m}$, for $m = 1, 2, \ldots$; the even partial sums form a non-decreasing sequence. Next,

$$A_{2m+1} - A_{2m} = a_{2m+1} \geqslant 0.$$

So, we have

$$A_{2m+1} \geqslant A_{2m} \geqslant A_2$$

since $\{A_{2m}\}$ is non-decreasing. Thus, $\{A_{2m+1}\}$ is bounded below (by A_2, a constant), for all m. It is also non-increasing, and so by Theorem 4.2–B is convergent. Suppose

$$\lim A_{2m+1} = \lambda. \tag{1}$$

Likewise, the sequence of even partial sums $\{A_{2m}\}$ is non-decreasing and bounded above (by A_1), and so is convergent, by Theorem 4.2–A. Let

$$\lim A_{2m} = \mu. \tag{2}$$

In order that the series $a_1 - a_2 + a_3 - \ldots$ converge, it is necessary to show that all sequences of partial sums converge to the same limit. So, the theorem will follow if we now prove that $\lambda = \mu$. Since

$$A_{2m+1} = A_{2m} + a_{2m+1},$$

we have, by Theorem 4.3–A,

$$\lim A_{2m+1} = \lim A_{2m} + \lim a_{2m+1}.$$

By hypothesis, $\lim a_{2m+1} = 0$; hence, by (1) and (2), $\lambda = \mu$.   ◆

Example 5.5.1.   The series $1 - \frac{1}{2} + \frac{1}{3} - \frac{1}{4} + \ldots$ converges; $\{1/n\} \downarrow 0$.

Example 5.5.2.   The series $1 - \frac{1}{4} + \frac{1}{9} - \frac{1}{16} + \ldots$ converges; $\{1/n^2\} \downarrow 0$.

5.6 Absolute Convergence

We have now discussed series of constant sign, and series of alternating sign. We shall later discuss series of mixed sign, of which the alternating series is a particular example. These types represent a classification of series according to their physical appearance, and we can find convergent series which belong to each of these classes. Since our purpose is discussing series is to establish whether or not they converge, we might try to classify series on the basis of convergence. By way of illustration, we observe that the series in Examples 5.5.1 and 5.5.2 both converge; on the other hand, if we consider two series closely connected with these, $1 + \frac{1}{2} + \frac{1}{3} + \ldots$ and $1 + \frac{1}{4} + \frac{1}{9} + \ldots$ (5.3.2 and 5.3.3), then the first diverges, while the second converges. This suggests a way of splitting up the class of convergent series and so, we can postulate that there are three basic classes of series:

  (i) those series, like 5.3.2, which are divergent;
 (ii) those series, like Example 5.5.1, which converge, but if we replace each term by its absolute value, become divergent;
(iii) those series, like that of Example 5.5.2, which converge, and remain convergent when each term is replaced by its absolute value.

It is at once apparent that all convergent series whose terms are of constant sign belong to class (iii). Series in class (iii) are given a special name; they are called "absolutely" convergent. So, we now formally make a new definition.

Definition.   The series Σb_n is called **absolutely convergent** if $\Sigma |b_n|$ is convergent.

It is evident that this is exactly the condition laid down for membership of class (iii) above.

Series in class (ii) are sometimes called **conditionally convergent** or **non-absolutely convergent**. These terms are self-explanatory; they imply convergence, but not absolute convergence. Since absolute convergence is a stronger condition on a series than convergence, it is to be expected that absolute convergence should imply convergence. We verify that this is the case.

Theorem 5.6–A. If Σa_n converges absolutely, then it converges.

We shall give two proofs, one using the Cauchy Condition for convergence (Section 5.2). This proof is the shorter, and we give it first.

First Proof. $\Sigma|a_n|$ convergent $\Rightarrow$ given $\varepsilon > 0$, there is an integer n_0 such that, for all pairs of integers $m > n > n_0$, we have

$$\|a_{n+1}| + |a_{n+2}| + \ldots + |a_m\| < \varepsilon \tag{1}$$

by the Cauchy Condition. But, if $m > n > n_0$,

$$|a_{n+1} + \ldots + a_m| \leqslant \|a_{n+1}| + \ldots + |a_m\| < \varepsilon \quad \text{by (1)}$$

$$\Rightarrow \Sigma a_n \text{ is convergent.} \qquad \blacklozenge$$

Second Proof. We introduce a new notation here, which we shall see in use later in this chapter, and which has an analogue in Chapter 8. Define p_n, q_n as follows:

$$p_n = \begin{cases} a_n & \text{if } a_n \geqslant 0 \\ 0 & \text{if } a_n < 0 \end{cases}, \qquad q_n = \begin{cases} 0 & \text{if } a_n \geqslant 0 \\ -a_n & \text{if } a_n < 0 \end{cases}.$$

Then, $p_n \geqslant 0$, $q_n \geqslant 0$ for all n. p_n thus denotes the positive terms of the series, and $-q_n$ the negative terms, so that

$$\Sigma a_n = \Sigma(p_n - q_n).$$

On the other hand, $|a_n|$ is always positive, and it is easy to verify that

$$|a_n| = p_n + q_n. \tag{2}$$

Now, (2) $\Rightarrow$ $p_n \leqslant |a_n|$, $q_n \leqslant |a_n|$, since $p_n \geqslant 0$, $q_n \geqslant 0$. So, if $\Sigma|a_n|$ is convergent, so also are Σp_n and Σq_n, by Theorem 5.4–B. Hence, by Theorem 5.2–C(i), $\Sigma a_n = \Sigma(p_n - q_n)$ is convergent. $\qquad \blacklozenge$

Corollary. If A_n, A_n^* denote the n-th partial sums of Σa_n and $\Sigma|a_n|$ respectively, then by Theorem 2.4–B,

$$|A_n| \leqslant A_n^* \Rightarrow \lim|A_n| \leqslant \lim A_n^*.$$

Thus, if Σa_n is absolutely convergent, the value of the sum (in absolute magnitude) does not exceed the sum of the absolute values of the terms of the series.

Note. Example 5.5.1 shows that Theorem 5.6–A does not have a converse.

The convergence of the series of absolute values is the distinguishing characteristic of an absolutely convergent series. But there is another distinction; the German, G. L. B. Riemann (1826–1866) discovered that a conditionally convergent series can be rearranged to give any desired sum. For an absolutely convergent series, on the other hand, every rearrangement has the same sum. This last fact we shall now prove.

We first define precisely what a rearrangement is.

Definition. Let f be a $(1, 1)$ function of N with range N. Let Σa_n and Σb_n be two series such that

$$a_n = b_{f(n)} \qquad n = 1, 2, 3, \ldots$$

Then, Σa_n is called a **rearrangement** of Σb_n.

Since f is $(1, 1)$ and $\mathscr{R}(f) = N$, f^{-1} exists as a function, and $b_n = a_{f^{-1}(n)}$, so that Σb_n is also a rearrangement of Σa_n.

Theorem 5.6–B. Let Σa_n be an absolutely convergent series, with sum s. Then, every rearrangement of Σa_n converges absolutely, also with sum s.

Proof. Let us denote the function f^{-1} by g, for convenience. Write $b_n = a_{g(n)}$. Since $\Sigma|a_n|$ is convergent, given $\varepsilon > 0$, there is an integer n_0 such that, for all $m > n > n_0$, we have

$$|a_{n+1}| + \ldots + |a_m| < \varepsilon.$$

This being true for all choices of $m > n$, let $m \to \infty$. Then, if $n > n_0$,

$$\sum_{k=n+1}^{\infty} |a_k| \leqslant \varepsilon. \tag{1}$$

We now wish to show that there is an integer m_0 such that, for all pairs $m > n > m_0$,

$$|b_{n+1}| + \ldots + |b_m| < k\varepsilon;$$

this will then prove Σb_n absolutely convergent, by the Cauchy condition. Now,

$$|b_{n+1}| + \ldots + |b_m| = |a_{g(n+1)}| + \ldots + |a_{g(m)}|$$

and the right-hand side will not exceed ε, in view of (1), provided that all the numbers $\{g(n+1), \ldots, g(m)\}$ exceed n_0.

Choose M (dependent, as we shall see, on n_0, and hence ultimately upon ε) so that the set $\{1, 2, \ldots, n_0\}$ is a subset of the set $\{g(1), \ldots, g(M)\}$; since the first set is finite, this is always possible.[†] Then, clearly, if $n > M$, $g(n) > n_0$. Hence, for all $m > n > M$, all members of the set $\{g(n+1), \ldots, g(m)\}$ exceed n_0, implying the absolute convergence of Σb_n.

---

† Consider the set of integers $\{1, 2, \ldots, n_0 + 1\}$; let K be the largest integer n such that $g(n) \in \{1, 2, \ldots, n_0 + 1\}$. Then, define M by setting $M \geqslant K + 1$.

We must also show that the sum of Σb_n is s. Let A_n, B_n denote the n-th partial sums of Σa_n, Σb_n respectively. Given $\varepsilon > 0$, we can choose an integer n_1 such that, for all $n > n_1$

$$|A_n - s| < \varepsilon,$$

and an integer n_2 as above such that

$$\sum_{k=n_2+1}^{\infty} |a_k| \leqslant \varepsilon.$$

Taking $n_3 = \max(n_1, n_2)$, we have

$$|A_{n_3} - s| < \varepsilon \quad \text{and} \quad \sum_{k=n_3+1}^{\infty} |a_k| \leqslant \varepsilon.$$

Now,

$$|B_n - s| \leqslant |B_n - A_{n_3}| + |A_{n_3} - s|$$
$$< |B_n - A_{n_3}| + \varepsilon.$$

If we choose M as before, then $n > M \Rightarrow g(n) > n_3$; and so, for $n > M$,

$$|B_n - A_{n_3}| = |b_1 + \ldots + b_n - a_1 - a_2 - \ldots - a_{n_3}|$$
$$= |a_{g(1)} + \ldots + a_{g(n)} - a_1 - \ldots - a_{n_3}|$$
$$\leqslant |a_{n_3+1}| + |a_{n_3+2}| + \ldots$$

since $\{1, 2, \ldots, n_3\} \subset \{g(1), \ldots, g(M)\}$, and so the terms $a_1, a_2, \ldots, a_{n_3}$ cancel out in the subtraction,

$$\leqslant \varepsilon$$
$$\Rightarrow |B_n - s| < 2\varepsilon \quad \text{for all } n > M,$$
$$\Rightarrow \lim B_n = s,$$

as required.   ◆

We shall merely sketch the proof of Riemann's Theorem on rearrangements of conditionally convergent series. Suppose we wish to find a rearrangement which converges to sum σ, say. We recall the definition of the sequences $\{p_n\}$, $\{q_n\}$ in Theorem 5.6–A. If Σa_n is conditionally convergent, then $\Sigma|a_n|$ is divergent, and so $\Sigma(p_n + q_n)$ is divergent. It follows that both Σp_n and Σq_n diverge; for, if both were convergent, their sum $\Sigma(p_n + q_n)$ would also converge, by Theorem 5.2–C(i), while if only one of them was divergent, then the same theorem would imply that $\Sigma(p_n - q_n)$ was divergent, again a contradiction.

So Σp_n, Σq_n both diverge; however, since Σa_n is convergent, $\lim a_n = 0$ (Theorem 5.2–D), and hence $\lim p_n = \lim q_n = 0$. Assuming $\sigma > 0$, the construction is as follows; take just enough terms from

Σp_n so that the sum of these exceeds σ. Suppose there are k_1 of them:

$$p_1 + p_2 + \ldots + p_{k_1} > \sigma.$$

Now, using the terms of Σq_n, subtract just enough terms (say m_1) to make the total sum to date less than σ; thus,

$$p_1 + p_2 + \ldots + p_{k_1} - q_1 - q_2 - \ldots - q_{m_1} < \sigma.$$

Proceed thus, adding and subtracting alternately just sufficient terms to reverse the inequality. This can be done indefinitely, since Σp_n, Σq_n diverge to $+\infty$. This gives a rearrangement of Σa_n whose sum is evidently something close to σ. The proof that the sum of this rearrangement is σ itself depends on the fact that the sequences $\{p_n\}$, $\{q_n\}$ have limit zero. We omit the details.

5.7 Series of Mixed Sign

We now return to consideration of series of mixed sign. The Alternating Series Test is, of course, limited in its application by its very nature. We include in this section an account of two tests for series of mixed sign, which are of a more general nature. Their real value, in fact, is in an adaptation to series of functions, which is, however, outside our scope in this volume. In both of these, we consider series of the form $\Sigma a_n b_n$, where $\{a_n\}$ and $\{b_n\}$ are sequences of real numbers; we show that the imposition of certain conditions on the sequences $\{a_n\}$, $\{b_n\}$ implies the convergence of the series whose n-th term is $a_n b_n$. We require two preliminary results; the first is purely algebraic.

Lemma 5.7.1. Let $\{a_n\}$, $\{b_n\}$ be sequences of real numbers. Let A_n, B_n, C_n denote the n-th partial sums of Σa_n, Σb_n and $\Sigma a_n b_n$ respectively. Then,

$$C_n - A_n b_n = \sum_{k=1}^{k=n-1} A_k(b_k - b_{k+1}).$$

Proof. $C_n = a_1 b_1 + a_2 b_2 + \ldots + a_n b_n$

$$= A_1 b_1 + (A_2 - A_1)b_2 + \ldots + (A_n - A_{n-1})b_n$$

$$= A_1(b_1 - b_2) + A_2(b_2 - b_3) + \ldots + A_{n-1}(b_{n-1} - b_n) + A_n b_n$$

whence

$$C_n - A_n b_n = \sum_{k=1}^{k=n-1} A_k(b_k - b_{k+1}). \qquad \blacklozenge$$

The second result is related to the first.

Lemma 5.7.2. Suppose that Σa_n is a series such that $\{A_n\}$ is a bounded sequence. Let $\{b_n\}$ be a non-increasing sequence of positive real numbers. Then, $\Sigma A_n(b_n - b_{n+1})$ is convergent, absolutely.

Proof. Suppose $|A_n| < K$, for all n. Let

$$D'_n = \sum_{k=1}^{k=n} |A_k(b_k - b_{k+1})|.$$

Then,

$$D'_n = \sum_{k=1}^{k=n} |A_k|(b_k - b_{k+1}),$$

since $\{b_n\}$ is non-increasing,

$$< K \sum_{k=1}^{k=n} (b_k - b_{k+1})$$

$$= K(b_1 - b_{n+1})$$

$$\leqslant Kb_1.$$

Hence, $\{D'_n\}$ is bounded above, and is increasing, since all the terms are positive. So, by Theorem 4.2–A, $\{D'_n\}$ is convergent.   ◆

We are now ready to prove the two tests for convergence of series. The first is due to the Norwegian, N. H. Abel (1802–1829).

Theorem 5.7–A (Abel's Test). Suppose that Σa_n is a convergent series; let $\{b_n\}$ be a non-increasing sequence of positive real numbers. Then, $\Sigma a_n b_n$ is convergent.

Proof. Let A_n denote the n-th partial sum of Σa_n, D_n the n-th partial sum of $\Sigma A_n(b_n - b_{n+1})$, C_n the n-th partial sum of $\Sigma a_n b_n$. Then,

$$\Sigma a_n \text{ convergent} \Rightarrow \{A_n\} \text{ convergent}$$

$$\Rightarrow \lim A_n = s, \quad \text{say.} \tag{1}$$

Also,

$$\text{Lemma 5.7.2} \Rightarrow \Sigma|A_n(b_n - b_{n+1})| \text{ convergent}$$

$$\Rightarrow \{D_n\} \text{ convergent, by Theorem 5.6–A}$$

$$\Rightarrow \lim D_n = d, \quad \text{say.} \tag{2}$$

Next, since $\{b_n\}$ is non-increasing and is bounded below (by zero), $\{b_n\}$ is convergent, say $\lim b_n = b$.
By Lemma 5.7.1,

$$C_n = \sum_{k=1}^{k=n-1} A_k(b_k - b_{k+1}) + A_n b_n$$

$$= D_{n-1} + A_n b_n$$

$$\Rightarrow \lim C_n = \lim(D_{n-1} + A_n b_n)$$

$$= d + sb \quad \text{(using Theorem 4.3–A yet again)}$$

$\Rightarrow \Sigma a_n b_n$ is convergent. ◆

Example 5.7.1. The series $\Sigma(1/n^2)\sin(\pi/n+1)$ is convergent.

Proof. Let $a_n = 1/n^2$; then Σa_n is convergent. If $b_n = \sin(\pi/n+1)$, then $b_{n+1} < b_n$, so $\{b_n\}$ is decreasing. It is also clear that $b_n > 0$; in fact, $\lim b_n = 0$. Hence, by Abel's Test, $\Sigma a_n b_n$ converges. ◆
A more powerful test is that due to the German, Dirichlet (1805–1859).

Theorem 5.7–B (Dirichlet's Test). Let Σa_n be a series with bounded partial sums; let $\{b_n\}$ be a non-increasing sequence of positive real numbers, such that $\lim b_n = 0$. Then $\Sigma a_n b_n$ is convergent.

Proof. Let A_n, D_n, C_n have the significance described in Theorem 5.7–A. Then, again, $\lim D_n$ exists, by Lemma 5.7.2, with value d, say. Now,

$$|A_n| < K \quad \text{and} \quad \lim b_n = 0 \Rightarrow \lim A_n b_n = 0.$$

But then,

$$C_n = D_{n-1} + A_n b_n$$
$$\Rightarrow \lim C_n = \lim(D_{n-1} + A_n b_n)$$
$$= d$$
$$\Rightarrow \Sigma a_n b_n \text{ is convergent.} \quad ◆$$

Corollary. The Alternating Series Test (Theorem 5.5–A) is a special case.

Proof. In Theorem 5.7–B, let

$$a_1 = a_3 = a_5 = \ldots = +1$$
$$a_2 = a_4 = a_6 = \ldots = -1$$

then, A_n is either $+1$ or 0, and so $\{A_n\}$ is bounded. Next, let $b_n = \alpha_n$, where $\{\alpha_n\}$ is decreasing with limit zero. Then, $\Sigma a_n b_n$ converges, by Theorem 5.7–B. But

$$\Sigma a_n b_n = \alpha_1 - \alpha_2 + \alpha_3 - \alpha_4 + \ldots$$

and the right-hand side is an alternating series, satisfying the conditions of Theorem 5.5–A. ◆

Example 5.7.2. The series $\Sigma(1/n)\sin(n\pi/2)$ is convergent.

Proof. Firstly, we observe that, if $u_n = 1/n \sin(n\pi/2)$, then

$$|u_n| = \frac{1}{n} \text{ if } n \text{ is odd, } u_n = 0, \text{ if } n \text{ is even}$$

and so the series is not absolutely convergent.

Let

$$a_n = \sin \frac{n\pi}{2}, \qquad b_n = \frac{1}{n};$$

then,

$$b_n \geqslant 0, \qquad b_{n+1} < b_n, \qquad \lim b_n = 0;$$

also, if $\{A_n\}$ denotes the partial sums of Σa_n, we have

$$A_{4k} = 0, \qquad A_{4k+1} = 1, \qquad A_{4k+2} = 1, \qquad A_{4k+3} = 0;$$

so, for all n, $0 \leqslant A_n \leqslant 1$ i.e. $\{A_n\}$ is bounded. Hence, by Theorem 5.7–B, $\Sigma a_n b_n$ converges. ◆

Example 5.7.3. The series $\Sigma(1/\sqrt{n}) \sin nx$, where $0 < \delta < x < \pi/2$, is convergent.

Proof. Let $a_n = \sin nx$, $b_n = 1/\sqrt{n}$. Clearly, $0 < b_{n+1} < b_n$, and $\lim b_n = 0$. By an elementary trigonometric calculation,

$$A_k = \sum_{n=1}^{n=k} \sin nx = \frac{\sin((k+1)/2)x \sin(kx/2)}{\sin(x/2)}$$

and so, since $|\sin \theta| \leqslant 1$,

$$|A_k| \leqslant \operatorname{cosec} \tfrac{1}{2}x$$

$$\leqslant K, \quad \text{since } 0 < \delta < x < \frac{\pi}{2}.$$

Hence the sequence $\{A_n\}$ is bounded, and the result follows by Theorem 5.7–B. ◆

5.8 Power Series

In Section 5.3, we encountered the geometric series

$$1 + r + r^2 + r^3 + r^4 + \ldots \tag{1}$$

which is convergent if $|r| < 1$, and divergent if $|r| \geqslant 1$. Now, in (1), r represents some real number, and so, if we consider r as a dummy whose domain is R, (1) can be thought of as representing a whole class of series, rather than just one, and the use of the dummy permits us to apply general techniques to determine the values of r for which the series converges. The series (1), with r as a dummy, is an example of a **real power series**, since the terms consist of powers of the real number r. The general form of a real power series allows multiples of these powers, and is given by

$$a_0 + a_1 r + a_2 r^2 + a_3 r^3 + \ldots \tag{2}$$

written as $\Sigma a_n r^n$, where r is a dummy with domain R, and $\{a_n\}$ is a given sequence of numbers. The sequence $\{a_n\}$ is labelled so as to start with a_0, simply for the convenience of having the same index as subscript in the sequence $\{a_n\}$ as appears in the exponent of r.

Now, different replacements for r give different series of real numbers. Some of these may converge, or even converge absolutely, and some may diverge. Our problem is to find a systematic way of classifying the values of r, using the results of Sections 5.4 to 5.7, into those for which the series (2) converges absolutely, converges conditionally, or diverges.

Firstly, we note that if $r = 0$, the series (2) is absolutely convergent (with sum a_0). Hence, there is a set S of real numbers such that, if $s \in S$, then $\Sigma a_n s^n$ is absolutely convergent. This set S is non-empty, since it contains 0. Next, if (2) converges absolutely for a number s, then it converges absolutely for all numbers r with $0 \leqslant |r| \leqslant |s|$. For then, $|a_n r^n| \leqslant |a_n s^n|$ and so, by the Comparison Test, $\Sigma|a_n r^n|$ is convergent. Thus, we can postulate that there is a greatest possible s with this property, or better, that there is a number ρ, given by

$$\rho = \sup\{|s| : s \in S\},$$

such that $\Sigma a_n r^n$ converges absolutely, if $0 \leqslant |r| < \rho$.

We shall therefore make the following definition:

Definition. Let S be the set of real numbers for which $\Sigma a_n r^n$ converges. Let ρ be the supremum of the *absolute values* of numbers in S, i.e. $\rho = \sup\{|s| : s \in S\}$. Then, ρ is called the **radius of convergence** of the power series (2).

The reason for the terminology *radius of convergence* is that power series are usually considered when r is a *complex* number. In that case, we find that the power series $\Sigma a_n r^n$ converges absolutely inside a circle, centre the origin. The radius ρ of this circle is then called the *radius of convergence*.

Clearly, if $|r| > \rho$, then $r \notin S$; but if $r \notin S$, then $\Sigma a_n r^n$ diverges, by definition of S. Thus, $\Sigma a_n r^n$ diverges if $|r| > \rho$. Our first theorem of this section shows that the number ρ represents a watershed between convergence and divergence, that $\Sigma a_n r^n$ cannot diverge if $|r| < \rho$.

Theorem 5.8–A. Let ρ be the radius of convergence of the power series $\Sigma a_n r^n$. Then if $|r| < \rho$, the series is absolutely convergent; if $|r| > \rho$, it is divergent.

Proof. Suppose that $|r| < \rho$. Then, since $\rho = \sup\{|s| : s \in S\}$, there is a number r_1 such that $|r| < |r_1| < \rho$, and $\Sigma a_n r_1^n$ is convergent. Then,

Theorem 5.2–D $\Rightarrow \lim a_n r_1^n = 0$

$\Rightarrow |a_n r_1^n| < M$, for all n.

$\Rightarrow |a_n r^n| = |a_n r_1^n| \, |r/r_1|^n$

$\qquad\qquad < M|r/r_1|^n$ for all n.

By the choice of r_1, $|r/r_1| < 1$, and so by Theorem 5.4–E, $\Sigma|a_n r^n|$ converges, i.e. $\Sigma a_n r^n$ is absolutely convergent. The case $|r| > \rho$ has been discussed already, in the preamble to the theorem. ◆

We have thus proved that if ρ is the radius of convergence of the power series, then $\Sigma a_n r^n$ is absolutely convergent throughout the whole interval $-\rho < r < \rho$. One interesting point about power series is that this interval is always symmetrical about the origin; in Exercises 15 (g) and (h), the reader will find that the range of x for which these series converge is not an interval symmetric about $x = 0$. This is because the series in (g) and (h) of Exercise 15 are not power series in the dummy x.

Theorem 5.8–A also says nothing about the behaviour of the power series at the points $-\rho$, ρ; examples can be constructed of series which converge absolutely at $\pm\rho$, which converge at $-\rho$, but diverge at ρ, or which diverge at $\pm\rho$. The number ρ itself may be zero, a positive real number, or $+\infty$.

Further investigation of power series requires machinery which we do not have at our disposal in this book.

5.9 Multiplication of Series—The Cauchy Product

Suppose that $\sum_{n=0}^{\infty} a_n r^n$ and $\sum_{n=0}^{\infty} b_n r^n$ are two real power series. If we multiply them together, forgetting about considerations of convergence for the moment, we naturally collect terms in the same power of r, thus obtaining a new power series, say $\Sigma c_n r^n$:

$$\Sigma c_n r^n = (\Sigma a_n r^n)(\Sigma b_n r^n)$$

$$= a_0 b_0 + (a_1 b_0 + a_0 b_1)r + (a_2 b_0 + a_1 b_1 + a_0 b_2)r^2 \ldots.$$

The general term c_n is given by

$$c_n = a_n b_0 + a_{n-1} b_1 + \ldots + a_0 b_n$$

$$= \sum_{k=0}^{k=n} a_{n-k} b_k. \tag{1}$$

In this section, we shall consider the product of two convergent series $\sum_{n=0}^{\infty} a_n$ and $\sum_{n=0}^{\infty} b_n$, and discuss the convergence of the product series $\sum_{n=0}^{\infty} c_n$, where c_n is given by (1).

Definition. If $\sum_{n=0}^{\infty} a_n$, $\sum_{n=0}^{\infty} b_n$ are two series of real numbers, the series $\sum_{n=0}^{\infty} c_n$, where $c_n = \sum_{k=0}^{k=n} a_{n-k} b_k$, is called the **Cauchy Product** of Σa_n and Σb_n.

The Cauchy product is only one of the many possible products; for if we multiply Σa_n and Σb_n together, we obtain a collection of terms of the form $a_m b_n$. The Cauchy product is a particular arrangement of these, in which those terms for which $m+n$ has the same value are bracketted together, and, as we have seen, it is an arrangement which arises naturally in the multiplication of power series.

We first of all consider the case when the series are of positive terms; if $\Sigma a_n = \alpha$, $\Sigma b_n = \beta$, then we might naturally expect the Cauchy product to converge to $\alpha\beta$. This is the case.

Theorem 5.9–A. Let Σa_n, Σb_n be series of *positive* terms, converging to α, β respectively. Then, their Cauchy product Σc_n is convergent, with sum $\alpha\beta$.

Proof. Let A_n, B_n, C_n denote the n-th partial sums of the series respectively, where $n = 0, 1, 2, \ldots$.

Since the terms are all positive, the sequences of partial sums are non-decreasing. Now

$$C_n = a_0 b_0 + (a_1 b_0 + a_0 b_1) + \ldots + (a_n b_0 + a_{n-1} b_1 + \ldots + a_0 b_n)$$

$$= a_0(b_0 + \ldots + b_n) + a_1(b_0 + \ldots + b_{n-1}) + a_2(b_0 + \ldots + b_{n-2}) + \ldots$$

$$+ a_{n-1}(b_0 + b_1) + a_n b_0,$$

$$\leqslant a_0(b_0 + \ldots + b_n) + a_1(b_0 + \ldots + b_n) + \ldots + a_n(b_0 + \ldots + b_n),$$

since all the terms are positive,

$$= A_n B_n. \tag{2}$$

On the other hand, $A_n B_n$ consists of terms of the form $a_m b_k$, where $0 \leqslant m+k \leqslant 2n$, though in fact the value $2n$ is obtained precisely once, namely, in the term $a_n b_n$. C_{2n} contains *all* terms $a_m b_k$ for which $0 \leqslant m+k \leqslant 2n$. Since $a_m b_k \geqslant 0$ for all choices of m and k, it follows that, because C_{2n} contains more terms than $A_n B_n$, we have

$$A_n B_n \leqslant C_{2n}$$

$$\Rightarrow \lim A_n B_n \leqslant \lim C_{2n}$$

$$\Leftrightarrow \alpha\beta \leqslant \lim C_{2n}. \tag{3}$$

On the other hand, by (2),

$$\lim C_n \leqslant \lim A_n B_n$$

$$= \alpha\beta.$$

This implies that $\{C_n\}$ is convergent; hence, $\lim C_n = \lim C_{2n}$, and so, using (3), we finally obtain $\lim C_n = \alpha\beta$. ◆

A "visual" proof of this result can be given as follows; we arrange the terms $a_m b_k$ in a square array, with a_m constant in any horizontal row, b_k constant in any vertical column:

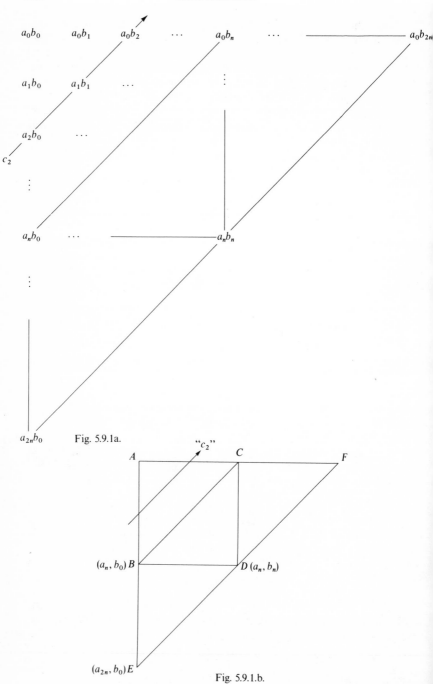

$$a_0b_0 \quad a_0b_1 \quad a_0b_2 \quad \cdots \quad a_0b_n \quad \cdots \quad\rule{2cm}{0.4pt}\quad a_0b_{2n}$$

$$a_1b_0 \quad a_1b_1 \quad \cdots$$

$$a_2b_0 \quad \cdots$$

$$c_2$$

$$a_nb_0 \quad \cdots \quad\rule{1cm}{0.4pt}\quad a_nb_n$$

$$a_{2n}b_0 \qquad \text{Fig. 5.9.1a.}$$

"c_2"

$A \qquad\qquad C \qquad\qquad\qquad F$

$(a_n, b_0)\,B \qquad\qquad D\,(a_n, b_n)$

$(a_{2n}, b_0)\,E$

Fig. 5.9.1.b.

Now, the terms c_n of the Cauchy product are represented by the sum of the terms in the diagonal lines sloping upwards to the right (e.g. $c_2 = a_2 b_0 + a_1 b_1 + a_0 b_2$ is the diagonal starting at the third term down in the first column and moving upwards to the third term along in the first row). Hence, $C_n = c_0 + c_1 + \ldots + c_n$ is represented in Fig. 5.9.1 by all terms $a_m b_k$ which lie inside or on the edge of the triangle ABC, and C_{2n} by terms inside or on the triangle AEF. On the other hand, $A_n B_n$ is the product of $(a_0 + \ldots + a_n)$ and $(b_0 + \ldots + b_n)$, and is clearly made up of all terms in or on the *square ABDC*. Since all the terms are non-negative, and from the figure we have $\triangle ABC < \square ABDC < \triangle AEF$, we conclude that $C_n \leqslant A_n B_n \leqslant C_{2n}$, and the proof ends as before.

We next go on to the case when the terms may not all be positive. In view of the remark on page 151 about conditionally convergent series, we cannot expect that, if Σa_n and Σb_n converge, with sums α and β respectively, the Cauchy product will converge to $\alpha\beta$; for the Cauchy product is a particular arrangement of the series $\Sigma a_k b_m$. On the other hand, absolute convergence of Σa_n and Σb_n will ensure that the Cauchy product converges to the product of the sums, by Theorem 5.6–B.

Theorem 5.9–B. Suppose that Σa_n, Σb_n converge absolutely, with sums α and β. Then, the Cauchy product is absolutely convergent, with sum $\alpha\beta$.

Proof. Let A_n, B_n, C_n be the n-th partial sums of Σa_n, Σb_n, and Σc_n respectively, A_n^*, B_n^* those of $\Sigma|a_n|$, $\Sigma|b_n|$; denote by $\Sigma \gamma_n$ the Cauchy product of $\Sigma|a_n|$ and $\Sigma|b_n|$, and write $\Gamma_n = \sum_{k=0}^{k=n} \gamma_k$.

Now, $\Sigma|a_n|$ and $\Sigma|b_n|$ are convergent, implying by Theorem 5.9–A that $\Sigma\gamma_n$ is convergent, and

$$\lim \Gamma_n = (\lim A_n^*)(\lim B_n^*). \tag{4}$$

Next,

$$|c_n| = |a_n b_0 + \ldots + a_0 b_n|$$
$$\leqslant |a_n||b_0| + \ldots + |a_0||b_n|$$
$$= \gamma_n.$$

Hence, by the Comparison Test, $\Sigma|c_n|$ is convergent i.e. Σc_n converges absolutely.

To show that its sum is $\alpha\beta$, consider the difference $A_n B_n - C_n$; $|A_n B_n - C_n|$ does not exceed the sum of the absolute values of the terms in this difference, and it is easy to see that this is $A_n^* B_n^* - \Gamma_n$. Thus,

$$|A_n B_n - C_n| \leqslant A_n^* B_n^* - \Gamma_n$$
$$\Rightarrow \lim(A_n B_n - C_n) = 0 \quad \text{by (4)}$$

$$\Rightarrow \lim C_n = (\lim A_n)(\lim B_n) \quad \text{by Theorem 4.3–A}$$
$$= \alpha\beta,$$

that is, Σc_n converges absolutely, with sum $\alpha\beta$.   ◆

Remark.   It is, in fact, possible to prove more than this. We record, without proof, two other results on the convergence of the Cauchy product. The first is due to Mertens, and was published in 1875.

Theorem 5.9–C (Mertens).   Suppose that Σa_n is absolutely convergent, with sum α, and Σb_n is convergent (not necessarily absolutely) with sum β. Then, the Cauchy product Σc_n is convergent, with sum $\alpha\beta$.
  The second result is due to Abel.

Theorem 5.9–D (Abel).   Suppose that Σa_n, Σb_n are convergent, with sums α, β respectively. Then, *if* the Cauchy product converges, its sum is $\alpha\beta$.

Exercises

1. Prove Theorem 5.2–E.
2. Show, by considering the *finite* series

$$\sum_{r=1}^{r=n} \left(\frac{1}{r} - \frac{1}{r+1} \right),$$

   that $\Sigma(1/n^2)$ is convergent.
3. Prove Theorem 5.4–C.
4. Show that

$$\sum \frac{1}{(n+\frac{1}{2})^2} \quad \text{and} \quad \sum \frac{n^2}{(3n+2)^4}$$

   converge, while

$$\sum \frac{n}{(4n-1)^2} \quad \text{and} \quad \sum \left(\frac{n^2-n+27}{n^4+12} \right)^{\frac{1}{4}}$$

   diverge.
5. Discuss the convergence or divergence of

   (a) $\displaystyle\sum \left(\frac{n}{n+1} \right)^{n^2}$ (d) $\displaystyle\sum \left(1 - \cos\frac{1}{n} \right)$

   (b) $\displaystyle\sum \frac{n^2}{2^n}$ (e) $\displaystyle\sum \ln\left(1 - \frac{1}{n} \right) \quad n \geqslant 2$

   (c) $\displaystyle\sum \frac{2^n+1}{3^n+1}$

(f) For each positive integer n, let $f(n) = [n \sin^2 n]$, the integral part of $n \sin^2 n$. Investigate the convergence of

$$\sum \frac{(-1)^{f(n)}}{n^p}.$$

6. Discuss the convergence or divergence of

(a) $\sum \dfrac{(-1)^{n+1}}{n}\left(1+\dfrac{1}{2}+\dfrac{1}{3}+\ldots+\dfrac{1}{n}\right)$

(b) $\sum \dfrac{(-1)^{n+1}}{\sqrt{n}} \cos n\theta$, θ not an odd multiple of π

(c) $\sum n^{-1-(1/n)}$

(d) $\sum (\sqrt{(1+n^2)}-n).$

7. The sequence $\{a_n\}$ is defined by

$$a_n = \begin{cases} -1/n & \text{if } n \text{ is divisible by 3} \\ 1/n & \text{otherwise} \end{cases}$$

Investigate the series Σa_n.

8. Prove that if Σu_n is a convergent series of positive terms, then Σu_n^2 also converges.

9. If $u_n > 0$, show that Σu_n, $\Sigma(u_n/1+u_n)$ converge or diverge together.

10. Show that the series whose n-th term is

$$\frac{1}{n} - \frac{1}{2n+1} - \frac{1}{2n+2}$$

is convergent.

11. Prove the following form of the Ratio Test:
Let $\{a_n\}$ be a sequence of positive real numbers. If
(i) $\lim \sup(a_{n+1}/a_n) = \lambda < 1$, then Σa_n converges;
(ii) $\lim \inf(a_{n+1}/a_n) = \mu > 1$, then Σa_n diverges;
(iii) $\mu \leqslant 1 \leqslant \lambda$, no conclusion can be drawn.

12. Formulate and prove a similar form of the Root Test.

13. Show that, if a is a positive constant, then $\Sigma[(-1)^n/(n+a)^s]$ is absolutely convergent if $s > 1$, and convergent, though not absolutely, if $0 < s \leqslant 1$.

14. Show, by the Root Test, that if $k \in N$, then $\Sigma n^k x^n$ converges if $0 \leqslant x < 1$.

15. Discuss the convergence, including absolute convergence, of the following series:

(a) $\sum \dfrac{k!x^k}{k^k}$

(b) $\sum \dfrac{x^{2n}}{n(n+1)}$

(c) $\sum \dfrac{x^n(1-x)^n}{n^2}$

(d) $\sum \dfrac{x^n}{(2n-1)(2n+1)}$

(e) $\sum \dfrac{nx^n}{(n+1)(n+2)(n+3)(n+4)}$

(f) $\sum \dfrac{(n!)^2 x^{2n}}{2n!}$

(g) $\sum \dfrac{x^n}{1-x^{2n}} \qquad (x \neq \pm 1)$

(h) $\sum \dfrac{1}{n}\left(\dfrac{2x}{1+x^2}\right)^n$.

16. Show that if ρ denotes the radius of convergence of $\Sigma a_n x^n$, ρ_1 the radius of convergence of $\Sigma n a_n x^{n-1}$, then $\rho \leqslant \rho_1$.

17. Show that, if $-1 < x < 1$, then

$$\tfrac{1}{2}(x - \tfrac{1}{2}x^2 + \tfrac{1}{3}x^3 - \ldots)^2 = \sum_{n=2}^{\infty} (-1)^n \frac{x^n}{n}\left(1 + \frac{1}{2} + \ldots + \frac{1}{n-1}\right).$$

18. Show that, if $-1 < x < 1$, then

(a) $\dfrac{1-x^2}{1-2x\cos\theta+x^2} = 1 + 2x\cos\theta + 2x^2\cos 2\theta + 2x^3\cos 3\theta + \ldots$

(b) $\dfrac{2x\sin\theta}{1-2x\cos\theta+x^2} = 2x\sin\theta + 2x^2\sin 2\theta + 2x^3\sin 3\theta + \ldots.$

CHAPTER 6

Continuous Functions

6.1 Limit Points

So far, our discussion of limits has been restricted to the limit of a sequence $\{s_n\}$. To prove the existence of the limit of a sequence, we required infinitely many values s_n, and we saw this specifically mentioned in the phrase "for all $n > n_0(\varepsilon)$" of the definition. We can think of the limit of the sequence $\{s_n\}$ as the final outcome of the behaviour of the values s_n as n becomes infinitely large, or, as we put it more usually, as $n \to \infty$ ("as n tends to infinity"). This object ∞ is called a "limit point", and before we go on to consider limits of functions and the idea of continuity, we first explore a little further the idea of a limit point.

Suppose E is a subset of the real numbers R. Then, we say that the point a is a limit point of E if we can find points of E as close as we please to a. The point a may or may not be itself a point of the set E. It is convenient to include as possible limit points the objects ∞ and $-\infty$, and for these, the definition has a slightly different appearance. We now give these various definitions explicitly.

Definition. Let E be a subset of R, a a real number. Then, the point a is called a **limit point** of E if, given any real $\delta > 0$, there is a point x of E, distinct from a, such that

$$|x-a| < \delta.$$

Note. The definition implies that there are infinitely many points of E distinct from a, whose distance from a is less than δ. For, suppose $x_1 \in E$ satisfies $|x_1-a| < \delta$, $x_1 \neq a$. Write $|x_1-a| = \delta_1$. By definition, there is a point $x_2 \in E$ such that $|x_2-a| < \delta_1$, $x_2 \neq a$. Since $|x_2-a| < \delta_1$, we have $x_2 \neq x_1$, and further $|x_2-a| < \delta_1 < \delta$. Proceeding thus, we can define a sequence $\{x_n\}$ so that $x_n \neq a$ and $|x_n-a| < \delta$, for all n.

For the cases ∞, $-\infty$, the definitions take the following forms.

Definition. ∞ is a limit point of E if, given any number $\alpha > 0$, there is a point x in E with $x > \alpha$. $-\infty$ is a limit point of E if given any number $\beta < 0$, there is a point y of E such that $y < \beta$.

Example 6.1.1. ∞ is a limit point of the set N. Further, it is the only limit point.

Proof. Let $\alpha > 0$. Then (Example 2.5.5) there is a number $n \in N$ such that $n > \alpha$. Hence, by definition, ∞ is a limit point. No real number $a \in N$ can be a limit point. For, suppose that n_0 is the positive integer closest to a; choose $\delta = \frac{1}{2}|a - n_0|$; then clearly, there is no integer n such that $|n - a| < \delta$ (Fig. 6.1.1). If $a \in N$, a is still not a limit point; choose $\delta = \frac{1}{2}$, and there is no element in N distinct from a whose distance from a is less than $\frac{1}{2}$.

Finally, $-\infty$ is not a limit point, since N contains no numbers less than zero. ◆

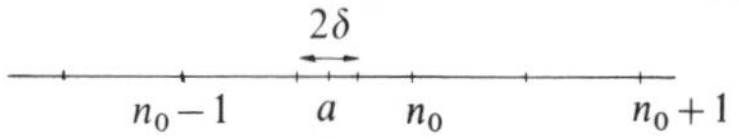

$$2\delta$$

$$n_0 - 1 \qquad a \quad n_0 \qquad\qquad n_0 + 1$$

Fig. 6.1.1.

Example 6.1.2. Let E be the open interval $\{x : a < x < b\}$, where a, b are real numbers. Then, all points of the set $\bar{E} = \{x : a \leqslant x \leqslant b\}$ are limit points of E, and are the only limit points.

Proof. First, let x_0 be a real number such that $a < x_0 < b$. Then, if $\delta > 0$, there are points y of E different from x_0 which satisfy $x_0 - \delta < y < x_0 + \delta$, by Theorems 2.6–C, 2.6–D. So x_0 is a limit point. Next, if $\delta > 0$, there are points y of E which satisfy $a < y < a + \delta$, again by Theorems 2.6–C, 2.6–D, and likewise points z of E such that $b - \delta < z < b$. So, every point of the set $\bar{E}$ is a limit point.

On the other hand, suppose $x_1 < a$. Write $a - x_1 = 2\delta$. Then, there are no points y of E which satisfy $|y - x_1| < \delta$. Hence, x_1 is not a limit point of E. Likewise if $x_2 > b$, x_2 is not a limit point of E. ◆

The reader should observe that the limit points of a set E may or may not belong to E. For instance, ∞ does not belong to N in Example 6.1.1, and neither a nor b belong to E in this example.

Example 6.1.3. Let $K = \{x \in R : a \leqslant x \leqslant b\}$. Then, every point of K is a limit point, and these are the only limit points.

The proof is exactly as in the previous example. Note this time that all the limit points of K belong to K.

The set of points $\{x \in R : |x - a| < \delta\}$ is called a **neighbourhood** (or a δ-*neighbourhood*) of a. The set of points $\{x \in R : 0 < |x - a| < \delta\}$ is called a **deleted neighbourhood** of a. The point a itself does not belong to a deleted neighbourhood of a, though it does belong to a neighbourhood of a. The set of points $\{x \in R : x > \alpha\}$, for some $\alpha \in R$ is called a **neighbourhood of** ∞.

We are now ready to proceed to limits of functions. We shall see that we can define the limit of a function at any limit point of its domain. In the case of sequences, the domain of the associated function in N, whose sole limit point (Example 6.1.1) is ∞, and so we have at most one limit for sequences. If this exists, we write it as $\lim s_n$. We shall see that a different notation is necessary for limits of functions.

6.2 Limit of a Function at ∞

We begin with the situation which resembles most closely the idea of the limit of a sequence.

Suppose f is a real valued function whose domain includes a neighbourhood of ∞. Then, as x gets larger, we can examine the behaviour of the function values $f(x)$; we classify certain types of behaviour as for sequences.

Definition. Let f be a real valued function defined on a neighbourhood of ∞. Then, $f(x)$ is said to **converge to the real number** λ, **as** x **tends to** ∞, if given $\varepsilon > 0$, there is a real number $x_0(\varepsilon)$ such that, for all $x > x_0(\varepsilon)$, we have

$$|f(x) - \lambda| < \varepsilon.$$

We write $\lim\limits_{x \to \infty} f(x) = \lambda$, or $f(x) \to \lambda$ as $x \to \infty$. Another notation is $\lim\limits_{\infty} f(x) = \lambda$, provided this is unambiguous. We shall also say "$f(x)$ has limit λ at ∞", instead of "$f(x)$ converges to λ as $x \to \infty$".

Pictorially, the definition asserts that all the points, on the graph of f, which lie to the right of the line $x = x_0(\varepsilon)$ are contained in the strip between the lines $y = \lambda \pm \varepsilon$ (see Fig. 6.2.1).

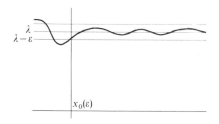

Fig. 6.2.1.

We can also formulate corresponding definitions when the limit is ∞ or $-\infty$. For example, in the former case we have

Definition. Let f be a real valued function defined on a neighbourhood of ∞. Then we say that the limit of $f(x)$ as $x \to \infty$ is ∞, if, given $A > 0$, there is a number $x_0(A)$ such that, for all $x > x_0(A)$, we have

$$f(x) > A.$$

We write $\lim\limits_{x \to \infty} f(x) = \infty$, or $f(x) \to \infty$ as $x \to \infty$. See Fig. 6.2.2.

Example 6.2.1. Let f be a real valued function defined on the set $\{x \in R : x > 0\}$. If $\lim\limits_{x \to \infty} f(x) = \lambda$, then the sequence $\{s_n\}$, where $s_n = f(n)$, converges to λ.

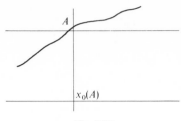

Fig. 6.2.2.

Proof. Let $\varepsilon > 0$. Then there is a number $x_0(\varepsilon)$ such that, for all $x > x_0(\varepsilon)$,

$$|f(x) - \lambda| < \varepsilon.$$

Denote by $n_0(\varepsilon)$ the least integer which exceeds $x_0(\varepsilon)$. Then if $n > n_0(\varepsilon)$, we have

$$|f(n) - \lambda| < \varepsilon$$

$$\Leftrightarrow |s_n - \lambda| < \varepsilon, \quad \text{for all } n > n_0(\varepsilon)$$

$$\Leftrightarrow \lim s_n = \lambda. \qquad \blacklozenge$$

The converse is false. Let f be the function given by

$$f(x) = \sin \pi x.$$

Then, the sequence $\{s_n\}$, given by $s_n = f(n)$, is convergent to zero (all the terms are zero), but $\lim\limits_{x \to \infty} f(x) \neq 0$, for we can find numbers x as large as we please for which $f(x) = 1$ (namely, $x = \frac{1}{2}(4m+1)$, $m \in N$).

We leave the reader to write out in full the meaning of the formula $\lim\limits_{x \to \infty} f(x) = -\infty$.

6.3 Limit of a Function at $-\infty$

We next consider limits at $-\infty$, since this bears a close resemblance to the definitions of Section 6.2. Throughout this section, we suppose f is defined in a neighbourhood of $-\infty$. By a process akin to that of Section 6.2, Section 4.1, Section 4.2, we ask about the behaviour of $f(x)$ as x gets large and negative. Without further comment, we state the following definitions.

Definition.   Let f be defined in a neighbourhood of $-\infty$. We say that $f(x)$ has the real number λ as **limit**, **as** $x \to -\infty$ (or that $f(x)$ **converges to** λ **as** $x \to -\infty$) if, given $\varepsilon > 0$, there is a number $x_0(\varepsilon)$ such that, for all $x < x_0(\varepsilon)$, we have

$$|f(x) - \lambda| < \varepsilon.$$

We write $\lim_{x \to -\infty} f(x) = \lambda$, $f(x) \to \lambda$ as $x \to -\infty$, or $\lim_{-\infty} f(x) = \lambda$. We also say that λ is "the limit of the function f at $-\infty$".

Definition. Let f be defined in a neighbourhood of $-\infty$. We say that the limit of $f(x)$ as $x \to \infty$ is ∞, if given $A > 0$, there is a number $x_0(A)$ such that, for all $x < x_0(A)$, we have

$$f(x) > A.$$

We write $\lim_{x \to -\infty} f(x) = \infty$, or $f(x) \to \infty$ as $x \to -\infty$.

Definition. Let f be defined in a neighbourhood of $-\infty$. Then, the limit of $f(x)$ as $x \to -\infty$ is $-\infty$, if given $B < 0$, there is a number $x_0(B)$ such that, for all $x < x_0(B)$, we have

$$f(x) < B.$$

We write $\lim_{x \to -\infty} f(x) = -\infty$, or $f(x) \to -\infty$ as $x \to -\infty$.

Example 6.3.1. Let f, g, h be given by

$$f(x) = x^2, \qquad g(x) = x^3, \qquad h(x) = \frac{1-x^2}{1+x^2},$$

for all $x \in R$.
Then, $\lim_{x \to -\infty} f(x) = \infty$; $\lim_{x \to -\infty} g(x) = -\infty$; $\lim_{x \to -\infty} h(x) = -1$.

Proof. (i) Let $A > 0$. Then,

$$f(x) > A \Leftrightarrow x^2 > A$$

$$\Leftrightarrow x > \sqrt{A}, \quad \text{or} \quad x < -\sqrt{A}.$$

Hence, if $x_0(A) < -\sqrt{A}$, we have, for all $x < x_0(A)$, $f(x) > A$; i.e. $\lim_{x \to -\infty} f(x) = \infty$. [Observe that $\lim_{x \to \infty} f(x) = \infty$, also.]

(ii) Let $B < 0$. Then,

$$g(x) < B \Leftrightarrow x^3 < B$$

$$\Leftrightarrow x < B^{\frac{1}{3}}.$$

Hence, if $x_0(B) < B^{\frac{1}{3}}$, we have for all $x < x_0(B)$, $g(x) < B$, i.e. $\lim_{x \to -\infty} g(x) = -\infty$. [Observe, in this case, that $\lim_{x \to \infty} g(x) = \infty$.]

(iii) Let $\varepsilon > 0$. Then

$$\left| \frac{1-x^2}{1+x^2} - (-1) \right| = \frac{2}{1+x^2}$$

$$< \varepsilon \Leftrightarrow x^2 > \frac{2}{\varepsilon} - 1$$

$$\Leftrightarrow x > \sqrt{\left(\frac{2}{\varepsilon} - 1\right)} \quad \text{or} \quad x < -\sqrt{\left(\frac{2}{\varepsilon} - 1\right)}.$$

Hence, if we take $x_0(\varepsilon) < -\sqrt{[(2/\varepsilon)-1]}$, we have

$$|h(x)+1| < \varepsilon$$

for all $x < x_0(\varepsilon)$ i.e. $\lim_{x \to -\infty} h(x) = -1$.

In this case, $\lim_{x \to \infty} h(x) = -1$, also. $\qquad\qquad\qquad$ ◆

The functions f, g, h in the above example are defined on R, and so on neighbourhoods of both ∞ and $-\infty$. We observe that the limit of g at ∞ is not the same as the limit of g at $-\infty$. Hence, the necessity for displaying which limit point of the domain is under consideration by the notation "$\lim_{x \to \infty} f(x) = \ldots$", "$\lim_{x \to -\infty} g(x) = \ldots$". We shall see this again in the next section.

6.4 Limit of a Function at a Real Number

Suppose that the real number a is a limit point of the domain E of the function f. The point a may or may not be a member of E (see Examples 6.1.2, 6.1.3), and so f may or may not be defined at a. Suppose, however, that f is defined in a *deleted* neighbourhood of a, i.e. the set of points $\{x : 0 < |x-a| < \delta\}$ is contained in E. We can then investigate the behaviour of the values $\{f(x)\}$, as the points x are taken closer and closer to the limit point a. The three situations in which we are interested are those for which the values $\{f(x)\}$ approach a real number λ, or ∞, or $-\infty$, as x approaches a. We arrive naturally at the following definition.

Definition. Let f be a real valued function defined on a set E. Suppose that the real number a is a limit point of E, and that f is defined on (at least) a deleted neighbourhood of a. We say that the **limit of** $f(x)$**, as x tends to** a, is λ if given $\varepsilon > 0$, there is a positive number δ (which will, in general, depend on ε, and is often written $\delta(\varepsilon)$), such that for all points x satisfying $0 < |x-a| < \delta$, we have

$$|f(x)-\lambda| < \varepsilon.$$

We write $\lim_{x \to a} f(x) = \lambda$, or $f(x) \to \lambda$ as $x \to a$, or $\lim_a f(x) = \lambda$.

The reader should note that, even if f is defined at the point a, we never consider or use the value $f(a)$, in the definition. Also, the limit λ may or may not be equal to $f(a)$.

When the limit is ∞ or $-\infty$, the definition is amended as in the previous sections.

Example 6.4.1. Let f be the function given by

$$f(x) = \begin{cases} 1+x^2 & \text{if } x \neq 0 \\ 0 & \text{if } x = 0. \end{cases} \qquad \text{(See Fig. 6.4.1).}$$

Then, $\lim_{x \to 0} f(x) = 1$.

Fig. 6.4.1.

Proof. Let $\varepsilon > 0$. Then, if $x \neq 0$,

$$|f(x)-1| = x^2$$
$$< \varepsilon \Leftrightarrow |x| < \sqrt{\varepsilon}.$$

Thus, if we choose $\delta(\varepsilon) \leqslant \sqrt{\varepsilon}$, we have for all x such that $0 < |x| < \delta(\varepsilon)$, $|f(x)-1| < \varepsilon$ i.e. $\lim_{x \to 0} f(x) = 1$. Note that $f(0) = 0$, so that $\lim_{x \to 0} f(x) \neq f(0)$. ◆

Example 6.4.2. Let f be the function given by

$$f(x) = \frac{x^2-1}{x-1}, \quad \text{for all } x \neq 1.$$

Show that $\lim_{x \to 1} f(x) = 2$.

Proof. Let $\varepsilon > 0$. Then, if $x \neq 1$,

$$|f(x)-2| = \left| \frac{x^2-1}{x-1} - 2 \right|$$
$$= |(x+1)-2|,$$

upon dividing top and bottom lines by $x-1$, which is permissible since $x \neq 1$; hence,

$$|f(x)-2| < \varepsilon \Leftrightarrow |x-1| < \varepsilon.$$

Hence, if $\delta(\varepsilon) \leqslant \varepsilon$, we have, for all x satisfying $0 < |x-1| < \delta(\varepsilon)$,

$$|f(x)-2| < \varepsilon$$

i.e. $\lim_{x \to 1} f(x) = 2$.

In this case, the point 1 is not in the domain of f, so $f(1)$ is not defined. ◆

Example 6.4.3. Let φ be the function given by

$$\varphi(x) = (x-1)^2, \quad \text{for all } x > 0.$$

Then,

$$\lim_{x \to 1} \varphi(x) = 0.$$

Proof. Let $\varepsilon > 0$. Then,

$$|\varphi(x) - 0| = (x-1)^2$$

$$< \varepsilon$$

$$\Leftrightarrow |x - 1| < \sqrt{\varepsilon}.$$

Hence, if we choose $\delta \leqslant \sqrt{\varepsilon}$, then for all x satisfying $0 < |x - 1| < \delta$, we have $|\varphi(x)| < \varepsilon$, i.e. $\lim_{x \to 1} \varphi(x) = 0$, so that $\lim_{x \to 1} \varphi(x) = \varphi(1)$. ◆

The situation in Example 6.4.3, where we have $\lim_{x \to 1} \varphi(x) = \varphi(1)$, is a special case. We shall discuss this phenomenon in detail in a later section. Examples 6.4.1 and 6.4.2 illustrate that there is no reason to expect that $\lim_{x \to a} f(x) = f(a)$; Example 6.4.2 shows that $f(a)$ need not be defined at all, while the previous example to it provides an illustration to show that even if $f(a)$ exists, it need not be the same as $\lim_{x \to a} f(x)$. This cannot be overemphasised.

Example 6.4.4. Let f be the function given by

$$f(x) = \begin{cases} x+1 & \text{if } x \geqslant 0 \\ x-1 & \text{if } x < 0. \end{cases}$$

Then, $\lim_{x \to 0} f(x)$ does not exist.

Proof. If we consider small, positive h, then $f(h) = 1 + h$, which is nearly 1. As h gets smaller, $1 + h$ is closer to 1. But $\lim_{x \to 0} f(x) \neq 1$. For, if $\lim_{x \to 0} f(x) = 1$, then given $\varepsilon > 0$, there is a $\delta(\varepsilon)$ such that for *all* x satisfying $0 < |x| < \delta$, we have $|f(x) - 1| < \varepsilon$. But take $\varepsilon = \frac{1}{2}$; there is no $\delta > 0$ such that for all x satisfying $0 < |x| < \delta$, we have $|f(x) - 1| < \frac{1}{2}$. For we can find points $k < 0$, as close to zero as we please, and

$$|f(k) - 1| = |k - 2| > \frac{1}{2} \quad \text{if } k < 0.$$

Hence, $\lim_{x \to 0} f(x) \neq 1$. We can show similarly that the limit cannot be any other real number. ◆

6.5 One-sided Limits of a Function

Let f be a function with domain E and range in R. If a is a limit point of E, it may be the case that there are points of E on only one side of the point a. For example, if E is the set $\{x \in R : a < x \leqslant b\}$, then a and b are limit points of E, but there are no points y of E which satisfy $y < a$ or $y > b$. The points of E lie on one side of the limit points a, b; this, however, is not true for the other limit points of E. We may also include ∞ and $-\infty$ in the same category as a, b above.

Since a is a limit point of E, we may again ask about the behaviour of $\{f(x)\}$ as x approaches the limit point a. Of course, since we are interested in the values $\{f(x)\}$, we consider only points x which lie in the domain of f, i.e. on one side of a.

Another situation which often arises is that exemplified in Example 6.4.4. We might consider f in that example to be the union of two functions, φ and ψ, given by

$$\varphi(x) = x + 1, \quad \text{for all } x \geqslant 0 \text{ (i.e. } \mathcal{D}(\varphi) = \{x \in R : x \geqslant 0\})$$

$$\psi(x) = x - 1, \quad \text{for all } x < 0 \text{ (i.e. } \mathcal{D}(\psi) = \{x \in R : x < 0\}).$$

Then, the point 0 is a limit point of $\mathcal{D}(\varphi)$, and all the points in $\mathcal{D}(\varphi)$ lie on one side only of 0. The same holds for the function ψ. We thus arrive at the problem posed above. We begin our investigation with two new definitions. These are not completely novel, but are refinements of a previous definition.

Definition. The set of points $\{x \in R : a \leqslant x < a + \delta\}$ is called a **right neighbourhood** of a. The set $\{x \in R : a < x < a + \delta\}$ is a **deleted right neighbourhood** of a. The point a has been "deleted" from the preceding set. Similarly, the set $\{x \in R : a - \delta < x \leqslant a\}$ is a **left neighbourhood** of a, and $\{x \in R : a - \delta < x < a\}$ is a **deleted left neighbourhood** of a.

Note. A neighbourhood of a is the union of a right and left neighbourhood of a. Note also that a neighbourhood of a is an open interval, though right- and left-neighbourhoods are not open intervals. The deleted right- and left-neighbourhoods are open intervals, however.

Definition. Let f be a real valued function defined on a set E, and suppose that a is a limit point of E, such that E contains (at least) a deleted right neighbourhood of a. Then, we say that **the limit of** $f(x)$ as x **tends to** a **from the right** is λ if, given $\varepsilon > 0$, there is a number $\delta(\varepsilon) > 0$ such that for all x satisfying $a < x < a + \delta(\varepsilon)$, we have

$$|f(x) - \lambda| < \varepsilon.$$

We write $\lim\limits_{x \to a+} f(x) = \lambda$, or $f(x) \to \lambda$ as $x \to a+$.

We leave the reader to write out in full the meaning of the statements "$\lim\limits_{x \to a+} f(x) = \infty$", "$\lim\limits_{x \to a+} f(x) = -\infty$". These limits are called "limits on the right" and are examples of one sided limits. We can also define limits on the left. By way of illustration, we have

Definition. Let f be a real valued function defined on a set E, and suppose that a is a limit point of E such that E contains (at least)

a deleted left neighbourhood of a. Then, we say that **the limits of $f(x)$, as x tends to a from the left**, is ∞, if given $A > 0$, there is a number $\delta(A) > 0$ such that, for all x satisfying $a - \delta(A) < x < a$, we have

$$f(x) > A.$$

We write $\lim_{x \to a-} f(x) = \infty$, or $f(x) \to \infty$ as $x \to a-$.

We leave the reader to write out in full the definitions $\lim_{x \to a-} f(x) = \lambda$, $\lim_{x \to a-} f(x) = -\infty$.

Example 6.5.1.   If $\lim_{x \to a} f(x) = \lambda$, then $\lim_{x \to a+} f(x) = \lim_{x \to a-} f(x) = \lambda$.

Proof.   Let $\varepsilon > 0$. Then, there is a number $\delta(\varepsilon) > 0$ such that for all x satisfying $0 < |x - a| < \delta(\varepsilon)$, we have

$$|f(x) - \lambda| < \varepsilon.$$

Now,

$$\{x : 0 < |x - a| < \delta(\varepsilon)\}$$
$$= \{x : a < x < a + \delta(\varepsilon)\} \cup \{x : a - \delta(\varepsilon) < x < a\}.$$

Hence, $|f(x) - \lambda| < \varepsilon$ for all x satisfying $a < x < a + \delta(\varepsilon)$

$$\text{i.e.} \quad \lim_{x \to a+} f(x) = \lambda.$$

Likewise, $|f(x) - \lambda| < \varepsilon$ for all x satisfying $a - \delta(\varepsilon) < x < a$

$$\text{i.e.} \quad \lim_{x \to a-} f(x) = \lambda. \qquad \blacklozenge$$

Example 6.5.2.   The converse of Example 6.5.1 is true; if $\lim_{x \to a+} f(x)$ and $\lim_{x \to a-} f(x)$ exist *and are equal*, then $\lim_{x \to a} f(x)$ exists and has the same value.

The proof is left to the reader. Example 6.4.4 shows that the condition $\lim_{x \to a+} f(x) = \lim_{x \to a-} f(x)$ is necessary. For, in that example, $\lim_{x \to 0+} f(x) = 1$, and $\lim_{x \to 0-} f(x) = -1$, so that the limits on the right and left both exist. But $\lim_{x \to 0} f(x)$ does not exist.

Example 6.5.3.   Show that $\lim_{x \to 0+} f(x) = \sqrt{2}$ where $f(x)$ is given by $f(x) = \sqrt{(2 + x)}$, for all $x \in R$.

Proof.   Let $\varepsilon > 0$. Then,

$$|f(x) - \sqrt{2}| = |\sqrt{(2 + x)} - \sqrt{2}|$$
$$= \left| \frac{(\sqrt{(2 + x)} - \sqrt{2})(\sqrt{(2 + x)} + \sqrt{2})}{\sqrt{(2 + x)} + \sqrt{2}} \right|$$

$$= \frac{|x|}{\sqrt{(2+x)} + \sqrt{2}}$$

$$< x/2\sqrt{2} \quad \text{if } x > 0$$

$$< \varepsilon \quad\quad \text{if } 0 < x < (2\sqrt{2})\varepsilon.$$

Hence, if we choose $\delta(\varepsilon) \leqslant (2\sqrt{2})\varepsilon$, the definition is satisfied, and
$$\lim_{x \to 0+} f(x) = \sqrt{2}. \qquad \blacklozenge$$

Example 6.5.4. Denote by $[t]$ the greatest integer not exceeding t.
Let f be defined by setting, for all $x \in R$, $f(x) = [1-x]$.
Then,
$$\lim_{x \to 0+} f(x) = 0, \qquad \lim_{x \to 0-} f(x) = 1.$$

Proof. Suppose $0 < x \leqslant 1$; then $0 \leqslant 1-x < 1$, and so $f(x) = 0$.
Hence, if $\varepsilon > 0$, choose $\delta(\varepsilon)$ to be any positive real number less than 1.
For all x satisfying $0 < x < \delta(\varepsilon)$, we have

$$|f(x)| = 0 < \varepsilon.$$

$$\Rightarrow \lim_{x \to 0+} f(x) = 0.$$

Next, if $-1 < x \leqslant 0$, we have $1 \leqslant 1-x < 2$; hence, for all x satisfying
$-1 < x \leqslant 0$, $f(x) = 1$. Thus, given $\varepsilon > 0$, choose $\delta(\varepsilon)$ to be any
positive number less than 1. Then, for all x satisfying $-\delta(\varepsilon) < x < 0$,
we have

$$|f(x)-1| = 0 < \varepsilon$$

$$\Rightarrow \lim_{x \to 0-} f(x) = 1. \qquad \blacklozenge$$

The graph of the function f of Example 6.5.4 is shown in Fig. 6.5.1.
We leave the following as an exercise for the reader: prove that, if K
is any integer, then

$$\lim_{x \to K+} f(x) = -K$$

$$\lim_{x \to K-} f(x) = -K+1.$$

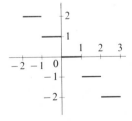

Fig. 6.5.1.

We have now seen fifteen varieties of definition: the limit value can be a real number λ, or ∞, or $-\infty$, while the limit point of the domain of the function may be ∞, or $-\infty$, or a real number a, and this last case also includes limits as $x \to a +$ or $x \to a -$. In view of this, it is plain to see why we adopt the notation $\lim\limits_{x \to a} f(x)$ and so on. We must be clear which limit point of $\mathscr{D}(f)$ we are concerned with, and even whether we want to restrict our attention to right or left neighbourhoods of it.

As we pointed out earlier, a sequence has a limit only at ∞, this being the only limit point of N. So there is no ambiguity about writing "$\lim s_n = \lambda$"; it can mean only that $s_n \to \lambda$ as $n \to \infty$. We shall use this as a distinguishing feature of sequences as opposed to functions. Thus, for example, $\lim x^n = 0$, for each x satisfying $-1 < x < 1$, means that the limit of the *sequence* $\{s_n\}$ is zero, where s_n is given by $s_n = x^n$, x being any real number such that $-1 < x < 1$; on the other hand $\lim\limits_{x \to 0} x^n = 0$, for each $n \in N$, means that the limit of the *function* f at 0 is zero, where f is given by $f(x) = x^n$, for any $n \in N$.

6.6 The Algebra of Limits

In this section, we shall establish theorems for limits of functions similar to those for sequences described in Section 4.3. We shall prove these results for the case when the limits of the functions f and g at the point a are defined. The same theorems are valid for limits at ∞ and $-\infty$, and for right and left limits at a. We first note the following consequence of the definition of limit: in order to show $\lim\limits_{x \to a} f(x) = \lambda$, it suffices to prove that, given $\varepsilon > 0$, there is a $\delta(\varepsilon) > 0$ such that, for all x satisfying $0 < |x-a| < \delta(\varepsilon)$, we have

$$|f(x)-\lambda| < K\varepsilon,$$

where K is a constant. (See the remark on page 111, following Theorem 4.1–A.)

Theorem 6.6–A.   Let f, g be functions defined on a set E, and suppose a is a limit point of E, with f and g defined in a deleted neighbourhood of a. Then, if $\lim\limits_{x \to a} f(x) = 0$ and $\lim\limits_{x \to a} g(x) = \mu$, where $\mu \in R$, then

$$\lim_{x \to a} fg(x) = \lim_{x \to a} f(x)g(x) = 0.$$

In particular, if g is a constant function, $\lim\limits_{x \to a} f(x)g(x) = 0$.

Proof.   Let $\varepsilon > 0$. Then, there is a number $\delta_1(\varepsilon) > 0$, such that, for all x satisfying $0 < |x-a| < \delta_1(\varepsilon)$, we have

$$|f(x)| < \varepsilon;$$

further, there is a number $\delta_2 > 0$ such that, for all x satisfying $0 < |x-a| < \delta_2$, we have

$$|g(x)-\mu| < 1 \qquad \text{(definition of limit with } \varepsilon = 1)$$

$$\Rightarrow |g(x)| < |\mu|+1, \quad \text{if } 0 < |x-a| < \delta_2.$$

Now, let $\delta(\varepsilon) = \min(\delta_1(\varepsilon), \delta_2)$; then if $0 < |x-a| < \delta(\varepsilon)$, we have

$$|fg(x)| = |f(x)||g(x)|$$

$$< (|\mu|+1)\varepsilon$$

$$\Rightarrow \lim_{x \to a} fg(x) = 0$$

by the remark preceding the theorem. ◆

Theorem 6.6–B. Suppose f, g are defined in (at least) a deleted neighbourhood of the limit point a, and that

$$\lim_{x \to a} f(x) = \lambda, \qquad \lim_{x \to a} g(x) = \mu.$$

Then,

(i) $\lim_{x \to a}(f + g)(x) = \lim_{x \to a}(f(x) + g(x)) = \lambda+\mu$;

(ii) $\lim_{x \to a}(f - g)(x) = \lim_{x \to a}(f(x)-g(x)) = \lambda-\mu$;

(iii) $\lim_{x \to a} fg(x) = \lim_{x \to a}(f(x)g(x)) = \lambda\mu.$

If λ or μ is infinite, then these results hold whenever the right-hand side of the equations above are meaningful.

Proof. (i) Let $\varepsilon > 0$. Then, there is a number $\delta_1(\varepsilon) > 0$ such that for all x satisfying $0 < |x-a| < \delta_1(\varepsilon)$, we have

$$|f(x)-\lambda| < \varepsilon;$$

further, there is a number $\delta_2(\varepsilon) > 0$ such that for all x satisfying $0 < |x-a| < \delta_2(\varepsilon)$,

$$|g(x)-\mu| < \varepsilon;$$

write $\delta = \min(\delta_1, \delta_2)$, so that both inequalities hold if $0 < |x-a| < \delta$; for such x,

$$|(f + g)(x)-(\lambda+\mu)| \leqslant |f(x)-\lambda|+|g(x)-\mu|$$

$$< 2\varepsilon$$

$$\Rightarrow \lim_{a \to a}(f + g)(x) = \lambda+\mu.$$

which is (i). (ii) is similar.

(iii) Define φ and ψ by setting, for all x in the neighbourhood of a,

$$\varphi(x) = f(x) - \lambda, \qquad \psi(x) = g(x) - \mu.$$

Then,

$$\lim_{x \to a} \varphi(x) = 0, \qquad \lim_{x \to a} \psi(x) = 0.$$

Further,

$$f(x)g(x) - \lambda\mu = \lambda\psi(x) + \mu\varphi(x) + \varphi(x)\psi(x).$$

By Theorem 6.6–A,

$$\lim_{x \to a} \lambda\psi(x) = \lim_{x \to a} \mu\varphi(x)$$

$$= \lim_{x \to a} \varphi(x)\psi(x) = 0.$$

Hence, by Theorem 6.6–B (i),

$$\lim_{x \to a} \{ \lambda\psi(x) + \mu\varphi(x) + \varphi(x)\psi(x) \} = 0$$

$$\Rightarrow \lim_{x \to a} f g(x) = \lambda\mu. \qquad \blacklozenge$$

Corollary. If $\lim_{x \to a} f(x) = \lambda$, and k is a constant, then $\lim_{x \to a} k f(x) = k\lambda$. As an application of the definition of limit, we have

Theorem 6.6–C. Suppose g is defined (at least) in a deleted neighbourhood of the limit point a of $\mathcal{D}(g)$. If $\lim_{x \to a} g(x) = \mu$, where μ is a nonzero real number, then there is a number $\delta > 0$ such that, for all x satisfying $0 < |x - a| < \delta$, we have

$$|g(x)| > \tfrac{1}{2}|\mu|.$$

Proof. Since $\lim_{x \to a} g(x) = \mu$, there is a $\delta > 0$ such that, for all x satisfying $0 < |x - a| < \delta$, we have

$$|g(x) - \mu| < \tfrac{1}{2}|\mu|.$$

(We take $\varepsilon = \tfrac{1}{2}|\mu|$ by Theorem 1.10–B); this implies that

$$-\tfrac{1}{2}|\mu| < |g(x)| - |\mu| < \tfrac{1}{2}|\mu| \qquad \text{(by Theorem 2.4–C)}$$

$$\Rightarrow |g(x)| > \tfrac{1}{2}|\mu|. \qquad \blacklozenge$$

We use this theorem to calculate the limit of a reciprocal.

Theorem 6.6–D. Suppose g is as in the previous theorem. Then,

$$\lim_{x \to a} 1/g(x) = 1/\mu.$$

Proof. Let $\varepsilon > 0$. Then, there is a $\delta(\varepsilon) > 0$ such that for all x satisfying $0 < |x - a| < \delta(\varepsilon)$, we have

$$|g(x) - \mu| < \varepsilon.$$

Now,

$$\left| \frac{1}{g(x)} - \frac{1}{\mu} \right| = \frac{|\mu - g(x)|}{|\mu| |g(x)|}$$

$$< \frac{2\varepsilon}{|\mu|^2},$$

if $0 < |x - a| < \delta(\varepsilon)$, by the inequality above and Theorem 6.6–C. Hence, by the remark preceding Theorem 6.6–A, $\lim_{x \to a} 1/g(x) = 1/\mu$. ◆

We now use this theorem in turn to calculate the limit of a quotient.

Theorem 6.6–E. Let f, g be real valued functions defined (at least) on a deleted neighbourhood of the limit point a. If $\lim_{x \to a} f(x) = \lambda$, and $\lim_{x \to a} g(x) = \mu$, where μ is a nonzero real number, then

$$\lim_{x \to a} f/g(x) = \lim_{x \to a} f(x)/g(x) = \lambda/\mu.$$

The proof follows immediately by Theorems 6.6–D and 6.6–B (iii). ◆

Example 6.6.1. Let f be the function defined on $\{x \in R : x > 1\}$ by

$$f(x) = \frac{\sqrt{(2x - 1)} - \sqrt{(2x^2 - 1)}}{\sqrt{(x + 1)} - \sqrt{(x^2 + 1)}};$$

evaluate $\lim_{x \to 1+} f(x)$.

Solution. We have, for $x > 1$,

$$f(x) = \frac{-2x(1 - x)\{\sqrt{(x + 1)} + \sqrt{(x^2 + 1)}\}}{\{\sqrt{(2x - 1)} + \sqrt{(2x^2 - 1)}\} x(x - 1)}$$

$$= \frac{2[\sqrt{(x + 1)} + \sqrt{(x^2 + 1)}]}{\sqrt{(2x - 1)} + \sqrt{(2x^2 - 1)}}.$$

Now the limits, as $x \to 1 +$, of the expressions in the square roots, are $\sqrt{2}, \sqrt{2}, 1$, and 1. Hence, by Theorems 6.6–B, 6.6–E applied to one sided limits, we have $\lim_{x \to 1+} f(x) = 2\sqrt{2}$. ◆

Example 6.6.2. Let φ be the function given by

$$\varphi(t) = \frac{1 + \cos \pi t}{\tan^2 \pi t}, \quad \text{for all } t \text{ in } (\tfrac{1}{2}, \tfrac{3}{2}).$$

Find $\lim_{t \to 1} \varphi(t)$.

Solution. Write $t = 1 + \theta$; then,

$$\varphi(t) = \varphi(1 + \theta)$$

$$= \frac{1 - \cos \pi\theta}{\tan^2 \pi\theta}$$

$$= \psi(\theta), \text{ say};$$

we must therefore find $\lim_{\theta \to 0} \psi(\theta)$. Now,

$$\psi(\theta) = \frac{(1 - \cos^2 \pi\theta)}{\tan^2 \pi\theta (1 + \cos \pi\theta)}$$

$$= \frac{\sin^2 \pi\theta}{\tan^2 \pi\theta (1 + \cos \pi\theta)}$$

$$= \frac{\cos^2 \pi\theta}{1 + \cos \pi\theta}.$$

Now $\lim_{\theta \to 0} \cos \pi\theta = 1$; hence by Theorems 6.6–B, 6.6–E, we have $\lim_{\theta \to 0} \psi(\theta) = \frac{1}{2}$. Hence $\lim_{t \to 1} \varphi(t) = \frac{1}{2}$. ◆

We now go on to results for functions analogous to that of Example 4.3.3 for sequences.

Theorem 6.6–F. Let f, g be real valued functions defined in a deleted neighbourhood of the limit point a. Suppose that $\lim_{x \to a} f(x) = \lambda$, $\lim_{x \to a} g(x) = \mu$. If, for all x in the deleted neighbourhood of a, we have $f(x) \geqslant g(x)$, then $\lambda \geqslant \mu$. If $f(x) > g(x)$ for all x in this neighbourhood, then we can still only conclude that $\lambda \geqslant \mu$.

The proof, which is similar to that of Example 4.3.3, is left to the reader. We have already defined, in Section 3.5, the ideas of bounded function, non-decreasing function and so on. We can establish theorems similar to those of Section 4.2 for sequences.

Theorem 6.6–G. Let f be defined on a deleted left neighbourhood of the limit point a of $\mathscr{D}(f)$. Suppose that f is non-decreasing on this neighbourhood (i.e. if $a - \eta < x_1 < x_2 < a$, then $f(x_1) \leqslant f(x_2)$). If f is bounded above, then $\lim_{x \to a-} f(x)$ exists. It has the value $\sup\{f(x) : (a - \eta < x < a)\}$. If f is not bounded above, then $\lim_{x \to a-} f(x) = \infty$. The proof is similar to that of Theorem 4.2–A. We can also formulate theorems for functions which are monotonic on right neighbourhoods.

Theorem 6.6–H. Let f be defined on a deleted right neighbourhood of the limit point a of $\mathscr{D}(f)$. Suppose that f is non-decreasing in this neighbourhood (i.e. $a < x_1 < x_2 < a + \eta \Rightarrow f(x_1) \leqslant f(x_2)$). If f is bounded below, then $\lim\limits_{x \to a+} f(x)$ exists, equal to $\inf\{f(x):(a < x < a+\eta)\}$; if f is not bounded below, then $\lim\limits_{x \to a+} f(x) = -\infty$.

There are clearly many variations on this theme, since we can combine right or left neighbourhoods with the various types of monotonic function. We leave the reader to formulate these.

Example 6.6.3. The function f given by $f(x) = \tan x$ is increasing in the set $\{x \in R : -(\pi/2) < x < \pi/2\}$. It is not bounded in this interval. We have $\lim\limits_{x \to (\pi/2)-} \tan x = \infty$ and $\lim\limits_{x \to (\pi/2)+} \tan x = -\infty$.

These results occur as part of Theorem 9.7–I (the proof of which is left as an exercise). See also Fig. 9.7.1.

Finally, in this section, we mention the Cauchy criterion (compare Theorem 4.5–A) for convergence of functions.

Theorem 6.6–I (Cauchy). Let f be a real valued function defined on a set E. Suppose that a is a limit point of E. Then, there is a number λ such that $\lim\limits_{x \to a} f(x) = \lambda$ if and only if, given $\varepsilon > 0$, there is a number $\delta(\varepsilon) > 0$ such that, for all pairs of points x, y of E satisfying $0 < |x-a| < \delta(\varepsilon), 0 < |y-a| < \delta(\varepsilon)$, we have

$$|f(x) - f(y)| < \varepsilon.$$

The proof is basically the same as for Theorem 4.5–A. The theorem is amended in the usual way if a is ∞ or $-\infty$.

6.7 Continuity

We now go on to consider "continuous" functions. These are functions whose graph is a continuous line. For example, the function f of Fig. 6.7.1 is continuous, while the function g in that figure is not continuous (though parts of its graph are continuous). We must try to establish what are the essential properties of a continuous function. We observe that the property possessed by the graph of f as a whole can be analysed into local properties, i.e. properties possessed by the

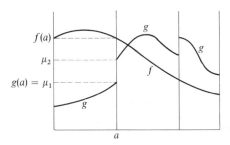

Fig. 6.7.1.

graph of f at each of its points. Let us see what local properties are possessed, say at the point a, by a continuous graph.

First, we note that the function f is defined at the point a; this is clearly necessary, for otherwise there is a point missing from the graph, which will then have a break, i.e. will not be "continuous".

Secondly, the function f is defined in a neighbourhood of a; there is a number $\delta > 0$ such that $f(x)$ is defined for all x such that $a - \delta < x < a + \delta$.

Finally, $\lim_{x \to a} f(x)$ exists, and has the value $f(a)$. These three properties seem to embody the intuitive ideas of what a continuous curve should be like. In Fig. 6.7.1, we also have the example of a curve g. Here, although g is defined at a, and in a neighbourhood of a, we have $\lim_{x \to a+} g(x) = \mu_2$, $\lim_{x \to a-} g(x) = \mu_1$ $(= g(a))$, but $\mu_1 \neq \mu_2$, and so $\lim_{x \to a} g(x)$ is not defined. So g is not "continuous" at a, and this bears out our expirical observation.

We are therefore led to the following definition.

Definition. Let f be a real valued function defined on a set E. Suppose that a is a limit point of E, and E contains a neighbourhood of a. Then, f is said to be **continuous** at a if $\lim_{x \to a} f(x) = f(a)$.

The hypothesis that E contains a neighbourhood of a means that $a \in E$, and so f is defined at a. We are no longer using deleted neighbourhoods. We have the following symbolic form of the definition, which we shall refer to frequently.

Definition. Let f be a real valued function, defined on a neighbourhood of the limit point a of $\mathscr{D}(f)$ (see Fig. 6.7.2). Then, f is **continuous** at a if, given $\varepsilon > 0$, there is a number $\delta(\varepsilon) > 0$ such that for all x satisfying $0 \leqslant |x - a| < \delta(\varepsilon)$, we have

$$|f(x) - f(a)| < \varepsilon.$$

We note that, since it is a requirement that f be defined at the limit point a, we do not have "continuity at ∞" or "continuity at $-\infty$". However, we can formulate a definition of one sided continuity; we merely replace $\lim_{x \to a} f(x)$ by the appropriate one sided limit.

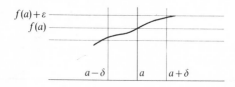

Fig. 6.7.2.

Definition. Let f be a real valued function defined on a right neighbourhood of the limit point a of $\mathscr{D}(f)$. Then, f is said to be **continuous on the right** at a, or **right-continuous** at a, if $\lim\limits_{x \to a+} f(x)$ exists, and has the value $f(a)$.

There is an analogous definition for *continuous on the left* at a; the condition is $\lim\limits_{x \to a-} f(x) = f(a)$.

Theorem 6.7–A. f is continuous at a if and only if it is continuous on the right, and on the left, at a.

Proof. This is immediate by Examples 6.5.1 and 6.5.2. ◆

A limit point a at which f is not continuous is called a **point of discontinuity**. A point of discontinuity a can occur because

(a) f is not defined at a; or

(b) $\lim\limits_{x \to a+} f(x)$ or $\lim\limits_{x \to a-} f(x)$, or both, do not exist; or

(c) even if both exist, $\lim\limits_{x \to a+} f(x)$ or $\lim\limits_{x \to a-} f(x)$, or both, are different from $f(a)$.

Example 6.7.1. Let f be given by, for all $x \in R$,

$$f(x) = [x^2].$$

Then, f is continuous at 0.

Proof. We have $f(0) = 0$. If $0 \leqslant |x| < 1$, then $0 \leqslant x^2 < 1 \Rightarrow f(x) = 0$. It follows that $\lim\limits_{x \to 0} f(x) = 0$. Hence, f is continuous at 0. ◆

Example 6.7.2. Let f be given by setting, for all $x \in R$,

$$f(x) = \begin{cases} x \sin 1/x, & \text{if } x \neq 0 \\ 0 & \text{if } x = 0. \end{cases}$$

Show that f is continuous at 0.

Proof. The formula $x \sin 1/x$ is meaningless if we put $x = 0$. So we *define* the value of f at 0 to be zero; we could define $f(0)$ to be anything we like, of course. Now, for all $x \neq 0$,

$$|f(x)| = |x \sin 1/x| \leqslant |x|$$

($|\sin 1/x| \leqslant 1$ by Theorems 9.7–H, 9.7–G (Corollary)).

Hence, if we take $\delta(\varepsilon)$ so that $\delta(\varepsilon) \leqslant \varepsilon$, we have $|f(x)| < \varepsilon$ for all x satisfying $0 \leqslant |x| < \delta(\varepsilon)$ i.e. $\lim\limits_{x \to 0} f(x) = 0$. Since $f(0) = 0$, f is continuous at zero.

Note that if we had defined $f(0)$ to be any number other than zero, then f would not be continuous at zero. ◆

Example 6.7.3. The function tan is not continuous at $\pi/2$.

Proof. This function is not defined at $\pi/2$. ◆

Example 6.7.4. Let ψ be the function given by setting, for $-1 < x \leqslant 1$,

$$\psi(x) = \lim(1 - x^n).$$

Then, ψ is continuous at zero, but discontinuous at 1.

Proof. $\psi(0) = 1$, clearly; next, if $|x| < 1$, we have $\lim x^n = 0$, by Example 4.1.6. Hence, if $|x| < 1$, we have $\psi(x) = 1$, and it follows that $\lim_{x \to 0} \psi(x) = 1$. So ψ is continuous at zero.

Next, $\psi(1) = 0$; for $0 < x < 1$, $\psi(x) = 1$, as before, and so $\lim_{x \to 1-} \psi(x) = 1 \neq \psi(1)$. Hence ψ is discontinuous at 1. ◆

We next show that continuity at a has local repercussions.

Theorem 6.7–B. Suppose that f is a real valued function which is continuous at a. If $f(a) \neq 0$, then there is a δ-neighbourhood of a such that, for all x satisfying $a - \delta < x < a + \delta$, $f(x)$ has the same sign as $f(a)$.

Proof. Let $\varepsilon = |f(a)|$. Then, since f is continuous, there is a number $\delta > 0$ such that, for $a - \delta < x < a + \delta$, we have

$$|f(x) - f(a)| < |f(a)|;$$

Suppose, first, that $f(a) > 0$; then the inequality above yields

$$-f(a) < f(x) - f(a) < f(a) \Rightarrow f(x) > 0,$$

from the left hand inequality. On the other hand, if $f(a) < 0$, we have $f(a) = -|f(a)|$, and so

$$f(a) < f(x) - f(a) < -f(a) \Rightarrow f(x) < 0,$$

from the right hand inequality. ◆

Before we continue with further results, we remark that many of these hold for one sided continuity, and the reader should investigate these. We first introduce the definition of continuous function.

Definition. Let f be defined on a set E. We say that f is **continuous** on E if f is continuous at a, for each $a \in E$.

For example, if $E = \{x \in R : a \leqslant x \leqslant b\}$, then f is continuous on E if f is continuous at x, for $a < x < b$, is right continuous at a and is left continuous at b.

We have an algebra of continuity similar to that of Section 6.6. We mention, without proof, the following theorems, and examples.

Theorem 6.7–C. If f and g are continuous on the set E, then so are $f + g$, $f - g$ and fg. Further, f/g is continuous for all points x of E such that $g(x) \neq 0$.

Example 6.7.5. The constant function and identity function are continuous on R. Hence, by Theorem 6.7–C, so is any polynomial function. A rational function is continuous at all points of R for which the denominator is nonzero.

Example 6.7.6. The functions sin, cos, exp are continuous on R (the proof must wait until Chapter 9). The function ln is continuous on the set $\{x \in R : x > 0\}$.

We have not so far considered the composition of functions. If f is defined on a set E, and g is defined in a neighbourhood of $f(a)$, we can ask about the behaviour of $g \circ f$ near a. The following theorem shows that continuity carries over to the composition of such functions.

Theorem 6.7–D. Let f be a real valued function which is continuous at the point a. Suppose g is a real valued function continuous at the point $f(a)$. Then $g \circ f$ is continuous at a.

Proof. Let $\varepsilon > 0$. Then, since g is continuous at $f(a)$, there is a number $\delta(\varepsilon) > 0$ such that, for all y satisfying $0 \leqslant |y - f(a)| < \delta(\varepsilon)$, we have

$$|g(y) - g(f(a))| < \varepsilon. \tag{1}$$

Next, since f is continuous at a, there is a number $\eta > 0$ such that for all x satisfying $0 \leqslant |x - a| < \eta$, we have

$$|f(x) - f(a)| < \delta. \tag{2}$$

The number η depends on δ, and hence ultimately upon ε. Hence, if $0 \leqslant |x - a| < \eta$, we have

$$|g(f(x)) - g(f(a))| < \varepsilon,$$

since y in equation (1) can be replaced by $f(x)$, in view of (2). That is, $\lim_{x \to a} g \circ f(x) = g \circ f(a)$.   ◆

Example 6.7.7. The corresponding result for composition is no longer valid if we relax the hypothesis to the following: $\lim_{x \to a} f(x) = \lambda$, $\lim_{y \to \lambda} g(y) = \mu$.

In this case, it is not true to say that $\lim_{x \to a} g \circ f(x) = \mu$. Counterexample: let f, g be given by

$$f(x) = [1 - x^2], \qquad g(y) = [1 - y^2] \quad \text{for all } x, y \in R.$$

f and g are thus the same function. Now, $\lim_{x \to 0} f(x) = \lim_{y \to 0} g(y) = 0$. So, in this case, $a = \lambda = \mu = 0$. But

$$g \circ f(x) = \begin{cases} 1 & \text{if } |x| < 1, \quad x \neq 0. \\ 0 & \text{if } x = 0. \end{cases}$$

Hence,

$$\lim_{x \to 0} g \circ f(x) = 1.   ◆$$

6.8 Continuous Functions

In this section, we investigate some important properties of continuous functions, especially when they are defined in a closed interval. For example, it is intuitively clear that a continuous function in a closed interval has a maximum value; for to say f is continuous means that, in Fig. 6.8.1, we must join the points $(a, f(a)), (b, f(b))$ by a continuous line. Since this means we cannot take our pen from the paper, it follows that f cannot take arbitrarily large values, positive or negative. The reader can test this for himself by trying to draw a continuous unbounded line from $(a, f(a))$ to $(b, f(b))$. We first begin with a different result, however, which is essential for that just mentioned. We show that a function continuous on a closed interval is bounded; from this, we know (Theorem 2.5–A) that the set $\{f(x)\}$ has a least upper bound, and the problem then is to show that this number is in fact a value of the function. The proof we shall give uses the method of repeated bisection. This technique, which occurs quite frequently in real analysis, depends on the completeness of the real numbers (Section 2.3).

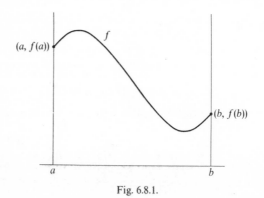

Fig. 6.8.1.

Before beginning the proof, we note the following exercises.

Example 6.8.1. If $f : E \to R$ is a bounded function, there is a number $K > 0$ such that, for all $x \in E$,

$$|f(x)| \leqslant K,$$

and conversely.

Proof. As Theorem 2.5–C. ◆

Example 6.8.2. If f is a real valued function, bounded in the closed interval $[a, c]$, and in the closed interval $[c, b]$, then it is bounded in $[a, b]$.

Proof. There exist $K_1, K_2 > 0$ such that

$$\text{for all } x \in [a, c], \qquad |f(x)| \leqslant K_1,$$

and

$$\text{for all } x \in [c, b], \qquad |f(x)| \leqslant K_2.$$

Write $K = \max(K_1, K_2)$; then, for all $x \in [a, b]$, we have

$$|f(x)| \leqslant K. \qquad \blacklozenge$$

This example remains true if we replace "bounded" by "bounded above". We shall use this result in a contrapositive form, *viz.* if f is not bounded above in $[a, b]$, and $a < c < b$, then it is not bounded above in at least one of $[a, c]$, $[c, b]$. We are now ready for the theorem.

Theorem 6.8–A. Let f be a real valued function, continuous in the closed interval $[a, b]$. Then, f is bounded in $[a, b]$.

Proof. Suppose, to the contrary, that f is not bounded above. We shall try to deduce a contradiction. We can also use the same approach if f is not bounded below; hence, it suffices to consider the one case.

Write $a = a_1$, $b = b_1$, and suppose that f is not bounded above in $[a_1, b_1]$. If c denotes the midpoint of $[a_1, b_1]$, then f is not bounded above in $[a_1, c]$, or is not bounded above in $[c, b_1]$, by the remark following Example 6.8.2.

If f is not bounded above in $[a_1, c]$, label the ends of this interval a_2 and b_2 respectively (i.e. $a_1 = a_2, c = b_2$). If f is bounded above in $[a_1, c]$, but not bounded above in $[c, b_1]$, label the ends of this interval a_2 and b_2 respectively, (i.e. $c = a_2, b_1 = b_2$). In either case we have

   (i) f is not bounded above in $[a_2, b_2]$;
   (ii) $a_1 \leqslant a_2$ and $b_2 \leqslant b_1$;
   (iii) $(b_2 - a_2) = \frac{1}{2}(b_1 - a_1)$.

Bisect $[a_2, b_2]$ at d; then f is not bounded above in at least one of the halves $[a_2, d]$, $[d, b_2]$. Choose such a one, and label its ends a_3, b_3 respectively. For example, if f is unbounded above in $[d, b_2]$, we write $d = a_3, b_2 = b_3$. We obtain a situation which satisfies the conditions (i), (ii), (iii), with appropriate modifications. Proceeding in this way, we obtain a sequence $\{[a_n, b_n]\}$ of closed intervals such that, for all n,

   (i) f is not bounded above in $[a_n, b_n]$;
   (ii) $a_{n-1} \leqslant a_n$ and $b_n \leqslant b_{n-1}$;
   (iii) $b_n - a_n = \frac{1}{2}(b_{n-1} - a_{n-1})$.

Now, since $a_{n-1} \leqslant a_n$, for all n, $\{a_n\}$ is a non-decreasing sequence of numbers. Likewise, $b_n \leqslant b_{n-1}$, for all n, so that $\{b_n\}$ is a non-increasing sequence. We therefore have

$$a_1 \leqslant a_n \leqslant b_n \leqslant b_1$$

$$\Rightarrow \{a_n\} \text{ is bounded above (by } b_1)$$

$$\Rightarrow \{a_n\} \text{ is convergent (Theorem 4.2-A)};$$

say $\lim a_n = \alpha$.

Similarly, $a_1 \leqslant b_n \Rightarrow \{b_n\}$ is bounded below

$$\Rightarrow \{b_n\} \text{ is convergent (Theorem 4.2-B)}$$

say $\lim b_n = \beta$.

Furthermore, $\alpha = \beta$; for $b_n - a_n = (\frac{1}{2})^{n-1} \cdot (b_1 - a_1)$ by (iii) repeatedly applied, and so $\lim(b_n - a_n) = 0$, since $(b_1 - a_1)$ is a constant; on the other hand $\lim(b_n - a_n) = \beta - \alpha$ (Theorem 4.3-A, Corollary 2), whence $\alpha = \beta$.

We consider two cases; when the number α is an end point of $[a, b]$, and when it is an interior point i.e. $a < \alpha < b$.

Case 1. $a < \alpha < b$. Since α is a point of (a, b), f is continuous at α; hence, there is a number $\delta > 0$ such that, for all satisfying $\alpha - \delta < x < \alpha + \delta$, we have

$$|f(x) - f(\alpha)| < 1 \Rightarrow f(x) < 1 + f(\alpha), \text{ in particular.}$$

But since $\lim a_n = \lim b_n = \alpha$, there is a number $n_0(\delta)$ such that for all $n > n_0(\delta)$, we have

$$\alpha - \delta < a_n \leqslant b_n < \alpha + \delta$$

i.e. the interval $[a_n, b_n]$ for $n > n_0$ is contained in $(\alpha - \delta, \alpha + \delta)$.
Hence, for all x satisfying $a_n \leqslant x \leqslant b_n$, we have

$$f(x) = 1 + f(\alpha)$$

so that f is bounded above in $[a_n, b_n]$, in contradiction of (i). Therefore, f is bounded above in $[a, b]$, by method (C) of indirect proof, (Section 1.10) with "r" as the statement (i).

Case 2.   Suppose $\alpha = a$ (the proof when $\alpha = b$ is similar). Then, f is right continuous at a, and so there is a $\delta > 0$ such that, for all x satisfying $a \leqslant x < a + \delta$, we have

$$|f(x) - f(a)| < 1 \Rightarrow f(x) < 1 + f(a), \text{ in particular.}$$

Now, $a_n = a$, for all n (since $\{a_n\}$ is nondecreasing, and $a_1 = a$), and $b_n \to a$. Hence, there is an integer $n_0(\delta)$ such that if $n > n_0(\delta)$, $a < b_n < a + \delta$. This implies that f is bounded above in $[a_n, b_n]$, for such n, again a contradiction, as above. ◆

This theorem is no longer valid if we replace "closed interval $[a, b]$" by "open interval (a, b)". To see this, we can consider the function

φ given by setting, for all $x \in (0, 1)$,

$$\varphi(x) = 1/x;$$

φ is continuous in $(0, 1)$; but it is not bounded there, for $\lim\limits_{x \to 0+} \varphi(x) = \infty \Rightarrow \varphi$ is unbounded above. This illustrates the principle that a theorem should contain no superfluous hypotheses; all the conditions imposed should be necessary. This we have tried to adhere to, but we point out that, occasionally, either for greater simplicity in the proof, or because we have a particular application in mind, we assume hypotheses which are stricter than they need be (i.e. the conclusion in question would be true under less restrictive conditions). The reader is left to construct an example showing that continuity is necessary also.

We now sharpen the result of Theorem 6.8–A, and show that the function f attains its supremum and infimum.

Theorem 6.8–B.   Let f be a real valued function continuous on the closed interval $[a, b]$. Denote by M, m the supremum and infimum, respectively, of f. Then, M and m are values of f, i.e. there are points $x_1, y_1 \in [a, b]$ such that

$$f(x_1) = M, \qquad f(y_1) = m.$$

Proof.   Suppose, to the contrary, that there is no value of f which equals M. Then, since $M = \sup\limits_{[a,b]} f(x)$, we have, for all $x \in [a, b]$,

$$f(x) < M.$$

Thus, $M - f(x) > 0$, for all $x \in [a, b]$.

It is clear that the function ψ given by $\psi(x) = M - f(x)$ is continuous in $[a, b]$, and ψ does not take the value zero. Hence, $1/\psi$ is continuous in $[a, b]$ (Theorem 6.7–C), and so is bounded (Theorem 6.8–A). There is therefore a number $K > 0$ such that

$$1/\psi(x) \leqslant K, \qquad \text{for all } x \in [a, b]$$

$$\Leftrightarrow M - f(x) \geqslant 1/K \quad \text{for all } x \in [a, b]$$

$$\Leftrightarrow f(x) \leqslant M - 1/K \quad \text{for all } x \in [a, b]$$

$$\Rightarrow M - 1/K \text{ is an upper bound of } \{f(x)\} \text{ in } [a, b]$$

$\Rightarrow\Leftarrow$ contradicting the definition of M as the least upper bound.

Hence, there must be a point $x_1 \in [a, b]$ such that $f(x_1) = M$. Similarly, there is a point $y_1 \in [a, b]$ such that $f(y_1) = m$. (This is an example of method (A) of indirect proof; part of the premises is p: "M is supremum of f." We deduce $\sim p$).

Again, the condition that $[a, b]$ be closed is essential. For if we take the identity function on $(0, 1)$, this is continuous there; also, the supremum is 1, but the identity function does not attain the value 1 in the open interval $(0, 1)$.

We again illustrate the method of repeated bisection in the following theorem. This says that if $f(a)$ and $f(b)$ are of opposite sign, so that the points $(a, f(a))$, $(b, f(b))$ lie on opposite sides of the x-axis, and f is continuous, then the graph of f joining $(a, f(a))$ to $(b, f(b))$ must cross the x-axis. This is once more a seemingly obvious result (Fig. 6.8.2). However, the reader might like to attempt a direct proof! We will again argue by contradiction.

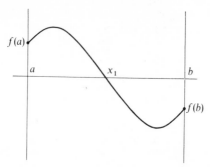

Fig. 6.8.2.

Theorem 6.8–C. Let f be a real valued function continuous on the closed interval $[a, b]$. If $f(a)$ and $f(b)$ are of opposite sign (i.e. $f(a)f(b) < 0$), then there is a point x_1 such that $a < x_1 < b$ and such that $f(x_1) = 0$.

Proof. We shall suppose, without loss of generality, that $f(a) > 0$, $f(b) < 0$. Assume the conclusion false i.e. that for all $x \in [a, b]$, $f(x) \neq 0$. Then, for each $x \in [a, b]$, either $f(x) > 0$, or $f(x) < 0$. Write $a = a_1$, $b = b_1$.

Bisect $[a, b]$ at c. Then, since $f(c) \neq 0$, either $f(c) > 0$, or $f(c) < 0$. If $f(c) > 0$, write $c = a_2$, and $b_2 = b_1$; if, however, $f(c) < 0$, write $c = b_2$ and $a_2 = a_1$. Then in either case, we shall have $f(a_2) > 0$ and $f(b_2) < 0$, so that $f(x)$ is of opposite sign at the ends of the interval $[a_2, b_2]$.

Next, bisect $[a_2, b_2]$ at d and repeat the performance. We have $f(d) \neq 0$, and so we label d as a_3 if $f(d) > 0$, and as b_3 if $f(d) < 0$. In the former case, we also write $b_3 = b_2$, and in the latter, $a_3 = a_2$; we therefore have $f(a_3) > 0$, $f(b_3) < 0$, in either case.

Proceeding thus, we obtain a sequence $\{[a_n, b_n]\}$ of closed intervals such that, for all n,

(i) $f(a_n) > 0$, $f(b_n) < 0$,

(ii) $a_{n-1} \leqslant a_n, b_n \leqslant b_{n-1}$;

(iii) $b_n - a_n = \frac{1}{2}(b_{n-1} - a_{n-1})$.

Now, as in Theorem 6.8–A, the conditions (ii) and (iii) imply that there is a real number α such that $\lim a_n = \lim b_n = \alpha$. By hypothesis $f(\alpha) \neq 0$. We again look at two cases.

Case 1. α is an interior point. If $a < \alpha < b$, then since f is continuous at α, it follows that there is a $\delta > 0$ such that $f(x)$ has the same sign as $f(\alpha)$ for all x satisfying $\alpha - \delta < x < \alpha + \delta$ (Theorem 6.7–B). But since $\lim a_n = \lim b_n = \alpha$, $\exists\, n_0(\delta)$ such that, for all $n > n_0(\delta)$

$$\alpha - \delta < a_n < b_n < \alpha + \delta\,;$$

this implies that, for such n, $f(a_n)$ and $f(b_n)$ have the same sign as $f(\alpha)$, and *hence the same sign as each other,* which contradicts (i).

Case 2. α is an end point. Here we use the same technique, except that f will be either right- or left-continuous (depending on which end point is α), rather than continuous. We omit the details.

Hence, by method (C) of indirect proof (Section 1.10), f must take the value zero somewhere in $[a, b]$. ◆

Corollary. If f is a continuous real valued function on an interval E, and $f(x_1)$, $f(x_2)$ are of opposite sign, (where $x_1 < x_2$), then f takes the value zero at a point x_3 such that $x_1 < x_3 < x_2$.

Proof. f continuous on $E \Rightarrow f$ continuous on $[x_1, x_2]$
$\Rightarrow$ result by Theorem 6.8–C. ◆

We now use this result to prove a fundamental theorem of analysis. This theorem is known as the Intermediate Value Theorem; it says the following: suppose f is a continuous real valued function on the closed interval $[a, b]$, so that (Theorem 6.8–B) f attains its supremum M and infimum m; now, in general, M will exceed m; the theorem we are about to prove says that not only are M and m values of f, but so is every real number between them. It is another pictorially obvious result:

If the curve f passes through P and Q and is *continuous,* then any line XY lying between $y = m$ and $y = M$ must intersect f (Fig. 6.8.3).

To put this result in another form, it states that the image of the bounded closed interval $[a, b]$ under a *continuous* function f is again a bounded closed interval, namely $[m, M]$. So continuity preserves the "topological" properties of the interval $[a, b]$.

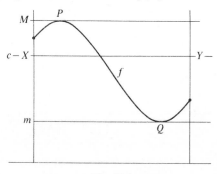

Fig. 6.8.3.

Theorem 6.8–D (Intermediate Value Theorem).

Let f be a continuous real valued function on the closed interval $[a, b]$. If f is not a constant function, i.e. if $M > m$, in the notation of Theorem 6.8–B, then f takes every value between m and M.

Proof. Let c satisfy $m < c < M$. We shall show that there is a point ξ, with $a < \xi < b$, such that $f(\xi) = c$.
Define the function g on $[a, b]$ by setting, for all $x \in [a, b]$,

$$g(x) = f(x) - c.$$

Then, g is continuous in $[a, b]$ (Theorem 6.7–C and Example 6.7.5). There are points x_1, x_2 of $[a, b]$ such that $f(x_1) = M$, $f(x_2) = m$, by Theorem 6.8–B. Hence, $g(x_1) > 0$ and $g(x_2) < 0$. It therefore follows, by the Corollary to Theorem 6.8–C, that $g(x_3) = 0$, for some x_3 between x_1 and x_2. That is,

$$f(x_3) - c = 0$$

or

$$f(x_3) = c. \qquad \blacklozenge$$

The reader will of course observe that the continuity of f is sufficient for the result. If f is not continuous, then f may or may not take every value between M and m, as is illustrated by the following examples.

Corollary 1. Let f be a continuous real valued function on the closed interval $[a, b]$ and suppose $f(a) \neq f(b)$. Then, f takes every value between $f(a)$ and $f(b)$.

Proof. Suppose $f(a) < f(b)$. Then, $m \leqslant f(a) < f(b) \leqslant M$. Hence, by Theorem 6.8–D, since f takes every value between m and M, it takes every value between $f(a)$ and $f(b)$, *a fortiori*. $\qquad \blacklozenge$

Corollary 2. Let f be continuous on the interval (a, b), where a or b may be infinite. If $m = \inf\{f(x) : a < x < b\}$ and $M = \sup\{f(x) : a < x < b\}$, then f takes every value in (m, M).
The proof is left to the reader.

Example 6.8.3. Let $[a, b]$ be the interval $[0, 1]$. Let f be given by

$$f(x) = \begin{cases} 1 - x, & 0 \leqslant x < \frac{1}{2} \\ x - 1, & \frac{1}{2} \leqslant x \leqslant 1. \end{cases}$$

Then, in this case $M = 1$, $m = -\frac{1}{2}$. There are no points x of $[0, 1]$ such that

$$0 < f(x) < \frac{1}{2}.$$

Here, f is not continuous (Fig. 6.8.4). $\qquad \blacklozenge$

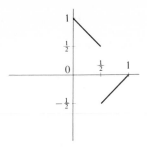

Fig. 6.8.4.

Example 6.8.4. Let g be defined on $[0, 1]$ by

$$g(x) = \begin{cases} x & \text{if } x \text{ is rational} \\ 1-x & \text{if } x \text{ is irrational.} \end{cases}$$

The function g is not continuous (except at the single point $\tfrac{1}{2}$); this is an exercise for the reader at the end of the chapter. The maximum of $g(x)$ is 1, the minimum is 0. Further, g takes every value between 0 and 1. To see this, let ξ be any number between 0 and 1; if ξ is rational, then g has the value ξ at the point ξ; if, on the other hand, ξ is irrational, then $g(1-\xi) = 1-(1-\xi) = \xi$, so that g has the value ξ at the point $(1-\xi)$. Further, of course, $0 < 1-\xi < 1$. ◆

6.9 Uniform Continuity

For a function f, continuous on a *closed* interval $[a, b]$, a special situation exists. We have regarded continuity, up to now, as a local property; f is continuous if it is continuous at each point x of its domain, and the formal definition involves a number δ, which depends on ε, and on x. For a closed interval, we obtain a "global" concept of continuity, in that a common standard applies to all the points of $[a, b]$, and these are not considered individually.

In order to develop this theory, we require a new definition, that of oscillation.

Definition. Let f be continuous in the closed interval $[\alpha, \beta]$. Let $M = \sup_{[\alpha,\beta]} f(x)$, $m = \inf_{[\alpha,\beta]} f(x)$. Then, the non-negative real number $M-m$ is called the **oscillation** of f in $[\alpha, \beta]$. We shall denote it by $\omega(f; \alpha, \beta)$.

Example 6.9.1. If $[\gamma, \delta]$ is an interval contained in $[\alpha, \beta]$, then $\omega(f; \gamma, \delta) \leqslant \omega(f; \alpha, \beta)$.

Proof. Since every point of $[\gamma, \delta]$ is a point of $[\alpha, \beta]$, it follows that $\sup_{[\gamma,\delta]} f(x) \leqslant \sup_{[\alpha,\beta]} f(x)$, $\inf_{[\alpha,\beta]} f(x) \leqslant \inf_{[\gamma,\delta]} f(x)$. The result is immediate. ◆

Now if $[a, b]$ is a closed interval, and $x_0, \ldots, x_n$ are points such that $a = x_0 < x_1 < x_2 < \ldots < x_{n-1} < x_n = b$, we say that $x_0, \ldots x_n$ form a **division** or **partition** of $[a, b]$, into the subintervals $[a, x_1], [x_1, x_2] \ldots [x_{n-1}, b]$.

We now come to the first of the two important theorems of this section.

Theorem 6.9–A. If f is a real valued function continuous on $[a, b]$, and $\varepsilon > 0$, then there is a partition of $[a, b]$ into a *finite* number of subintervals, such that in each subinterval the oscillation of f is less than ε.

Proof. A constructive direct proof seems out of the question. Therefore, we argue by the method of contradiction. For the purposes of this proof, call $[a, b]$ "divisible" if we can divide it into a finite number of subintervals, in each of which the oscillation of f is less than ε. We observe that if $[\alpha, \beta]$ has mid-point γ, and $[\alpha, \gamma]$ and $[\gamma, \beta]$ are each divisible, so then is $[\alpha, \beta]$, for the sum of two finite numbers is finite. Hence, if $[\alpha, \beta]$ is not divisible, at least one of $[\alpha, \gamma], [\gamma, \beta]$ must not be divisible.

We now begin the proof proper. Suppose the theorem is false, i.e. $[a, b]$ is not divisible. Then, at least one half of $[a, b]$ is not divisible. Label such a half $[a_2, b_2]$; we take $a_1 = a, b_1 = b$. Since $[a_2, b_2]$ is not divisible, at least one half of it is not divisible. Label such a half $[a_3, b_3]$. This method of repeated bisection yields a sequence $\{[a_n, b_n]\}$ of closed intervals such that

(i) $[a_n, b_n]$ is not divisible;

(ii) $a_n \leqslant a_{n+1}$ & $b_{n+1} \leqslant b_n$;

(iii) $b_{n+1} - a_{n+1} = \frac{1}{2}(b_n - a_n)$.

As before, we have $\lim a_n = \lim b_n = \alpha$. Now, if $a < \alpha < b$, we have, since f is continuous at α, that there is a $\delta > 0$ such that, for all x satisfying $0 \leqslant |x - \alpha| < \delta$,

$$|f(x) - f(\alpha)| < \frac{\varepsilon}{2}.$$

If n is sufficiently large, $\alpha - \delta < a_n < b_n < \alpha + \delta$; write

$$M_n = \sup_{[a_n, b_n]} f(x) = f(x_n),$$

say,

$$m_n = \inf_{[a_n, b_n]} f(x) = f(y_n).$$

Then,

$$\omega(f; a_n, b_n) = M_n - m_n$$

$$= |f(x_n) - f(\alpha)| + |f(\alpha) - f(y_n)|$$

$$< \varepsilon$$

which contradicts the hypothesis that $[a_n, b_n]$ is not divisible. Hence, the theorem follows, by method (C) of Section 1.10. The proof when $\alpha = a$ or $\alpha = b$ is similar. ◆

We use this result in the next theorem, which describes the special situation we mentioned at the start of the section.

Theorem 6.9–B. Suppose f is a real valued function continuous in the closed interval $[a, b]$. Given $\varepsilon > 0$, there is a number $\delta(\varepsilon) > 0$ such that for *all pairs* of points x_1, x_2 in $[a, b]$ satisfying $0 \leqslant |x_1 - x_2| < \delta$, we have

$$|f(x_1) - f(x_2)| < \varepsilon.$$

Proof. By Theorem 6.9–A, there is a partition of $[a, b]$ into a finite number of subintervals, in each of which the oscillation of f is less than $\frac{1}{2}\varepsilon$. Let $\delta(\varepsilon)$ be the length of the shortest subinterval. Suppose now that x_1 and x_2 are points of $[a, b]$ whose distance apart is less than $\delta(\varepsilon)$. Then, only two possibilities can arise: (i) x_1 and x_2 belong to the *same* subinterval of the partition, in which case

$$|f(x_1) - f(x_2)| < \frac{\varepsilon}{2} < \varepsilon,$$

or else (ii) x_1 and x_2 belong to adjoining subintervals; in this case, let ξ be the common end point of these subintervals. Then,

$$|f(x_1) - f(x_2)| \leqslant |f(x_1) - f(\xi)| + |f(\xi) - f(x_2)|$$
$$< \frac{\varepsilon}{2} + \frac{\varepsilon}{2}$$

and the theorem follows. ◆

The two cases mentioned above are illustrated in Fig. 6.9.1. x_1 and x_2 cannot be separated by a complete subinterval, for since the smallest subinterval has length δ, this would imply that $|x_1 - x_2| > \delta$.

We use Theorem 6.9–B to formulate a new definition, that of uniform continuity on a set.

Definition. Let f be a real valued function defined on an interval E. Then f is called **uniformly continuous** on E if, given $\varepsilon > 0$, there is a $\delta(\varepsilon) > 0$ such that for all pairs of points x_1, x_2 of E satisfying $0 \leqslant |x_1 - x_2| < \delta(\varepsilon)$, we have

$$|f(x_1) - f(x_2)| < \varepsilon.$$

Fig. 6.9.1.

In symbolic language, f is uniformly continuous on E if $\forall\, \varepsilon > 0$, $\exists\, \delta(\varepsilon) > 0$ s.t. $\forall\, x_1, x_2 \in E$ with $|x_1 - x_2| < \delta, |f(x_1) - f(x_2)| < \varepsilon$.

The theorem above can thus be expressed in the following form: A function continuous on a closed interval $[a, b]$ is uniformly continuous there.

Example 6.9.2. Theorem 6.9–B holds only under the hypothesis that the interval is closed. If the interval is not closed, f can be continuous without being uniformly continuous.

Proof. Consider the function f defined on $(0, 1)$ by

$$f(x) = 1/x.$$

Then, f is continuous on $(0, 1)$. But f is not uniformly continuous on this set. To show this, we consider the negation of the definition above; f is not uniformly continuous means (by Rule (iii) of Section 1.9) that

$$\exists\, \varepsilon > 0 \text{ s.t. } \quad \forall\, \delta > 0, \quad \exists\, x_1, x_2 \in E \text{ s.t. } |x_1 - x_2| < \delta,$$

and $|f(x_1) - f(x_2)| \geqslant \varepsilon$.

Now, let $\varepsilon > 0$; whatever $\delta > 0$ we care to take, we can certainly find a point x_2 of $(0, 1)$ such that $0 < x_2 < \delta$ and $0 < x_2 < 1/\varepsilon$. Now, take $x_1 = \frac{1}{2}x_2$; then, clearly, $|x_1 - x_2| < \delta$. Further,

$$
\begin{aligned}
|f(x_1) - f(x_2)| &= 1/x_1 - 1/x_2 \\
&= 2/x_2 - 1/x_2 \\
&= 1/x_2 \\
&> \varepsilon.
\end{aligned}
$$

So, f is not uniformly continuous on $(0, 1)$.   ◆

Note. In this example, we can take ε to be any positive number. In some circumstances, we may have to look harder for a suitable ε, and any ε will not just do. In Exercise 20 at the end of this chapter, for instance, we must take $\varepsilon \leqslant 2$ (why?).

Let us compare the definition of *uniform* continuity with the definition of continuity of f on E. The latter reads: f is continuous on E if $\forall\, x_1 \in E$, f is continuous at x_1, i.e. $\forall\, x_1 \in E$, $\forall\, \varepsilon > 0$, $\exists\, \delta(\varepsilon) > 0$ s.t. $\forall\, x_2 \in E$ with $|x_1 - x_2| < \delta, |f(x_1) - f(x_2)| < \varepsilon$.

What is the difference? It is this: in the latter definition (of continuity), the number δ is quantified after x_1—hence δ may be chosen to depend on ε and x_1; in the former case (of uniform continuity), δ is quantified before x_1, and so the chosen δ must do for every x_1 (i.e. δ depends on ε, but is independent of x_1). It is in this sense that uniform continuity is a global, rather than a local, concept. The reader should also note that we talk of uniform continuity only "on a set", and never "at a point".

6.10 The Inverse Function Again

Suppose that f is a function of the interval A into R, and that f^{-1} exists as the inverse function of $f(A)$ into A. One question which it is natural to ask in this chapter is the following—if f is continuous, is f^{-1} continuous also? We might suspect that, since there is so close a relationship between f and f^{-1}, it is likely that a property of one will be transmitted to the other, and in fact, this suspicion is strengthened if we consider examples like the identity function on R (which is continuous, and whose inverse function is again the identity), or the function f given by $f(x) = x^3$ (continuous, and whose inverse function is φ, given by $\varphi(y) = y^{\frac{1}{3}}$, also continuous). We invite the reader to think of other examples of $(1, 1)$ continuous functions, and consider whether their inverse functions are continuous.

We are thus predisposed towards trying to prove that the answer to our question above is "yes". This means that we look for a direct proof, rather than cast around for counterexamples.

Let us see what we have to do; to show f^{-1} continuous, we must show that it is continuous at every c in $f(A)$, i.e. given $\varepsilon > 0$, we must show there is a $\delta > 0$ such that, for all y satisfying $0 \leqslant |y - c| < \delta$, we have $|f^{-1}(y) - f^{-1}(c)| < \varepsilon$.

Now since y, c belong to $f(A)$, $c = f(\xi)$, and $y = f(x)$, for points ξ, x of A. So, we have to show that, given $\varepsilon > 0$, for all y in $(c - \delta, c + \delta)$,

$$|f(\xi) - f(x)| < \delta \Rightarrow |\xi - x| < \varepsilon.$$

On the other hand, we know that f is continuous i.e. given $\varepsilon' > 0$, there is a $\delta' > 0$ such that

$$|\xi - x| < \delta' \Rightarrow |f(\xi) - f(x)| < \varepsilon'. \tag{1}$$

We therefore are trying, in a sense, to reverse the implication. In general, this cannot be done; if the points ξ, x satisfy the condition $|f(\xi) - f(x)| < \varepsilon'$ of (1), there is no guarantee that $|\xi - x| < \delta'$ for the δ' of (1) (see Fig. 6.10.1, where f is continuous, but note that $|f(\xi) - f(x')| < \varepsilon'$ although $|\xi - x'| > \delta'$).

This shows that if $\delta > 0$, then we cannot find an $\varepsilon > 0$ such that $|f(\xi) - f(x)| < \varepsilon$ implies that $|\xi - x| < \delta$. For by choosing a small enough δ, we can never cut out the situation of points like x'', where $f(x'') = f(\xi)$, but $|x'' - \xi| > \delta$.

In our situation, however, we may be able to do better. For we have the additional hypothesis that f is $(1, 1)$. The situation of Fig. 6.10.1 will therefore not occur; if f is continuous and $(1, 1)$ the graph of f will be a continuous line which never crosses the same horizontal line twice, which means f is either increasing or decreasing. (Experiment with drawing continuous $(1, 1)$ functions on an interval!.) So, there will be only one segment of the graph of f [namely, that passing through $(\xi, f(\xi))$], which lies between the horizontal lines $y = f(\xi) + \varepsilon'$, $y = f(\xi) - \varepsilon'$.

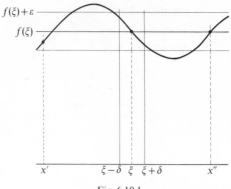

Fig. 6.10.1.

Assuming that f is increasing, we obtain the situation of Fig. 6.10.2. If we now look at the ε-neighbourhood of ξ, its image under f is the interval $(f(\xi-\varepsilon),\ f(\xi+\varepsilon))$, i.e. LK. Moreover, since the graph is $(1, 1)$ we observe that if δ is less than both MK and ML, the corresponding points on the horizontal axis necessarily lie within the segment QR. Putting this into formal language, this means that if $|y-c| < \delta$, where $\delta < \min(LM, MK)$, then

$$|f^{-1}(y) - f^{-1}(c)| < \varepsilon$$

i.e. f^{-1} is continuous at c.

In order to prove our result, therefore, we must justify the remark above that if f is continuous and $(1, 1)$, then it is either increasing or decreasing. This we do by easy stages. We begin by showing that if a and c belong to A, and b lies between them, then $f(b)$ lies between $f(a)$ and $f(c)$. This might, at first sight, seem to be enough; if we confine our attention to functions continuous and $(1, 1)$ on closed intervals, it is enough (why?). If, as we do, we concern ourselves with functions defined

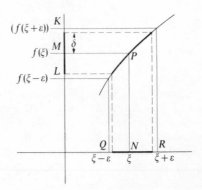

Fig. 6.10.2.

on any interval, then there are a few more subtleties to be examined. These we shall see in Theorem 6.10–C, which will also show the necessity for Theorem 6.10–B.

Theorem 6.10–A. Let f be continuous and $(1, 1)$ on some interval E of the real line. Suppose a, b, c are points of E with $a < b < c$. Then, either $f(a) < f(b) < f(c)$, or $f(c) < f(b) < f(a)$.

Proof. Since f is $(1, 1)$, $f(a) \neq f(c)$; suppose $f(a) < f(c)$. Now b is different from a, c, so $f(b)$ is distinct from $f(a)$ and $f(c)$. There are only three possibilities:

(i) $f(a) < f(b) < f(c)$,

which is the one we want;

(ii) $f(b) < f(a)$,
(iii) $f(c) < f(b)$;

we shall show the last two cannot hold. If case (ii) were true, consider the interval $[b, c]$. By Theorem 6.8–D, Corollary 1, f takes every value between $f(b)$ and $f(c)$, and in particular, $f(a)$. But then there is a point in $[b, c]$ (which therefore cannot be the point a) at which f takes the value $f(a)$. This contradicts the hypothesis that f is $(1, 1)$; hence (ii) cannot be true. If case (iii) holds, consider the interval $[a, b]$. By the same theorem, f takes every value between $f(a)$ and $f(b)$—in particular, $f(c)$. So we have two points (c, and a point in (a, b)) where f has the same value. This is impossible if f is $(1, 1)$. So (iii) is ruled out, and therefore (i) must hold. Similarly, if we suppose, at first, that $f(c) < f(a)$, and proceed in exactly the same way, we find that $f(c) < f(b) < f(a)$. ◆

An immediate consequence of this is the following.

Theorem 6.10–B. Suppose f is a continuous real valued $(1, 1)$ function defined on an interval E of R, and let a, $b \in E$, with $f(a) < f(b)$. If c is a point of E, and $c < a$, then $f(c) < f(a)$; if $c > b$, then $f(c) > f(b)$.

Proof. Suppose $c < a$; then $f(c) < f(b)$. For, if $f(c) > f(b)$, we can apply Theorem 6.10–A to $[c, b]$, and conclude that $f(a) > f(b)$, which is false. Also, since $b \neq c$, $f(b) \neq f(c)$, since f is $(1, 1)$. Therefore $f(c) < f(b)$.

If we now apply Theorem 6.10–A to $[c, b]$, we have $f(c) < f(a) < f(b)$; in particular, $f(c) < f(a)$.

If $c > b$, the proof is similar.   ◆

This allows us to prove the conditional converse of Theorem 3.5–A.

Theorem 6.10–C. Let f be a *continuous* real valued $(1, 1)$ function on an interval A. Then, f is either increasing or decreasing on A.

Proof. Let x_1, x_2 be distinct points of A, and suppose $x_1 < x_2$. Now f is $(1, 1)$, so $f(x_1) \neq f(x_2)$. We shall suppose $f(x_1) < f(x_2)$, and deduce that f is increasing on A (it is clearly no use trying to prove f

decreasing, since $x_1 < x_2$, and $f(x_1) < f(x_2)$). If $f(x_1) > f(x_2)$, we would prove f decreasing. This will be left to the reader.

We thus compare any two values, and show that all other pairs of values satisfy the same relation.

To show f increasing, we must prove that if y_1, y_2 are *any* two numbers in A with $y_1 < y_2$, then $f(y_1) < f(y_2)$. So let $y_1 < y_2$ be two points in $[a, b]$. Now, if $y_1 = x_1$, $y_2 = x_2$, we have $f(y_1) = f(x_1) < f(x_2) = f(y_2)$. If $y_1 = x_1 < y_2 < x_2$, then by Theorem 6.10–A, either

$$f(x_1) = f(y_1) < f(y_2) < f(x_2)$$

or

$$f(x_1) = f(y_1) > f(y_2) > f(x_2);$$

the second possibility is eliminated, because $f(x_1) < f(x_2)$ by hypothesis.

If $y_1 = x_1 < x_2 < y_2$, then again by Theorem 6.10–A,

$$f(y_1) = f(x_1) < f(x_2) < f(y_2)$$

or

$$f(y_1) = f(x_1) > f(x_2) > f(y_2);$$

once more, the second possibility is ruled out, since $f(x_1) < f(x_2)$.

In a similar way, the situations when $y_2 = x_2$ and y_1 is less than, or greater then x_1, yield the result that $f(y_1) < f(y_2)$ on appeal to Theorem 6.10–A.

If $y_1 = x_2$, then we have $x_1 < y_1 < y_2$. Here again, by Theorem 6.10–A, $f(x_1) < f(y_1) = f(x_2) < f(y_2)$, or $f(x_1) > f(y_1) > f(y_2)$; the second is impossible, since $f(x_1) < f(x_2) = f(y_1)$. The case when $y_2 = x_1$ is exactly similar.

There remain the cases when neither of y_1, y_2 coincide with x_1, x_2. These give six different situations, which however are easily treated.

   (i) $y_1 < y_2 < x_1 < x_2$; by Theorem 6.10–B, $f(y_1) < f(x_1)$; hence, by Theorem 6.10–A, $f(y_1) < f(y_2) < f(x_1)$.

  (ii) $y_1 < x_1 < y_2 < x_2$; by Theorem 6.10–B, $f(y_1) < f(x_1)$; by Theorem 6.10–A, $f(x_1) < f(y_2) < f(x_2)$. So $f(y_1) < f(x_1) < f(y_2)$.

 (iii) $y_1 < x_1 < x_2 < y_2$; by Theorem 6.10–B, $f(y_1) < f(x_1)$; by the same theorem, $f(x_2) < f(y_2)$. Since $f(x_1) < f(x_2)$, the result follows.

 (iv) $x_1 < y_1 < y_2 < x_2$; by Theorem 6.10–A, $f(x_1) < f(y_1) < f(x_2)$; by Theorem 6.10–A again, $f(y_1) < f(y_2) < f(x_2)$.

  (v) $x_1 < y_1 < x_2 < y_2$; by Theorem 6.10–A, $f(y_1) < f(x_2)$; by Theorem 6.10–B, $f(x_2) < f(y_2)$. Hence, $f(y_1) < f(y_2)$.

 (vi) $x_1 < x_2 < y_1 < y_2$; by Theorem 6.10–B, $f(x_2) < f(y_2)$; hence by Theorem 6.10–A, $f(x_2) < f(y_1) < f(y_2)$.   ◆

We are now ready to prove the main result of this section.

Theorem 6.10–D. Let f be a continuous real valued $(1, 1)$ function defined on an interval A. Then, f^{-1}, the inverse function of f, is also continuous.

Proof. Let c be an element of the range of f. We shall show that f^{-1} is continuous at c.

Since $c \in \mathcal{R}(f)$, we may write

$$c = f(\xi), \qquad \xi \in A.$$

We want to prove that given $\varepsilon > 0$, there is a $\delta > 0$ such that, for all y in $\mathcal{R}(f)$ satisfying $|y - c| < \delta$, we have

$$|f^{-1}(y) - f^{-1}(c)| < \varepsilon.$$

To this end, let $\varepsilon > 0$. By Theorem 6.10–C, f is either increasing or decreasing. We may suppose, without loss, that it is increasing. Then, we have

$$f(\xi - \varepsilon) < f(\xi) < f(\xi + \varepsilon)$$

(since obviously $\xi - \varepsilon < \xi < \xi + \varepsilon$).
If we write $\delta = \min\{f(\xi) - f(\xi - \varepsilon), f(\xi + \varepsilon) - f(\xi)\}$, then

$$f(\xi - \varepsilon) \leqslant f(\xi) - \delta \leqslant f(\xi) + \delta \leqslant f(\xi + \varepsilon).$$

Hence, for all y satisfying $f(\xi) - \delta < y < f(\xi) + \delta$, we have

$$f(\xi - \varepsilon) < y < f(\xi + \varepsilon).$$

By Exercise 34 of Chapter 3, if f is increasing, so is f^{-1}. Hence,

$$f^{-1}(f(\xi - \varepsilon)) < f^{-1}(y) < f^{-1}(f(\xi + \varepsilon))$$

i.e.

$$\xi - \varepsilon < f^{-1}(y) < \xi + \varepsilon.$$

But, since $\xi = f^{-1}(c)$, this is equivalent to the statement

$$|f^{-1}(c) - f^{-1}(y)| < \varepsilon.$$

We have therefore shown that, for all y satisfying $c - \delta < y < c + \delta$,

$$|f^{-1}(c) - f^{-1}(y)| < \varepsilon.$$

Hence, f^{-1} is continuous at c.   ◆

Exercises

1. Find the limit points of the following sets:
   (a) The integers Z.
   (b) The rationals Q.
   (c) All numbers of the form $1/n$, $n \in N$.
   (d) All numbers of the form $2^{-m} + 3^{-n}$, $m, n \in N$.

2. Prove the following results on limits:

(a) $\lim\limits_{x \to \infty} \{\sqrt{x} - \sqrt{(x-1)}\} = 0$

(b) $\lim\limits_{x \to \infty} \{\sqrt{(x + \ln x)} - \sqrt{x}\} = 0$

(c) $\lim\limits_{x \to -\infty} \dfrac{e^x - e^{-x}}{e^x + e^{-x}} = -1$

(d) $\lim\limits_{x \to \infty} [\ln x] = \lim\limits_{x \to \infty} \ln[x] = \infty$

(e) $\lim\limits_{x \to 0+} \dfrac{\sqrt{(x(1+x))} - \sqrt{x}}{x\sqrt{x}} = \frac{1}{2}$

(f) $\lim\limits_{x \to 1-} \dfrac{\sqrt{(1-x^2)} - \sqrt{(2(1-x))}}{(1-x)^{\frac{3}{2}}} = -\dfrac{1}{2\sqrt{2}}$.

3. Suppose f and g are defined for $x \neq 0$ by setting

$$f(x) = \frac{x}{\alpha}\left[\frac{\beta}{x}\right], \quad g(x) = \frac{\beta}{x} \cdot \left[\frac{x}{\alpha}\right],$$

where $\alpha > 0$, $\beta > 0$ and $[t]$ denotes the greatest integer not exceeding t.
Find

$$\lim\limits_{x \to 0+} f(x), \qquad \lim\limits_{x \to 0+} g(x), \qquad \lim\limits_{x \to 0-} f(x), \qquad \lim\limits_{x \to 0-} g(x).$$

4. Consider the function f given by

$$f(x) = \frac{x^3 + 8}{x + 2}$$

for all $x \neq -2$. Extend the function f so that it is defined, and *continuous*, at -2.

5. Prove that if f is continuous at a, so is $|f|$.

6. Give an example of a function f such that f is not continuous but $|f|$ is continuous. Show that f^2 can be continuous when f is not.

7. Let f be continuous on $[a, b]$, and suppose $f(x) = 0$ for every rational x in $[a, b]$. Prove that $f(x) = 0$, for all x in $[a, b]$.

8. Show that $[x] \sin \pi x$ is continuous for all x in R.

9. A function f satisfies the equation

$$f(x + y) = f(x) + f(y)$$

for all x, y. Show that

(a) If f is continuous at the point a, then it is continuous for all x.

(b) If f is continuous, then $f(x) = kx$, for some constant k.

10. A function f is called **even** if $f(x) = f(-x)$, **odd** if $f(-x) = -f(x)$. Show that any continuous function f can be written as the sum of an even continuous function and an odd continuous function.

11. The function g defined on $[0, 1]$ is given by

$$g(x) = \begin{cases} x & \text{if } x \text{ is rational} \\ 1-x & \text{if } x \text{ is irrational.} \end{cases}$$

Show that g takes every value between 0 and 1 inclusive, but that it is continuous only at the point $\frac{1}{2}$.

12. Let f, g be two continuous functions. Show that $\max(f, g)$ and $\min(f, g)$ are also continuous, where, for all x,

$$\max(f, g) = \begin{cases} f(x) & \text{if } f(x) \geqslant g(x) \\ g(x) & \text{if } f(x) < g(x) \end{cases},$$

$$\min(f, g) = \begin{cases} f(x) & \text{if } f(x) \leqslant g(x) \\ g(x) & \text{if } f(x) > g(x) \end{cases}.$$

13. Let f be continuous on $[a, b]$. Define a function g as follows:

$$g(a) = f(a)$$

$$g(x) = \max\{f(y) : a \leqslant y \leqslant x\}.$$

Prove that g is continuous on $[a, b]$, and that g is non-decreasing.

14. The functions f, g and h are given by setting, for x in $[0, 1]$,

(a) $f(x) = \begin{cases} 0 & \text{if } x \text{ is irrational} \\ 1 & \text{if } x \text{ is rational} \end{cases}$

(b) $g(x) = \begin{cases} 0 & \text{if } x \text{ is irrational} \\ x & \text{if } x \text{ is rational} \end{cases}$

(c) $h(x) = \begin{cases} 0 & \text{if } x \text{ is irrational} \\ 1/q & \text{if } x \text{ is rational, } x = p/q \text{ in lowest terms, } x \neq 0. \\ 1 & \text{if } x = 0. \end{cases}$

Prove that f is never continuous, g is continuous only at 0, and h is continuous at x only if x is irrational.

15. Suppose, for all x, that $f^2(x) = g^2(x)$, and $f(x) \neq 0$. If f, g are continuous, show that either $f(x) - g(x) = 0$, for all x, or $f(x) + g(x) = 0$, for all x. Show why continuity is necessary.

16. If f is continuous on $[a, b]$, and increasing on (a, b), show that f is increasing on $[a, b]$.

17. If f is continuous on $[a, b]$ and on $[b, c]$, and is increasing on (a, b) and (b, c), then f is increasing on $[a, c]$.

18. Prove Theorems 6.6–F, 6.6–G, 6.6–H, 6.6–I.

19. Let f be continuous on $[a, b]$. If $a < c < b$, show that $\omega(f; a, b) \leqslant \omega(f; a, c) + \omega(f; c, b)$.

20. Show that $\sin 1/x$ is not uniformly continuous on any interval $(0, a)$.

21. Suppose E_1, E_2 are closed intervals on the real line. If f is continuous on E_1 and on E_2, show that f is uniformly continuous on $E_1 \cup E_2$.

22. Let f be continuous on R. Let A be the set of points x such that $f(x) = 0$. Show that every limit point of A is in the set A (such a set is called **closed**).

23. Show that to each value of x, there corresponds one value of y such that $x = y + y^5$, and that this value is a continuous, increasing function of the dummy x.

Part Four: The Calculus

In the next chapters, we shall consider that branch of Analysis usually called *The Calculus*. This traditionally falls into two parts; one of these is *The Derivative* or *Differentiation*, the other being *The Integral* or *Integration*.

Historically, these two parts arose quite separately, having been developed for different purposes. *Integration* was used for finding areas and volumes, while *Differentiation* was concerned with change and rate of change, and with certain extremal problems. However, as these subjects were thoroughly investigated, it became clear that, far from being distinct disciplines, the two ideas were closely connected, in a very special way. It turned out, in fact, that the processes of differentiation and integration were (almost) reverses of each other.

Our programme will be to treat the ideas separately, although to begin with, in Chapter 7, we shall exhibit the special relationship between the two processes for a particular example. The remainder of Chapter 7 deals with the derivative of a function; Chapter 8 then discusses Integration, beginning with an account of its development as a tool for finding areas, and continuing with a discussion of the principal properties of the integral. Also in this chapter, we show how the integral and derivative are related (this result is known as the *fundamental theorem of the Calculus*). The last chapter in Part Four deals with the elementary functions and their properties, including, of course, the property of differentiability.

CHAPTER 7

The Derivative

7.1 Introduction

Consider a function f which describes the speed of a moving vehicle at certain times, as illustrated in Fig. 7.1.1. We have time measured horizontally (this is the domain of f), and speed measured vertically. Suppose that when $t = 0$, f takes the value 42. The function (or, if we like, its graph) tells us pictorially that the speed increases at first, then drops, climbs to a peak after about six seconds, and then settles at about 45 feet per second. This is the visible data which we can immediately read off from the graph; but there is, in fact, a great deal of additional information concealed in the diagram below. For example, we know that if we travel for t seconds at a speed of v feet per second, then the *distance travelled* is vt feet; or, if we travel for t_1 seconds at v_1 feet per second, and then for t_2 seconds at v_2 feet per second, the distance travelled is $v_1 t_1 + v_2 t_2$ feet (see Figs 7.1.2 and 7.1.3).

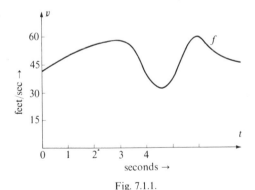

Fig. 7.1.1.

In each case, the distance travelled is, of course, the area "under the graph", taken between 0 and t, or between 0 and t_2. By applying this principle to Fig. 7.1.1, we might conclude that the area "under f" between 0 and t represented the total distance travelled in that time. This is the area OMPN in Fig. 7.1.4. So, the diagram yields information about total distance travelled with respect to time. This aspect will be dealt with in detail in the next chapter.

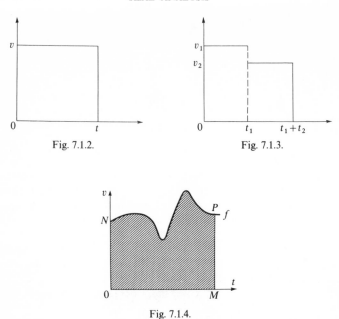

Fig. 7.1.2.   Fig. 7.1.3.

Fig. 7.1.4.

The diagram also tells us, if we look for it, not only about changes in speed, but also about the *rate* at which the speed changes. This is called "acceleration", and we use this word whether the speed is increasing or decreasing. We see that as speed increases, the graph rises (this is fairly obvious); but not only this: the more quickly the speed increases or decreases, the steeper the graph becomes. So, the rate of change in speed at time t might be measured by measuring the steepness of the graph at t.

But how do we measure the steepness of a graph? Let us try to proceed by simple stages. It is clear that the speed at t itself is no help at all—we need to know the speed at times near to t, in order to calculate whether the change is large or small, positive or negative. In the very simplest case, if the speed is constant, then the change from time to time is nil, and the rate of change will likewise be nil (Fig. 7.1.2).

Now consider what happens in the case where the speed is increasing constantly (Fig. 7.1.5). If the speed alters constantly, the graph will be a straight line, and the steepness of this line is clearly determined by the angle α marked on Fig. 7.1.5. But equally (corresponding angles), $PP_2K = P_1PK_1 = \alpha$. How is this related to speed and time? By a simple piece of trigonometry; we have

$$\frac{P_1K_1}{K_1P} = \frac{PK}{KP_2} = \tan \alpha$$

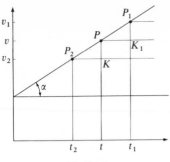

Fig. 7.1.5.

that is,

$$\frac{v_1 - v}{t_1 - t} = \frac{v - v_2}{t - t_2} = \tan \alpha. \tag{1}$$

So, the steepness of the speed curve at time t (which is the rate of change in speed at time t) can be measured in terms of the symbols v and t, using times t_1, t_2 near to t.

We now move on to the general situation, when the speed may be always changing. We have again got to measure the rate of change in speed "at" some time t. The reader will have realised, perhaps, that what we want is the tangent to the graph at t, or at least a measure of its steepness. Let us see how this comes about. As we do so, we will also see how to measure it in terms of v and t (which is, of course, the only specific data we have). If t_1 is a time near t, and v_1 is the speed at time t_1, then the ratio $(v_1 - v)/(t_1 - t)$, the change in speed divided by the change in time, is an approximate measure of the rate of change in speed "at" t. It is not an exact measure, because we do not know what is happening between the times t and t_1. The situation could be like that in Fig. 7.1.6 or it could be like that in Fig. 7.1.7. In each case, $(v_1 - v)/(t_1 - t)$ is the same, but the situations they come from are

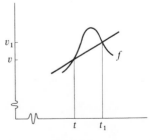

Fig. 7.1.6.

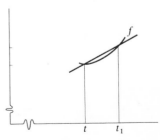

Fig. 7.1.7.

quite different. However, if we choose to take t_1 closer to t, this margin
of error will be reduced. Carrying this to its logical conclusion, we
see that we can eliminate the error if we use a limiting technique;
we look at the limit, as $t_1 \to t$, of the quotient $(v_1 - v)/(t_1 - t)$. Then,
we have a measure (which depends only on v and t, the data presented)
for the rate of change in speed. This is the idea which we will formalise
and investigate in the present chapter; if f is a function, we shall
introduce a new function, called the *derivative* of f, and denoted by
Df. The value of this function at a point x (i.e. $Df(x)$) will be the same
as the slope of the tangent to the graph of f at x (if this exists). Here,
slope has a technical meaning; the slope of a tangent $= \tan \alpha$, where
α is the angle between the tangent and the positive x-axis.

Before we proceed with this programme, let us again consider
briefly the example described in this section; we have suggested at
the beginning that the *area OMPN* in Fig. 7.1.4 represented the total
distance travelled up to time t. This idea of area, as we have said,
properly belongs to the next chapter, on *Integration*, and we are not
going to discuss it in detail here. But we could very well consider the
rate of change in total distance travelled. How do we measure rate
of change in distance? We may observe that the greater the distance
travelled in a given time, the greater the (average) speed during that
time. By taking shorter and shorter intervals of time from t, we see
that the rate of change in total distance, at time t, is given by the *speed*
at time t. It is no accident that speed is usually described as so many
"feet per second", or "miles per hour", which is of course just change
in distance divided by change in time (30 m.p.h. means that distance
travelled would change by 30 miles if time changed by one hour).
This is just another way of expressing a formula like $(d_1 - d)/(t_1 - t)$.
Moreover, this rate of change is what we are going to generalise as
the *derivative Df*. We can draw the graph of the function which
measures distance travelled up to time t. Suppose we call this function
F. Then, the rate of change in distance at time t, is represented by the
tangent to the graph of F at t i.e. by $DF(t)$ (see Fig. 7.1.8). But we have

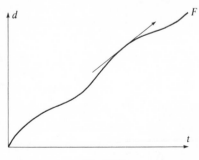

Fig. 7.1.8.

seen above that the rate of change in distance travelled is given by the speed; thus, "$DF(t)$" = $f(t)$, where f is given by Fig. 7.1.1. On the other hand, if area represents total distance travelled up to time t, and we denote this by $Af(t)$, then it plainly follows that $Af(t) = F(t)$. Putting all this together, we discover that "$DAf(t)$" = $f(t)$. The number $Af(t)$ or $F(t)$ is called the "integral of f from 0 to t"; we thus see that the integral and the derivative are essentially inverse processes. For, if we take a function f, and *integrate* it—so obtaining Af—and then find the *derivative* of this i.e. DAf, we discover that we are back where we started, with the function f again. The same thing is very nearly true in the reverse order—if we find the *derivative*, assuming there is one, and then integrate it, we get back to where we started, or at least to within a constant of f. These important results will be proved in Section 8.5. In the meantime, we begin our rigorous investigation of the concept of the derivative.

7.2 The Derivative of a Function

Let E be an open interval of R, f a mapping of E into R. Let $x_0 \in E$, and h be a small, nonzero real number such that $x_0 + h$ is also in E. The graph of f might look like the sort of thing we saw in Fig. 7.1.1.

Definition. With the notation just described, define a function of the nonzero real numbers into R by setting

$$\varphi(h) = \frac{f(x_0 + h) - f(x_0)}{h}.$$

Then, φ is called the **chord-function** of f at x_0. It is sometimes written Cf_{x_0}.

The terminology arises because $\varphi(h)$ measures the slope of the chord joining the points $(x_0, f(x_0))$ and $(x_0 + h, f(x_0 + h))$ on the graph of f (see Fig. 7.2.1).

Definition. Let f be a function of E into R, $x_0 \in E$, h a nonzero number. Let φ be defined as in the definition above. If $\lim_{h \to 0} \varphi(h)$ exists,

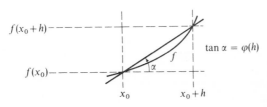

Fig. 7.2.1.

then we say that f is **differentiable** at x_0, and we write

$$Df(x_0) = \lim_{h \to 0} \varphi(h) = \lim_{h \to 0} \frac{f(x_0 + h) - f(x_0)}{h}.$$

Other notations include $f'(x_0)$ and $(d/dx)f(x_0)$. It is plain that $\lim_{h \to 0} \varphi(h)$ measures the slope of the tangent to the graph of f at x_0, or, the rate of change of f at x_0, as we guessed above.

Again, suppose that $E \subset R$, $f : E \to R$.

Definition. Denote by E_1 the subset of E consisting of all points x of E at which f is differentiable. We can define a new function of E_1 into R, whose image at the point x of E_1 is $Df(x)$. This new function is denoted by Df, and is called the **derivative** of f.

Strictly speaking, we should talk of Df as the *first* derivative of f. For, since $Df : E_1 \to R$, we can find a subset E_2 of E_1, at all points of which Df is differentiable. (Of course, E_2 could be empty.) According to the last definition, we can define a function $D(Df)$ of E_2 into R, the derivative of Df. This function is usually denoted by $D^2 f$, and is called the *second derivative* of f.

Definition. The **n-th derivative** of f, denoted by $D^n f$, is defined to be the derivative of $D^{n-1} f$, for $n = 2, 3, \ldots$.

What kind of function has a derivative, you may ask? Or, if f is differentiable at the point x_0, what can we say about the function f? The answer to the second question is contained in the following theorem; the same theorem provides a partial (if negative) answer to the first question.

Theorem 7.2–A. If f is differentiable at x_0, then it is continuous at x_0.

Proof. By definition,

$$Df(x_0) = \lim_{h \to 0} \frac{f(x_0 + h) - f(x_0)}{h}.$$

We wish to show that $\lim_{h \to 0} f(x_0 + h) = f(x_0)$. If $h \neq 0$, we may write

$$f(x_0 + h) - f(x_0) = h \frac{f(x_0 + h) - f(x_0)}{h}$$

$$\Rightarrow \lim_{h \to 0} f(x_0 + h) - f(x_0) = [\lim_{h \to 0} h] \cdot Df(x_0) \quad \text{(Theorem 6.6–B)}$$

$$\Rightarrow \lim_{h \to 0} f(x_0 + h) - f(x_0) = 0$$

$$\Leftrightarrow \lim_{h \to 0} f(x_0 + h) = f(x_0)$$

$$\Leftrightarrow f \text{ is continuous at } x_0. \qquad \blacklozenge$$

In this proof, the reader will notice that two of the steps are not reversible. For example, if $\lim_{x \to 0} f(x) = \lim_{x \to 0} g(x)$, then it does not follow that $f(x) = g(x)$ for $x \neq 0$. We cannot therefore expect a converse to the theorem. We show this by a counterexample.

Corollary. f continuous at $x_0 \not\Rightarrow f$ is differentiable at x_0.

Proof. Consider the function defined for all real numbers by

$$f(x) = |x|.$$

Then, f is continuous at 0; $\lim_{x \to 0} f(x) = 0 = f(0)$. Consider the chord-function of f at 0:

$$Cf_0(h) = \frac{|h|}{h} = \begin{cases} 1 & \text{if } h > 0 \\ -1 & \text{if } h < 0. \end{cases}$$

It follows that $\lim_{h \to 0} Cf_0(h)$ does not exist i.e. f is not differentiable at 0. ◆

The next theorem also reveals something of the behaviour of f.

Theorem 7.2–B. Suppose f is differentiable at x_0; if $Df(x_0) > 0$, then $f(x_0 + h) > f(x_0)$ if h is small and positive, while $f(x_0 + h) < f(x_0)$ if h is small and negative; if $Df(x_0) < 0$, then the inequalities are reversed.

Proof. Let $\varepsilon > 0$. If h is small, we have

$$\left| \frac{f(x_0 + h) - f(x_0)}{h} - Df(x_0) \right| < \varepsilon \tag{1}$$

$$\Rightarrow \begin{cases} h[Df(x_0) - \varepsilon] < f(x_0 + h) - f(x_0) < h[Df(x_0) + \varepsilon] & \text{if } h > 0 \\ h[Df(x_0) + \varepsilon] < f(x_0 + h) - f(x_0) < h[Df(x_0) - \varepsilon] & \text{if } h < 0. \end{cases} \tag{2}$$

Suppose $Df(x_0) > 0$; we can take $\varepsilon < Df(x_0)$, and the inequalities (2) will hold for suitably small values of h. Then,

$$Df(x_0) - \varepsilon > 0 \tag{3}$$

$$\Rightarrow h[Df(x_0) - \varepsilon] > 0 \quad \text{if } h > 0;$$

clearly also,

$$h[Df(x_0) - \varepsilon] < 0 \quad \text{if } h < 0.$$

Thus, if h is small and positive, we have

$$f(x_0 + h) - f(x_0) > h[Df(x_0) - \varepsilon] > 0$$

$$\Rightarrow f(x_0 + h) > f(x_0);$$

if h is small and negative, we have

$$f(x_0+h) - f(x_0) < h[Df(x_0)-\varepsilon] < 0$$

$$\Rightarrow f(x_0+h) < f(x_0), \qquad \text{as required.}$$

A similar argument applies if $Df(x_0) < 0$. ◆

In proving this result, we write down, in (1), part of the information given in the hypotheses; (2) processes this for use in this particular problem—we isolate the term $f(x_0+h) - f(x_0)$. In (3), we make use of the rest of the information given. Using a reverse argument, we see that the problem is solved for $h > 0$ if we can guarantee that $Df(x_0)-\varepsilon$ is positive; since $Df(x_0)$ is fixed, while ε is alterable, this is always possible.

7.3 The Algebra of Derivatives

Here, we look at algebraic relations between the derivatives of functions.

Theorem 7.3–A. Let E be an open interval in R, f and g two functions of E into R. Then, we have the following relations, whenever Df, Dg are defined:

(i) $D(f \pm g) = Df \pm Dg$

(ii) $D(fg) = f \cdot Dg + g \cdot Df$.

Let E_1 be the subset of E such that, on E_1, Df and Dg are defined, and g is never zero. Then, on E_1,

(iii) $D(f/g) = \dfrac{g \cdot Df - f \cdot Dg}{g^2}$.

The proof follows from the definition by using appropriate algebraic devices. For instance, in proving (ii), we use the relation

$$f(x_0+h)g(x_0+h) - f(x_0)g(x_0)$$

$$= [f(x_0+h) - f(x_0)]g(x_0+h) + [g(x_0+h)-g(x_0)]f(x_0).$$

Now divide by h, and take the limit at 0. By Theorem 7.2–A, $g(x_0+h) \to g(x_0)$, and the result follows by Theorem 6.6–B.

In (iii), we split the problem in two; we have

$$\frac{1}{g(x_0+h)} - \frac{1}{g(x_0)} = -\frac{g(x_0+h)-g(x_0)}{g(x_0)g(x_0+h)}$$

Now, if $g(x_0) \neq 0$, and $Dg(x_0)$ exists, then $g(x_0+h) \neq 0$ for all sufficiently small h [why?]. Divide by h, and take the limit at 0. Then, $g(x_0+h) \to g(x_0)$ in the denominator, and the rest of the right-hand side has limit $-Dg(x_0)$. So,

$$D\left(\frac{1}{g}\right)(x_0) = -\frac{Dg(x_0)}{\{g(x_0)\}^2}.$$

To obtain (iii), apply (ii) to the product $f \cdot (1/g)$. ◆

Corollary. By taking g to be a constant function, and using Exercise 7 at the end of this chapter, we obtain the special case

$$D(kf) = k \cdot Df, \text{ where } k \text{ is a real number.}$$

From this, and (i), we observe that D is a linear operator on the vector space of functions differentiable at x_0 (or, if applicable, differentiable at all points of E_1).

7.4 The Chain Rule

In Chapter 3, we discussed composite functions. We further investigated these in Chapter 6, asking about their continuity. It is therefore reasonable, since a composite function is a function, to ask if and when it has a derivative function. We would further expect this derivative, should it exist, to depend in a fairly explicit way on the functions which are composed. Our next theorem states under what conditions the composite function is differentiable, and shows how to evaluate the derivative, when it exists, in a simple way. This formula is often called the *chain rule*.

Theorem 7.4–A (The Chain Rule). Let f be continuous on a closed interval E of R. Suppose g is defined on $f(E)$, and let φ be the function of E into R given by $\varphi(x) = g \circ f(x) = g(f(x))$, for all x in E. Then, if
(a) x_0 is an interior point of E,
(b) $f(x_0)$ is an interior point of $f(E)$,
(c) f is differentiable at x_0,
(d) g is differentiable at $f(x_0)$,
φ is differentiable at x_0, and $D\varphi(x_0) = Dg(f(x_0)) \cdot Df(x_0)$; the derivative function $D\varphi$, where it exists, is given by

$$D\varphi = (Dg \circ f) \cdot Df.$$

Proof. We wish to evaluate

$$\lim_{k \to 0} \frac{\varphi(x_0 + k) - \varphi(x_0)}{k} = \lim_{k \to 0} \frac{g(f(x_0 + k)) - g(f(x_0))}{k}. \tag{1}$$

Now, f continuous at x_0

$$\Rightarrow f(x_0 + k) - f(x_0) \to 0 \quad \text{as} \quad k \to 0$$

$$\Rightarrow f(x_0 + k) - f(x_0) = h,$$

where $k \to 0 \Rightarrow h \to 0$. Thus, we can replace $f(x_0 + k)$ by $f(x_0) + h$. By (1),

$$C\varphi_{x_0}(k) = \frac{g(f(x_0) + h) - g(f(x_0))}{k}.$$

If $h \neq 0$ when $k \neq 0$, we can multiply top and bottom to obtain

$$C\varphi_{x_0}(k) = \frac{g(f(x_0)+h)-g(f(x_0))}{h} \cdot \frac{h}{k}.$$

Let us now take the limit of this as $k \to 0$; then, $h \to 0$, and so

$$\lim_{k \to 0} \frac{g(f(x_0)+h)-g(f(x_0))}{h} = \lim_{h \to 0} \frac{g(f(x_0)+h)-g(f(x_0))}{h}$$

$$= \lim_{h \to 0} Cg_{f(x_0)}(h)$$

$$= Dg(f(x_0)),$$

while

$$\lim_{k \to 0} \frac{h}{k} = \lim_{k \to 0} \frac{f(x_0+k) - f(x_0)}{k}$$

$$= Df(x_0),$$

and the result then follows as required.

There is, however, one problem. It may happen that, for $k \neq 0$, we have $h = f(x_0+k) - f(x_0) = 0$. In this case, the argument above is not valid. We can amend it, nevertheless, as follows: let us write $f(x_0) = y_0$, $f(x) = y$, for each x in E.

Since g is differentiable at y_0, we have

$$\lim_{h \to 0} Cg_{y_0}(h) = Dg(y_0) \Rightarrow \frac{g(y)-g(y_0)}{y-y_0} - Dg(y_0) = \mu(y) \qquad (2)$$

for all $y \neq y_0$. We thus define a function μ on all of $f(E)$, apart from y_0. Since $\lim_{y \to y_0} \mu(y) = 0$ [because $Dg(y_0)$ exists], we define μ at y_0 to make it continuous there: $\mu(y_0) = 0$. Then, by Theorem 6.7–D, $\mu \circ f$ is continuous at x_0, and

$$\lim_{x \to x_0} \mu(f(x)) = 0. \qquad (3)$$

By (2),

$$g(y)-g(y_0) = (y-y_0)Dg(y_0)+(y-y_0)\mu(y)$$

and this equation holds for $y = y_0$ also, so that

$$g(f(x))-g(f(x_0)) = [f(x) - f(x_0)]Dg(f(x_0))+[f(x) - f(x_0)]\mu(f(x)).$$

Divide by $x-x_0$ where $x \neq x_0$; here, $x-x_0$ corresponds to k above. Then,

$$\frac{g(f(x))-g(f(x_0))}{x-x_0} = \frac{f(x) - f(x_0)}{x-x_0}[Dg(f(x_0))+\mu(f(x))].$$

We now take the limit at x_0; the left-hand side has limit $D\varphi(x_0)$, while on the right-hand side, the first term has limit $Df(x_0)$ and $\lim_{x \to x_0} \mu(f(x)) = 0$ by (3), so that we obtain finally

$$D\varphi(x_0) = Df(x_0) \cdot Dg(f(x_0))$$

and the proof is complete.   ◆

7.5 Inverse Functions and their Derivatives

Let f be a function of E into R. Then, if f is (1, 1), we can define an inverse function $f^{-1}: f(E) \to R$. If f is continuous as well as (1, 1), then f is strictly monotonic, by Theorem 6.10–C. Moreover, f^{-1} is continuous and monotonic. Again, we may ask when f^{-1} is differentiable. The answer is given in the following theorem.

Theorem 7.5–A. Let $f: E \to R$ be continuous in the open interval $(x_0 - a, x_0 + a)$, and differentiable at x_0 with $Df(x_0) \neq 0$. Denote by g the inverse function of f, supposing that it exists. Then, g is differentiable at $f(x_0)$, and

$$Dg(f(x_0)) = \frac{1}{Df(x_0)}.$$

Proof. Suppose that k is a small nonzero number; let

$$\beta = g(f(x_0) + k) - g(f(x_0)) \tag{1}$$

k being so chosen that $f(x_0) + k$ is again in $f(E)$. Then,

$$g(f(x_0) + k) = \beta + g(f(x_0))$$
$$= \beta + x_0, \quad \text{since } g = f^{-1}$$
$$\Rightarrow f(x_0) + k = f(x_0 + \beta), \quad \text{since } f \circ g \text{ is the identity,}$$
$$\Rightarrow k = f(x_0 + \beta) - f(x_0).$$

Now, f is differentiable at x_0, so that, for small h,

$$f(x_0 + h) - f(x_0) = hDf(x_0) + h\mu(h)$$

where $\lim_{h \to 0} \mu(h) = 0$. Replacing h by β (also small), we have

$$k = \beta \cdot Df(x_0) + \beta \cdot \mu(\beta) \Rightarrow g(f(x_0) + k) - g(f(x_0)) = \frac{k}{Df(x_0) + \mu(\beta)} \tag{2}$$

where $\lim_{\beta \to 0} \mu(\beta) = 0$.

By (1), since g is continuous at $f(x_0)$, we have that $k \to 0 \;\Rightarrow\; \beta \to 0$. Dividing (2) by k, therefore,

$$\frac{g(f(x_0)+k)-g(f(x_0))}{k} = \frac{1}{Df(x_0)+\mu(\beta)}$$

and, upon taking the limit as $k \to 0$, we obtain the result.   ◆

Heuristic note. We mention the following "proof", which is valid enough under the conditions laid down above, but which rather conceals their necessity. Since $g \circ f$ is the identity, we have

$$g(f(x)) = x.$$

Using the chain rule,

$$D[g(f(x))] = 1 \quad \text{i.e. } Dg(f(x)) . Df(x) = 1$$

and so, if $Df(x) \neq 0$,

$$Dg(f(x)) = \frac{1}{Df(x)}.$$

7.6 Differentiable Functions and Rolle's Theorem

Let f be a function defined on a set E, taking values in R. If x_0 is in E, and $Df(x_0)$ exists, then we have said (Section 7.2) that f is *differentiable at* x_0.

Definition.   If f is differentiable at every point x of E, then f is said to be **differentiable on** E.

Consider a function defined on a closed interval $[a, b]$ in R, and continuous there. If the graph of this function f is smooth, then it is intuitively plausible (Fig. 7.6.1) that there is a point c between a and b at which the tangent to the graph is parallel to the chord joining the

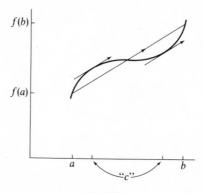

Fig. 7.6.1.

points $(a, f(a))$ and $(b, f(b))$. In Fig. 7.6.1 there are two possible choices for c. On the other hand, if f is not continuous, it is easy to construct examples for which this is not the case; it may also fail to happen if f is not "smooth". For instance, take $f(x) = |x|$, $a = -1$, $b = 1$. The chord here is parallel to the horizontal axis, but no point of the graph has a tangent with this property; at the most likely point, $(0, 0)$, the function has no derivative, and no tangent (Fig. 7.6.2).

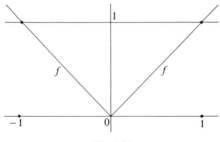

Fig. 7.6.2

Since, geometrically speaking, we are examining certain tangents, it follows that, in order to provide an adequate supply, we have to insist that the function be differentiable on (a, b). This is a "smoothness" condition, analytically speaking, but we have already seen the connection between the tangent at a point on a curve (a geometrical idea) and the derivative at that point (an analytic idea). We begin by looking at the special case of this result when we have $f(a) = f(b) = 0$. The chord is then the horizontal axis, and the conclusion will be that there is a point where the tangent is horizontal. This theorem was first proved by the French mathematician, Michel Rolle (1652–1719).

Theorem 7.6–A (Rolle).   Let f be continuous on $[a, b]$, differentiable on (a, b), and suppose that $f(a) = f(b) = 0$. Then, there is a point c, satisfying $a < c < b$, such that $Df(c) = 0$.

Proof.   If f is a constant function, then Df is the zero function (Exercise 7), and the theorem is established. c can be any point of (a, b). Suppose, then, that f is not constant. Then, f takes positive and/or negative values in (a, b). Consider the first possibility; by Theorem 6.8–B, f attains its maximum in (a, b) and this will be positive. Suppose it is attained at c; then, $a < c < b$, since $f(a) = f(b) = 0$. We now look at $Df(c)$; if it is nonzero, then it will be either positive or negative. Suppose that $Df(c) > 0$; then by Theorem 7.2–B, there are points x of (a, b) such that $f(x) > f(c)$, contradicting the maximality of $f(c)$. Similarly, if $Df(c) < 0$, Theorem 7.2–B again tells us that there are points x of (a, b) such that $f(x) > f(c)$. Hence, we must have $Df(c) = 0$.

It is intuitively clear from a geometrical picture that the maximum or minimum of f will be the point c in question. Hence, we turn all our attention on this point. The rest of the proof is a logical elimination of all possibilities other than the one we require. Note, too, that all the hypotheses are necessary. Continuity is necessary, but by itself is not sufficient. The function must also have a derivative. To see this, we construct examples of a function, not continuous, which has no tangent parallel to the chord joining $(a, f(a))$ to $(b, f(b))$ (see Fig. 7.6.3). This shows that continuity is required. Figure 7.6.2 shows, though, that this is not enough. We must have the additional property of differentiability.

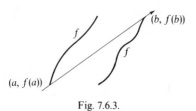

Fig. 7.6.3.

Example 7.6.1.   Let g be given by $g(x) = \pi \cos \pi x - 4(1 - 2x)$. Show that g has exactly one zero in the open interval $(0, \frac{1}{2})$.

Solution.   We have

$$g(0) = \pi - 4 < 0$$

$$g(\tfrac{1}{4}) = \frac{\pi}{\sqrt{2}} - 2 > 0$$

g is clearly continuous, so by Theorem 6.8–C g is zero between 0 and $\frac{1}{4}$, say at c. Also, by direct substitution, $g(\frac{1}{2}) = 0$, and hence, by Rolle's theorem, Dg is zero between c and $\frac{1}{2}$. If g were zero at a second point d in $(0, \frac{1}{2})$, say with $c < d$, then Dg would be zero twice—once between c and d, and once between d and $\frac{1}{2}$, by Rolle's theorem. But

$$Dg(x) = -\pi^2 \sin \pi x + 8,$$

so that $Dg(x) = 0$ if and only if $\sin \pi x = 8/\pi^2$. This has a solution in $(0, \frac{1}{2})$ since $8 < \pi^2$, and has exactly one solution since $\sin$ is increasing in $(0, \frac{1}{2}\pi)$. Hence Dg is zero precisely once, implying that g is zero precisely once in $(0, \frac{1}{2})$.   ◆

7.7 The Mean Value Theorem

We now proceed to the general situation described at the beginning of the last section.

Theorem 7.7–A (The Mean Value Theorem). Let f be continuous on $[a, b]$, differentiable on (a, b). Then, there is a point c such that $a < c < b$, for which

$$Df(c) = \frac{f(b) - f(a)}{b - a}. \tag{1}$$

The right-hand side of (1) represents the slope of the chord joining the points $(a, f(a))$, $(b, f(b))$, so the conclusion is that there is a point c between a and b where the tangent (given by $Df(c)$) is parallel to the chord, as we suggested originally.

In order to prove the result, we shall appeal to Theorem 7.6–A. However, at present, not all the conditions of Rolle's theorem are satisfied. We require a function whose values at a and b are zero, and whose maximum or minimum value occurs at the critical point c. Such a function would be that which measures the distance from $P(x, f(x))$ to the point on the line AB directly below P i.e. to the point on AB with abscissa x. For, since the graph of f passes through A and also through B, the distance PL (Fig. 7.7.1) would in these cases be zero,

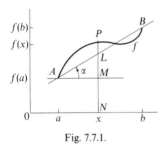

Fig. 7.7.1.

as we require. This new function depends intimately on f, and so would, we hope, have the same properties of continuity and differentiability. Its value at x, i.e. PL, is easily calculated from Fig. 7.7.1:

$$PN = f(x), \quad \text{so that} \quad PM = f(x) - f(a).$$

Now, $LM = (x - a) \tan \alpha$, where α is the slope angle of AB; that is,

$$LM = \frac{f(b) - f(a)}{b - a} (x - a)$$

whence

$$PL = PM - LM$$

$$= f(x) - f(a) - \frac{f(b) - f(a)}{b - a} (x - a).$$

This function is illustrated in Fig. 7.7.2 for the case when f is given by Fig. 7.7.1.

We are now ready to prove the Mean Value Theorem. We extrapolate from Fig. 7.7.1.

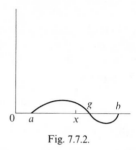

Fig. 7.7.2.

Proof. Define a function g by setting, for each x in $[a, b]$,

$$g(x) = f(x) - f(a) - \frac{f(b) - f(a)}{b-a}(x-a).$$

Then, g is continuous on $[a, b]$, by Theorem 6.7–C, and is differentiable on (a, b) by Theorem 7.3–A. Also, $g(a) = g(b) = 0$, by direct substitution. The conditions of Rolle's theorem are thus satisfied, and so there is a point c with $a < c < b$ such that $Dg(c) = 0$. But, Dg is given by

$$Dg(x) = Df(x) - \frac{f(b) - f(a)}{b-a} \cdot 1$$

so that

$$0 = Dg(c) = Df(c) - \frac{f(b) - f(a)}{b-a}$$

or

$$Df(c) = \frac{f(b) - f(a)}{b-a}. \qquad \blacklozenge$$

The Mean Value theorem has several important corollaries.

Corollary 1. If f is continuous on $[a, b]$, and Df is the zero function on (a, b), then f is a constant function. (Compare this with Exercise 7.)

Proof. Let x be any point of (a, b). By the Mean Value theorem,

$$f(x) - f(a) = (x-a)Df(c) \qquad (a < c < x)$$

$$= 0, \quad \text{since } Df \text{ is the zero function.}$$

Hence, $f(x) = f(a)$, for all x satisfying $a \leqslant x \leqslant b$, which is to say, f is a constant function on $[a, b]$. ◆

Corollary 2. If f, g are continuous on $[a, b]$, and $Df = Dg$ on (a, b), then f and g differ by a constant.

Proof. Apply Corollary 1 to the function $f - g$. ◆

Corollary 3. If f is continuous on $[a, b]$, and $Df(c) > 0$ for all c in (a, b), then f is increasing.

Proof. Let x_1, x_2 be points of $[a, b]$ with $x_1 < x_2$. We must show that $f(x_1) < f(x_2)$. By the Mean Value theorem, applied to $[x_1, x_2]$,

$$f(x_1) - f(x_2) = (x_1 - x_2)Df(c) \qquad x_1 < c < x_2,$$
$$< 0 \quad \text{since } x_1 < x_2, \text{and } Df(c) > 0$$

and so the result follows. ◆

Note. Compare this proof with that of Theorem 7.2–B.

7.8 Higher Derivatives

We have seen, in Section 7.2, how to define higher derivatives of a function f iteratively. In the present section, we examine some results on higher derivatives, notably the theorem of Taylor. First, however, we show how to evaluate the higher derivatives of a product. This result is ascribed to the German, Leibniz (1646–1716).

Theorem 7.8–A. Suppose f, g are functions which have derivatives of all orders up to and including the n-th. Then, the product fg has a derivative of order n, given by

$$D^n(fg) = f \cdot D^n g + n \cdot Df \cdot D^{n-1}g + \frac{1}{2!}n(n-1)D^2f \cdot D^{n-2}g + \ldots + g \cdot D^n f$$

$$= \sum_{j=0}^{j=n} \binom{n}{j} D^j f \cdot D^{n-j}g.$$

Proof. One method of proof is by induction, using the relation

$$\binom{n}{j} + \binom{n}{j+1} = \binom{n+1}{j}.$$

The reader should prove the result by this method (see Exercise 15).

A second proof is as follows: by immediate differentiation,

$$D(fg) = f \cdot Dg + g \cdot Df$$
$$D^2(fg) = f \cdot D^2g + 2Df \cdot Dg + g \cdot D^2f$$
$$D^3(fg) = f \cdot D^3g + 3Df \cdot D^2g + 3D^2f \cdot Dg + g \cdot D^3f,$$

and so, after proceeding in this way for n steps, we find that

$$D^n(fg) = \sum_{j=0}^{j=n} \beta_j D^j f \cdot D^{n-j} g,$$

where the numbers β_j are independent of the functions f and g. Since they are therefore the same for any two functions f, g, we can choose the latter so as to make the task of finding β_j as easy as possible. We choose f, g to be the functions given by

$$f(x) = e^{\alpha x}, \qquad g(x) = e^x$$

so that

$$fg(x) = e^{(1+\alpha)x}.$$

Now, on the one hand, by elementary calculus,

$$D^n(fg)(x) = (1+\alpha)^n \cdot e^{(1+\alpha)x}$$

while the right-hand side of the equation above becomes

$$\beta_0 e^{\alpha x} \cdot e^x + \beta_1 \alpha \cdot e^{\alpha x} \cdot e^x + \beta_2 \alpha^2 e^{\alpha x} \cdot e^x + \ldots + \beta_n \alpha^n e^{\alpha x} \cdot e^x.$$

Equating both sides, and multiplying by the nonzero number $e^{-(1+\alpha)x}$, we obtain

$$(1+\alpha)^n = \beta_0 + \beta_1 \alpha + \beta_2 \alpha^2 + \ldots + \beta_n \alpha^n.$$

This being true for all α, it follows that the right-hand side is the binomial expansion of $(1+\alpha)^n$, whence $\beta_j = \binom{n}{j}$.   ◆

Example 7.8.1. If $f(x) = \sin(m \arcsin x)$, show that
$$(1-x^2)D^{n+2}f(x) - (2n+1)x \cdot D^{n+1}f(x) + (m^2 - n^2)D^n f(x) = 0.$$

Solution. By immediate differentiation,

$$Df(x) = \cos(m \arcsin x) \cdot \frac{m}{(1-x^2)^{\frac{1}{2}}}$$

by Theorem 7.4–A, whence

$$(1-x^2)^{\frac{1}{2}} Df(x) = m \cos(m \arcsin x)$$

$$\Rightarrow (1-x^2)(Df(x))^2 = m^2 \cos^2(m \arcsin x)$$

$$\Rightarrow 2(1-x^2)Df(x) \cdot D^2 f(x) - 2x(Df(x))^2$$

$$= -\frac{2m^3 \cos(m \arcsin x) \cdot \sin(m \arcsin x)}{(1-x^2)^{\frac{1}{2}}}$$

$$\Rightarrow [(1-x^2)D^2 f(x) - xDf(x) + m^2 f(x)] \cdot Df(x) = 0$$

$$\Rightarrow (1-x^2)D^2 f(x) - xDf(x) + m^2 f(x) = 0, \tag{1}$$

since f is not constant; apply Leibniz's theorem, of order n, to each of the terms:

$D^n[(1 - x^2)D^2f(x)]$

$$= (1 - x^2)D^{n+2}f(x) - 2nxD^{n+1}f(x) - n(n-1)D^nf(x) + 0$$

$$D^n[-xDf(x)] = -xD^{n+1}f(x) - nD^nf(x) + 0$$

$$D^n[m^2 f(x)] = m^2D^nf(x).$$

Upon adding, the left-hand side is $D^n(0) = 0$. The right-hand side is as required. ◆

Our next task is to prove an important generalisation of the Mean Value theorem. This result is due to the English mathematician, Brook Taylor (1667–1752).

Theorem 7.8–B (Taylor). Let $f, Df, D^2f, \ldots, D^nf$ be defined in an interval surrounding the point a. If the point $a + h$ is also a point of this interval, then there is a point c between a and $a + h$ such that

$$f(a+h) = f(a) + hDf(a) + \ldots + \frac{h^{n-1}}{n-1!}D^{n-1}f(a) + \frac{h^n}{n!}D^nf(c). \qquad (2)$$

Proof. We first observe that Theorem 7.7–A is the special case of Taylor's theorem with $n = 1$. The method of proof follows that of the Mean value theorem in constructing a function which will satisfy the conditions of Rolle's theorem.

Define a function g by setting, for each point x,

$$g(x) = f(a+h) - f(x) - (a+h-x)Df(x) - \ldots - \frac{(a+h-x)^{n-1}}{n-1!}D^{n-1}f(x).$$

Then, g is continuous and differentiable, with

$$Dg(x) = -\frac{(a+h-x)^{n-1}}{n-1!}D^nf(x). \qquad (3)$$

Now, $g(a + h)$ is clearly zero. If we put $x = a$, we find that

$$g(a) = f(a+h) - f(a) - hDf(a) - \ldots - \frac{h^{n-1}}{n-1!}D^{n-1}f(a) \qquad (4)$$

which of course is *not* zero, in general. So g does not satisfy all the conditions of Rolle's theorem. However, we can adjust this by introducing another new function F, defined as follows:

$$F(x) = g(x) - \frac{(a+h-x)^n}{h^n}g(a).$$

It is clear that F is also continuous and differentiable. Moreover,

$$F(a+h) = F(a) = 0,$$

so that F satisfies the conditions of Rolle's theorem, and so, by that theorem, there is a point c between a and $a+h$ at which $DF(c)$ is zero. Now, we can calculate DF;

$$DF(x) = Dg(x) + \frac{n}{h^n}(a+h-x)^{n-1}g(a)$$

$$= (a+h-x)^{n-1}\left[-\frac{1}{(n-1)!}D^nf(x) + \frac{n}{h^n}g(a) \right].$$

Hence,

$$0 = DF(c) = (a+h-c)^{n-1}\left[-\frac{1}{n-1!}D^nf(c) + \frac{n}{h^n}g(a) \right].$$

Since c is *between* a and $a+h$, $a+h-c \neq 0$, and so

$$g(a) = \frac{h^n}{n!}D^nf(c)$$

and the result follows upon substituting for $g(a)$ in (4). ◆

The term $(h^n/n!)D^nf(c)$ is called **Lagrange's form** of the remainder, after the mathematician Lagrange (1736–1813). This term can be expressed differently, in ways known as Cauchy's form and Taylor's form of the remainder. See Exercise 34 at the end of this chapter, for more about these. There is also an integral form, which is derived in Theorem 8.7–C.

We shall denote the remainder term in Theorem 7.8–B by R_n.

Before proceeding further, it may be worthwhile to look a little more closely at the proof above. The reader may feel that it is vaguely unsatisfactory (from his viewpoint) that the function g should be, as it were, pulled from a hat, like a conjurer's rabbit. That g, or rather, the associated function F, does the trick, is undeniable. The reader may wonder, however, what led us to choose this particular function, and indeed, how we formulated the result in the first place, since it is not geometrically obvious. We will therefore digress to try to indicate the reasons.

Firstly, suppose that f is a polynomial function, given, say, by

$$f(x) = \alpha_0 + \alpha_1 x \ldots + \alpha_n x^n.$$

Then, if a, $a+h$ are in the domain of f, we can define a function g by setting

$$f(a+h) = c_0 + c_1 h + \ldots + c_n h^n \tag{5}$$

$$= g(h),$$

say, by substitution and the binomial theorem, where $c_0, \ldots, c_n$ are numbers independent of h, and depend only on f and a. So, if f is defined in an interval surrounding a, then we can regard the right-hand side of (5) as the function-value at h of the polynomial function g. Now, from (5),

$$g(0) = f(a) = c_0,$$

so that we have found the value of c_0. To find c_1, we differentiate; on the one hand,

$$Dg(0) = c_1$$

while, on the other, using the chain rule,

$$Dg(h) = Df(a+h) \Rightarrow c_1 = Dg(0) = Df(a).$$

Successive differentiation yields

$$c_k = \frac{1}{k!} D^k f(a) \qquad (k = 2, 3, \ldots, n)$$

and so, upon putting in these values for c_k in (5), we obtain (2) (Taylor's theorem) with a as the point c. We observe that, since f is a polynomial of degree n, $D^{n+1}f = D^{n+2}f = \ldots \equiv 0$. The question now arises whether an expansion of this kind is possible for non-polynomial functions which are suitably differentiable. If f is differentiable at least n times, and we assume that we can express $f(a+h)$ as a series of powers of h, namely,

$$f(a+h) = c_0 + c_1 h + \ldots + c_n h^n + c_{n+1} h^{n+1} + \ldots$$

then a procedure like that above gives

$$c_0 = f(a), \ldots, \qquad c_{n-1} = \frac{1}{n-1!} D^{n-1} f(a), \ldots$$

but now the "polynomial" does not automatically stop; we have the "remainder" $c_n h^n + \ldots$, which of course we can write as

$$h^n [c_n + c_{n+1} h + \ldots] \quad \text{i.e. } \mu h^n.$$

The problem now is to find a closed form for μ in terms of the function f. This explains at least part of the conclusion of the theorem; we feel that we can express a function as a polynomial, with the prescribed coefficients $(1/k!) D^k f(a)$, plus a remainder. To show how this remainder has the form $(h^n/n!) D^n f(c)$, we return to the Mean Value theorem, which, we recall, is the case $n = 1$ of Taylor's theorem. We want to show that

$$f(a+h) = f(a) + h \cdot Df(c_1).$$

Now, we can always write

$$f(a+h) = f(a) + h\mu_1 \Rightarrow -f(a+h) + f(a) + h\mu_1 = 0. \qquad (6)$$

There is nothing mysterious about this; we merely define μ_1 as the real number which satisfies (6). Consider the function F_1 given by

$$F_1(x) = -f(a+h) + f(x)+(a+h-x)\mu_1;$$

we choose F_1 so that $F_1(a)$ becomes the left-hand side of (6). Also, $F_1(a+h) = 0$, and, since F_1 is clearly continuous and differentiable, it satisfies the conditions of Rolle's theorem, implying that $DF_1(c_1) = 0$, for some c_1 between a and $a+h$. But

$$DF_1(x) = Df(x)-\mu_1 \Rightarrow 0 = DF_1(c_1) = Df(c_1)-\mu_1$$

$$\Rightarrow \mu_1 = Df(c_1), \quad \text{as required.}$$

Let us proceed to the next case. We write

$$f(a+h) = f(a)+h \cdot Df(a)+\mu_2 h^2$$

$$\Rightarrow -f(a+h) + f(a)+h \cdot Df(a)+\mu_2 h^2 = 0. \tag{7}$$

Again, we define a function F_2 so that $F_2(a)$ is the left-hand side of (7), and $F_2(a+h) = 0$. This we can accomplish by writing

$$F_2(x) = -f(a+h) + f(x)+(a+h-x)Df(x)+\mu_2(a+h-x)^2.$$

The device we use is as follows: in (7), retain $-f(a+h)$ as it is, since it is this that we are trying to calculate, but otherwise, replace "a" by "x", and "h" by "$a+h-x$".

F_2 satisfies the condition of Rolle's theorem, and so there is a point c_2 between a and $a+h$ such that $DF_2(c_2) = 0$. But,

$$DF_2(x) = Df(x)-Df(x)+(a+h-x)D^2f(x)-2\mu_2(a+h-x)$$

$$\Rightarrow 0 = DF_2(c_2) = (a+h-c_2)[D^2f(c_2)-2\mu_2]$$

$$\Rightarrow \mu_2 = \tfrac{1}{2}D^2f(c_2), \quad \text{since } a+h-c_2 \neq 0$$

which is precisely what we want for the case $n = 2$.

In general, then, if we assume a polynomial expression for $f(a+h)$, we have the "unknown" μ_n as the coefficient of the highest power h^n:

$$f(a+h) = f(a)+h \cdot Df(a)+\ldots+\frac{h^{n-1}}{n-1!}D^{n-1}f(a)+\mu_n h^n$$

$$\Rightarrow -f(a+h) + f(a)+h \cdot Df(a)+\ldots+\mu_n h^n = 0. \tag{8}$$

In the left-hand side of (8), retain $-f(a+h)$ but otherwise replace "a" by "x", and "h" by "$a+h-x$", so creating a function F_n whose value at a is automatically zero, by virtue of (8). We have

$$F_n(x) = -f(a+h) + f(x)+(a+h-x)Df(x)+\ldots+(a+h-x)^n\mu_n.$$

F_n is continuous, differentiable, and $F_n(a+h) = 0$. Hence, F_n satisfies the conditions of Rolle's theorem. There is therefore a point c_n between

a and $a+h$ (so that $a+h-c_n \neq 0$) such that $DF_n(c_n) = 0$. Now, we have

$$DF_n(x) = (a+h-x)^{n-1}\left[\frac{1}{n-1!}D^nf(c_n)-n\mu_n\right]$$

after cancellation, and so we obtain

$$\mu_n = \frac{1}{n!}\,D^nf(c_n)$$

as required.

So we have the general formula for Taylor's theorem as expressed in Theorem 7.8–B. The special case of this theorem when a is the point zero is called Maclaurin's Theorem, after the Scottish mathematician, Colin Maclaurin (1698–1746).

Theorem 7.8–C (Maclaurin). Suppose that $f, Df, \ldots, D^nf$ are defined and continuous in an interval surrounding 0. If h is a point of this interval, then there is a point c between 0 and h such that

$$f(h) = f(0)+h\,.\,Df(0)+\ldots+\frac{h^{n-1}}{n-1!}D^{n-1}f(0)+\frac{h^n}{n!}D^nf(c).$$

7.9 Applications of Taylor's Theorem

Definition. Suppose that f has derivatives of all orders; suppose that, as $n \to \infty$ in Theorem 7.8–B, $R_n \to 0$. (R_n, we recall, is the remainder term.) We obtain the expression

$$f(a+h) = \sum_{n=0}^{\infty} \frac{1}{n!}D^nf(a)\,.\,h^n$$

which is called the **Taylor Series** of f at the point a.

When $a = 0$, the Taylor series is called the **Maclaurin Series**.

In this section, we look at some applications of Taylor's theorem, through the medium of examples.

Example 7.9.1.   If f is given by

$$f(x) = x^6 + 14x^5 - 4x^3 + 21x^2 + x - 19,$$

express $f(x)$ in powers of $x-1$, and hence find the value of f at the point $1\cdot15$ correct to four places of decimals.

Solution. We note the derivatives of f:

$$Df(x) = 6x^5 + 70x^4 - 12x^2 + 42x + 1; \qquad Df(1) = 107$$
$$D^2f(x) = 30x^4 + 280x^3 - 24x + 42; \qquad D^2f(1) = 328$$
$$D^3f(x) = 120x^3 + 840x^2 - 24; \qquad D^3f(1) = 936$$
$$D^4f(x) = 360x^2 + 1680x; \qquad D^4f(1) = 2040$$

$$D^5f(x) = 720x + 1680; \qquad\qquad D^5f(1) = 2400$$

$$D^6f(x) = 720; \qquad\qquad\qquad D^6f(1) = 720$$

We also observe that $D^kf(x) = 0$ for $k = 7, 8, 9, \ldots$.
By Taylor's theorem,

$$f(1+h) = f(1) + h\,.\,Df(1) + \ldots + \frac{h^6}{6!}D^6f(1)$$

$$= 14 + 107h + 164h^2 + 156h^3 + 85h^4 + 20h^5 + h^6. \qquad (1)$$

If we now put $x = 1 + h$ (that is, $h = x - 1$), (1) expresses $f(x)$ in powers of $x - 1$, as required.

To find $f(1\cdot15)$, we must put $h = 0\cdot15$ in (1); then,

$$f(1\cdot15) = 14 + 16\cdot05 + 3\cdot69 + 0\cdot5625 + 0\cdot04303 + 0\cdot00152 + 0\cdot00001$$

$$= 34\cdot31106$$

$$= 34\cdot3111, \text{ to four decimal places.} \qquad\qquad \blacklozenge$$

Example 7.9.2. If f is given by

$$f(x) = x^3 - 3x + \frac{1}{x-4}$$

find a formula for computing f in the interval $[1, 1\cdot1]$, which will be accurate to seven decimal places. Find $f(1\cdot05)$ to this accuracy.
Solution. Write, for $1 \leqslant x \leqslant 1\cdot1$,

$$f(x) = f(1) + (x-1)Df(1) + \frac{1}{2!}(x-1)^2D^2f(1) + \ldots$$

The remainder term, after n terms, will be by Taylor's theorem,

$$R_n = \frac{1}{n!}(x-1)^nD^nf(c) \qquad 1 < c < 1\cdot1$$

so that

$$|R_n| = \frac{1}{n!}|x-1|^n|D^nf(c)| \leqslant \frac{1}{n!10^n}|D^nf(c)| \qquad (2)$$

since $1 \leqslant x \leqslant 1\cdot1$. We now calculate $D^nf(x)$;

$$Df(x) = 3x^2 - 3 - (x-4)^{-2}$$

$$D^2f(x) = 6x + 2!(x-4)^{-3}$$

$$D^3f(x) = 6 - 3!(x-4)^{-4}$$

$$D^4f(x) = 4!(x-4)^{-5}$$

and so,

$$D^n f(x) = (-1)^n . n!(x-4)^{-n-1} \quad \text{if } n \geqslant 4$$
$$\Rightarrow |D^n f(c)| < n! 2 \cdot 9^{-(n+1)} \quad \text{since } c > 1, \quad \text{if } n \geqslant 4$$
$$\Rightarrow |R_n| < 10^{-n} . 2 \cdot 9^{-(n+1)} \quad \text{by (2) above, if } n \geqslant 4.$$

We require R_n to be of the order of 10^{-8} (seven places of decimals means $0 \cdot 0000001 = 10^{-7}$). We will achieve this if

$$10^{-n} . 2 \cdot 9^{-(n+1)} < 10^{-8}$$
$$\Leftrightarrow 10^8 < 10^n . 2 \cdot 9^{n+1}.$$

Now, if $n = 6$, $3^{n+1} = 3^7$, which is approximately $2 . 10^3$, and then, $10^6 . 3^{6+1} > 2 . 10^9 > 10^8$. On the other hand, if we take $n = 5$, then 3^{5+1} is about $7 . 10^2$, which means $10^5 . 3^{5+1} < 8 . 10^7 < 10^8$. To be quite safe, therefore, we take six terms of the series. The required formula is

$$f(x) = f(1) + (x-1)Df(1) + \ldots + \frac{1}{5!}(x-1)^5 D^5 f(1).$$

By direct calculation,

$$f(1) = -2 \cdot 33333333 \qquad Df(1) = 0 \cdot 11111111$$

$$\frac{1}{2!} D^2 f(1) = 2 \cdot 962962963 \qquad \frac{1}{3!} D^3 f(1) = 0 \cdot 98765432$$

$$\frac{1}{4!} D^4 f(1) = -0 \cdot 004115226 \qquad \frac{1}{5!} D^5 f(1) = -0 \cdot 001371742.$$

From this, $f(1 \cdot 05)$ can be computed to seven decimal places; we find that $f(1 \cdot 05) = -2 \cdot 3313581$. ◆

Example 7.9.3. Examine the function $(1+x)^\alpha$ with a view to finding a Maclaurin series.

Write

$$f(x) = (1+x)^\alpha; \qquad \text{then,}$$
$$Df(x) = \alpha(1+x)^{\alpha-1}, \qquad D^2 f(x) = \alpha(\alpha-1)(1+x)^{\alpha-2}$$
$$D^k f(x) = \alpha(\alpha-1) \ldots (\alpha-k+1)(1+x)^{\alpha-k}.$$

So, by Taylor's theorem, we have

$$f(x) = 1 + \alpha x + \frac{1}{2!}\alpha(\alpha-1)x^2 + \ldots + \frac{\alpha(\alpha-1) \ldots (\alpha-k+2)}{k-1!}x^{k-1}$$

$$+ \frac{\alpha(\alpha-1) \ldots (\alpha-k+1)}{k!}(1+c)^{\alpha-k}x^k,$$

where $|c| < |x|$. Consider the series

$$\sum_{k=0}^{\infty} \frac{\alpha(\alpha-1)\dots(\alpha-k+1)}{k!} x^k = \sum_{k=0}^{\infty} u_k \qquad (3)$$

(i.e. the series obtained by continuing the series above without the remainder term). Now,

$$\left| \frac{u_{k+1}}{u_k} \right| = \left| \frac{\alpha-k}{k+1} \right| |x| \to |x|$$

so that the series (3) converges if $|x| < 1$. [**Note**. We cannot say at this stage that (3) converges to $(1+x)^{\alpha}$.] Hence, in particular,

$$\lim u_k = \lim \frac{\alpha(\alpha-1)\dots(\alpha-k+1)}{k!} x^k = 0$$

by Theorem 5.2–D, if $|x| < 1$. We now show that $\lim R_k = 0$, where

$$R_k = \frac{\alpha(\alpha-1)\dots(\alpha-k+1)}{k!}(1+c)^{\alpha-k}x^k.$$

Firstly, if $0 < x < 1$, we have $0 < c < 1$, so that $1 < 1+c$. Writing

$$R_k = \frac{\alpha(\alpha-1)\dots(\alpha-k+1)}{k!} x^k \left(\frac{1}{1+c} \right)^k (1+c)^{\alpha},$$

we have $(1+c)^{\alpha}$ constant, and $(1/1+c) < 1$, whence $\lim R_k = 0$, by the remark above. This leaves the range $-1 < x < 0$; here, the same technique is not sufficient. Instead, we use Cauchy's form of the remainder (see Exercise 34). Then, if $0 < \theta < 1$,

$$R_k = \binom{\alpha}{k-1} . x . (1+\theta x)^{\alpha-1} \left(\frac{1-\theta}{1+\theta x} \right)^{k-1} x^{k-1}.$$

Next,

$$|1+\theta x|^{\alpha-1} < \begin{cases} 1 \text{ if } \alpha \geqslant 1, \text{ since } 1+\theta x < 1 \\ (1+x)^{\alpha-1} \text{ if } \alpha < 1 \end{cases}$$

so we can say $|(1+\theta x)^{\alpha-1}| < M$; also

$$-1 < x < 0 \Rightarrow -\theta < \theta x < 0$$
$$\Rightarrow 1-\theta < 1+\theta x$$
$$\Rightarrow \frac{1-\theta}{1+\theta x} < 1;$$

therefore,

$$|R_k| < \alpha M|x| . \binom{\alpha}{k-1} |x|^{k-1} \to 0$$

since $|x| < 1$, by the same argument as before. So, for $-1 < x < 0$, $R_k \to 0$. Since the remainder term thus has limit zero, we have the following Maclaurin series for $(1+x)^z$, any α:

$$(1+x)^z = 1 + \alpha x + \frac{1}{2!}\alpha(\alpha-1)x^2 + \frac{1}{3!}\alpha(\alpha-1)(\alpha-2)x^3 + \dots$$

and this series converges, for $-1 < x < 1$, to $(1+x)^z$.   ◆

Remark. There is a very important result in Analysis, which is beyond the scope of this book. Therefore, we will merely state that the Taylor series is unique, i.e. if $\Sigma a_k x^k$ and $\Sigma b_k x^k$ are both Taylor series for the function f about 0, then, for all k, $a_k = b_k$.

Warning. The fact that a function has derivatives of all orders does not mean that it has a Taylor series, nor that $\lim R_k = 0$. The reader is invited to examine the function g given by

$$g(x) = \begin{cases} 0 & \text{if } x = 0 \\ e^{-(1/x^2)} & \text{if } x \neq 0. \end{cases}$$

It is easy to verify that $D^k g$ exists, for all k, and that $D^k g(0) = 0$. Hence the Maclaurin series is $0+0+0+\dots$ which converges to zero (not $e^{-(1/x^2)}$). Also, R_k can be shown to be $e^{-(1/x^2)}$, which does not have limit zero at ∞, unless $x = 0$.

7.10 Maxima and Minima

Consider a function f, continuous and differentiable, whose graph might be something like that of Fig. 7.10.1. There are occasions when it is necessary to find out the coordinates of the "peaks" A, C, E and "depressions" B, D, F, or indeed, to know whether such exist. Presumably, one could plot the graph of the given function f, and calculate the coordinates of the appropriate points (if any exist) empirically. But this is clearly a time-consuming and inaccurate process, and is therefore

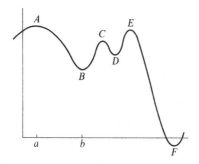

Fig. 7.10.1.

unsatisfactory. Let us see, then, if we can not devise a more powerful method. To do this, let us analyse what happens at a point like A or B. We see that the graph rises to A and then falls away; conversely, it descends to B and then climbs away from the value there. Similar occurrences happen at C, D, E, and F, provided that we concentrate our attention on the immediate vicinity of these points. In other words, if A has first coordinate a, the graph tells us that $f(a+h) \leqslant f(a)$, for all small enough h (positive and negative). Likewise, if B has first coordinate b, we can say that $f(b+h) \geqslant f(b)$ for all small enough h, positive and negative. Analogous statements hold for the points C, D, E, and F. This allows us to formulate a definition.

Definition.   A point a is called a **maximum** of f if f is defined in an interval surrounding a, and, for all sufficiently small values of h, $f(a+h) \leqslant f(a)$. The real number $f(a)$ is called a **maximum value** of f.
   Slightly stronger is the following.

Definition.   A point a is called a **proper maximum** of f if f is defined in an interval surrounding a, and for all values of h sufficiently small, and *nonzero*, $f(a+h) < f(a)$. The number $f(a)$ is then called a **proper maximum value** of f.
   The distinction between the two definitions is illustrated in Fig. 7.10.2. By analogy, we can formulate definitions of **minimum, minimum value, proper minimum**, and **proper minimum value**. It merely requires reversal of the inequalities above. We leave the reader to write them out in full. In Fig. 7.10.2, a_1 is a maximum of f, since $f(a_1+h) \leqslant f(a_1)$, but it is not a proper maximum, since (for example) $f(a_2) = f(a_1)$. But a_3 is a proper maximum, since for all small nonzero h, $f(a_3+h) < f(a_3)$.
   The reader may have noticed that in the definitions above, the conditions that f be continuous and differentiable, mentioned at the beginning of this section, have been omitted. It is easy to see that they would be superfluous. For instance, to see that the definitions hold even if the function f is not differentiable at some points, take f to be

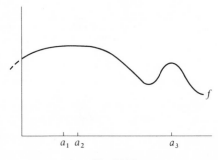

Fig. 7.10.2.

the function $f(x) = |x|$. Then, it is simple to verify that 0 is a proper minimum. The reader can no doubt construct examples where continuity is not required.

The statements embodied in the definitions are sufficient to establish whether a given point a is a maximum or minimum; but they still do nothing to help us find a simple way of sifting out such points, and it is clearly absurd to test each point in turn. We again fall back on intuition, and look at the graph in Fig. 7.10.1. It does not represent *all* possibilities, since f is assumed continuous and differentiable, but it does represent some. We notice that at the points A, B, C, D, E, F, the tangents are horizontal, or, to put it analytically, if x is near a and $x < a$, then $Df(x) > 0$ (the function is increasing), but when $x > a$, $Df(x) < 0$, since the function is decreasing [look back to Theorem 7.2–B]. So, if the derivative is continuous, which happens to be the case with our particular graph, we should have $Df(a) = 0$. Geometrically, this is to say the tangent is horizontal at a. We now put all this formally, without recourse to visual graphs.

Theorem 7.10–A.   Suppose that f has a maximum or minimum at the point a, and that Df is defined at a. Then, $Df(a) = 0$.

Proof (by contradiction).   Suppose a is a maximum. If $Df(a) \neq 0$, it is either positive or negative; if $Df(a) > 0$, then $f(a+h) > f(a)$ for small positive values of h, by Theorem 7.2–B, contradicting the hypothesis that a is a maximum. If $Df(a) < 0$, then we have $f(a+h) > f(a)$ for small negative h, also by Theorem 7.2–B, and again a contradiction. Hence, $Df(a) = 0$. A similar argument applies if a is a minimum.   ◆

Theorem 7.10–A provides a clue to finding maxima and minima. It, however, does not distinguish them. To do this, we again observe from our graphical example Fig. 7.10.1 that on the left of the maxima A, C, E, Df is positive, while on the right, Df is negative. At the minima B, D, F, Df is negative on the left and positive on the right. Therefore, we can formulate the following theorem to distinguish between maxima and minima.

Theorem 7.10–B.   Suppose that f has a derivative throughout an interval containing a, and that $Df(a) = 0$. Then,
  (i) a is a *maximum* if $Df(x) \geqslant 0$ for $x < a$, and $Df(x) \leqslant 0$ for $x > a$, x being close to a in each case;
  (ii) a is a *minimum* if $Df(x) \leqslant 0$ for $x < a$, and $Df(x) \geqslant 0$ for $x > a$, where x is close to a.

Proof.   (i) Suppose $a+h$ is a point of the interval in which Df is defined. Then, by the Mean Value theorem,

$$f(a+h) - f(a) = h \cdot Df(c),$$

where c is between a and $a+h$. Hence,

$$h < 0 \;\Rightarrow\; Df(c) \geqslant 0 \text{ (by the hypothesis of the theorem)}$$
$$\Rightarrow\; h \cdot Df(c) = f(a+h) - f(a) \leqslant 0$$
$$\Rightarrow\; f(a+h) \leqslant f(a).$$

On the other hand,

$$h > 0 \;\Rightarrow\; Df(c) \leqslant 0$$
$$\Rightarrow\; h \cdot Df(c) = f(a+h) - f(a) \leqslant 0$$
$$\Rightarrow\; f(a+h) \leqslant f(a).$$

So, for all h, positive and negative, $f(a+h) \leqslant f(a)$, i.e. a is a maximum, by definition. (ii) is similar.

Corollary. If, in Theorem 7.10–B, the inequalities are replaced by strict inequalities, "maximum" can be replaced by "proper maximum", and "minimum" by "proper minimum".

Theorem 7.10–A shows that if Df exists at a, then the condition $Df(a) = 0$ is *necessary* for a maximum or minimum. It is clearly not *sufficient* for one or the other, since it fails to distinguish them; but it is not even sufficient for *either* to occur. To see this, we look at Theorem 7.10–B, which gives sufficient conditions for each; one possibility not covered by this theorem is the situation where $Df(a) = 0$, and $Df(x) > 0$ for both $x < a$ and $x > a$. Another is the situation $Df(a) = 0$, $Df(x) < 0$ for $x < a$ and $x > a$. The former is illustrated in Fig. 7.10.3, which is the graph of the cubing function. Here, at 0, $Df(0) = 0$, but 0 is neither a maximum nor a minimum. This counter-example shows that $Df(a) = 0$ is not by itself sufficient to give a maximum or minimum.

Yet another possibility is that Df be undefined at a. We have already mentioned the example $f(x) = |x|$, which has a proper minimum at 0, but $Df(0)$ is not defined. A final possibility is that a maximum or

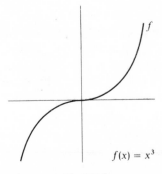

$$f(x) = x^3$$

Fig. 7.10.3.

minimum may occur at the boundary of the domain of f. For instance, suppose f is given by $f(x) = +\sqrt{(1-x^2)}$, for $-1 \leqslant x \leqslant 1$. Then, f has a maximum at 0, and minima at 1 and -1, the boundary of the domain of f (Fig. 7.10.4).

At this point, we shall collect all the information we have, and tabulate it. Before doing so, we shall require one further definition.

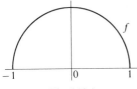

Fig. 7.10.4.

Definition. A point a such that $Df(a) = 0$ is called a **stationary point** of f.

It is so called, because at such a point, the graph is neither rising nor falling—it is "stationary". In order to find the maxima and minima, we must therefore

(1) find the stationary points of f;

(2) find the points at which Df is not defined;

(3) find the boundary points (if any) of the domain of f;

(4) check the stationary points using Theorem 7.10–B;

(5) check all other possible points using the original definition.

Definition. A stationary point of f which is not a maximum or a minimum is called a **point of inflection** (sometimes spelt "inflexion"). At such a point, the tangent crosses the graph. That is to say, on one side of a point of inflection, the tangent is above the graph, while on the other side, the tangent is below the graph.

Verification of the statements is left to the reader.

7.11 A Further Test for Maxima and Minima

In establishing the test for maxima and minima described in Theorem 7.10–B, we made use of the Mean Value theorem. Since Taylor's theorem is a more general result than the Mean Value theorem, we may expect to obtain a result based on it. The theorem we obtain is as follows.

Theorem 7.11–A. Suppose that $f, Df, \ldots, D^n f$ are defined and continuous in an interval surrounding a. Suppose also that

$$Df(a) = \ldots = D^{n-1}f(a) = 0, \quad \text{but } D^n f(a) \neq 0.$$

Then,

  (i) if n is odd, f has neither a maximum nor a minimum at a, (f has a point of inflection at a);

  (ii) if n is even, and $D^n f(a) > 0$, f has a proper *minimum* at a;
   if n is even, and $D^n f(a) < 0$, f has a proper *maximum* at a.

Proof. Let $a+h$ be a point of the interval surrounding a. Then, by Taylor's theorem,

$$f(a+h) = f(a)+\frac{h^n}{n!}\,D^n f(c),$$

where c is between a and $a+h$, using the fact that all derivatives up to and including the $(n-1)$-th vanish at a. Next, $D^n f$ continuous at a and nonzero implies that $D^n f(x)$ has the same sign as $D^n f(a)$ if x is sufficiently close to a, by Theorem 6.7–B. Now, we distinguish the cases:

  (i) suppose n is odd; then, if $D^n f(a) > 0$, we have

$$h < 0 \;\Rightarrow\; h^n < 0 \;\Rightarrow\; \frac{h^n}{n!}D^n f(c) < 0 \;\Rightarrow\; f(a+h) < f(a),$$

$$h > 0 \;\Rightarrow\; h^n > 0 \;\Rightarrow\; \frac{h^n}{n!}D^n f(c) > 0 \;\Rightarrow\; f(a+h) > f(a),$$

so that a is neither a maximum nor a minimum, and clearly, the same holds if $D^n f(a) < 0$.

  (ii) Now suppose n is even, and $D^n f(a) > 0$; then,

$$\left.\begin{array}{l} h < 0 \\ h > 0 \end{array}\right\} \;\Rightarrow\; h^n > 0 \;\Rightarrow\; \frac{h^n}{n!}D^n f(c) > 0 \;\Rightarrow\; f(a+h) > f(a),$$

which means that a is a proper minimum.
On the other hand, if n is even, and $D^n f(a) < 0$,

$$\left.\begin{array}{l} h < 0 \\ h > 0 \end{array}\right\} \;\Rightarrow\; h^n > 0 \;\Rightarrow\; \frac{h^n}{n!}D^n f(c) < 0 \;\Rightarrow\; f(a+h) < f(a)$$

so that a is a proper maximum, and the theorem is therefore established.   ◆

Example 7.11.1.   Find the maxima and minima of the function f given by

$$f(x) = x^3 - 7x^2 + 8x - 2, \quad \text{for all } x.$$

Solution.   There are no boundary points of the domain of f, and Df is defined at all points of R, since f is a polynomial. Hence, any maxima or minima will lie among the stationary points of f. To find these, we solve the equation $Df(x) = 0$: i.e.

$$3x^2 - 14x + 8 = 0$$

$$\Leftrightarrow x = \tfrac{2}{3} \quad \text{or} \quad x = 4.$$

We now use Theorem 7.11–A. $D^2f(x) = 6x - 14$, so that

$$D^2f(\tfrac{2}{3}) = -10$$

$$D^2f(4) = +10.$$

Thus, by Theorem 7.11–A, with $n = 2$, we conclude that $\tfrac{2}{3}$ is a maximum, and 4 is a minimum. The maximum and minimum values of f are respectively $\tfrac{14}{27}$ and -16.   ◆

7.12 Cauchy's Extension of The Mean Value Theorem

In this section, we shall look at a generalisation of the Mean Value theorem. We recall that the Mean Value theorem states that, with certain provisos,

$$f(a+h) - f(a) = h \cdot Df(c) \tag{1}$$

where c is between a and $a+h$.

If, then, we have two functions f, g, continuous and differentiable, we might apply the Mean Value theorem to both, obtaining (1), and also, for some point d between a and $a+h$,

$$g(a+h) - g(a) = h \cdot Dg(d) \tag{2}$$

whence, by (1) and (2),

$$\frac{f(a+h) - f(a)}{g(a+h) - g(a)} = \frac{Df(c)}{Dg(d)}.$$

The method just employed suggests that, in general, the points c and d will be distinct, for the functions f, g are randomly chosen. Cauchy's contribution here was to discover that there is a point μ between a and $a+h$ such that the quotient

$$\frac{f(a+h) - f(a)}{g(a+h) - g(a)}$$

is equal to the quotient of Df and Dg, *both evaluated at one and the same point μ.*

The Mean Value theorem is, of course, a special case of this result. To see this, take g to be the identity function $g(x) = x$. Then, the Mean Value theorem is given by (1); on the other hand,

$$g(a+h) - g(a) = (a+h) - a$$

$$= h,$$

and we have $Dg(x) = 1$ for all x. Hence,

$$\frac{f(a+h) - f(a)}{h} = \frac{f(a+h) - f(a)}{g(a+h) - g(a)}$$

$$= \frac{Df(c)}{Dg(c)}$$

$$= Df(c) \quad [\text{since } Dg(c) = 1]$$

which is the Mean Value theorem. We therefore prove

Theorem 7.12–A (Cauchy's or Extended Mean Value theorem). Suppose that f and g are continuous and differentiable in an interval surrounding the point a, and let $a+h$ be a point of this interval. If

(i) $g(a) \neq g(a+h)$,

(ii) Df and Dg do not vanish at the same point x, then there is a point μ between a and $a+h$ such that

$$\frac{f(a+h) - f(a)}{g(a+h) - g(a)} = \frac{Df(\mu)}{Dg(\mu)}.$$

Proof. Let us write

$$\frac{f(a+h) - f(a)}{g(a+h) - g(a)} = k;$$

condition (i) implies that k is neither infinite nor indeterminate. Then,

$$- f(a+h) + f(a) + k[g(a+h) - g(a)] = 0. \tag{3}$$

We follow a procedure like that described on pages 227 and 228. If we put

$$F(x) = - f(a+h) + f(x) + k[g(a+h) - g(x)],$$

then $F(a+h) = 0$ automatically, and $F(a) = 0$ in consequence of (3). Since F is evidently continuous and differentiable, we can use Rolle's theorem; there is a point μ between a and $a+h$ such that

$$DF(\mu) = 0.$$

But,

$$DF(x) = Df(x) - k \cdot Dg(x)$$

$$\Rightarrow \quad 0 = Df(\mu) - k \cdot Dg(\mu).$$

Now, if $Dg(\mu) = 0$, this would imply that $Df(\mu)$ is also zero, in contradiction of condition (ii). Thus, $Dg(\mu) \neq 0$, and so, dividing by it,

$$k = \frac{Df(\mu)}{Dg(\mu)}. \qquad \blacklozenge$$

Cauchy's Mean Value theorem is sometimes expressed in a determinantal form. Let φ be given by

$$\varphi(x) = \begin{vmatrix} f(x) & f(a) & f(b) \\ g(x) & g(a) & g(b) \\ 1 & 1 & 1 \end{vmatrix}$$

φ is continuous and differentiable; further, $\varphi(a) = 0$, for the first two columns of the determinant are then equal, and similarly, $\varphi(b) = 0$. Hence, by Rolle's theorem, $D\varphi(c) = 0$ for some c in (a, b). But,

$$D\varphi(c) = \begin{vmatrix} Df(c) & f(a) & f(b) \\ Dg(c) & g(a) & g(b) \\ 0 & 1 & 1 \end{vmatrix}$$

and this, when expanded, gives the result of Theorem 7.12–A (with $b = a+h$ and $c = \mu$). This form also opens up possibilities for generalisation, by replacing the last row of the determinant above with a function h, say, defined on $[a, b]$.

7.13 L'Hôpital's Rule (an application of Cauchy's mean value theorem)

A powerful application of Theorem 7.12–A occurs in the calculation of certain limits and quotients. For example, it is known that the limit at 0 of $(\sin x)/x$ is $+1$. If, however, we try to substitute $x = 0$ in the quotient, we obtain $(\sin 0)/0 = 0/0$, and this is indeterminate. The general problem is to evaluate such expressions as

$$\lim_{x \to a} \frac{f(x)}{g(x)}. \tag{1}$$

The problem is, of course, easy if $\lim_{x \to a} f(x)$, $\lim_{x \to a} g(x)$ both exist and $\lim_{x \to a} g(x) \neq 0$, for then we can use Theorem 6.6–E. If $\lim_{x \to a} f(x) \neq 0$, and $\lim_{x \to a} g(x) = 0$, then (1) does not exist, except as ∞ or $-\infty$; but if $\lim_{x \to a} f(x) = \lim_{x \to a} g(x) = 0$, application of Theorem 6.6–E gives an indeterminate, and this case merits further investigation.

Suppose, for instance, that f, g are continuous and differentiable in an interval surrounding a, with $f(a) = g(a) = 0$. We might use Taylor's theorem on f and g: set

$$\varphi(h) = f(a+h) = 0+h \,.\, Df(a)+\tfrac{1}{2}h^2 \,.\, D^2f(a)+\ldots$$
$$\psi(h) = g(a+h) = 0+h \,.\, Dg(a)+\tfrac{1}{2}h^2 D^2g(a)+\ldots$$

so that

$$\lim_{x \to a} \frac{f(x)}{g(x)} = \lim_{h \to 0} \frac{\varphi(h)}{\psi(h)};$$

then, for $h \neq 0$,

$$\frac{\varphi(h)}{\psi(h)} = \frac{Df(a) + \frac{1}{2}h \cdot D^2 f(a) + \ldots + (h^{n-1}/n!)D^n f(c)}{Dg(a) + \frac{1}{2}h \cdot D^2 g(a) + \ldots + (h^{n-1}/n!)D^n g(d)}$$

$$\Rightarrow \lim_{x \to a} \frac{f(x)}{g(x)} = \lim_{h \to 0} \frac{\varphi(h)}{\psi(h)} = \frac{Df(a)}{Dg(a)} \quad \text{by Theorem 6.6–E.}$$

The required limit would appear to have the value $Df(a)/Dg(a)$. If we test this out on $(\sin x)/x$, we find that the derivatives of the top and bottom lines are $\cos x$ and 1 respectively, so that

$$\lim_{x \to 0} \frac{\sin x}{x} = \lim_{x \to 0} \frac{\cos x}{1} = 1 \,;$$

this agrees with the known result, so we feel hopeful about the technique. Of course, we have made a lot of assumptions about the functions f and g. We now try to formulate a theorem which will provide a rigorous, watertight justification for the procedure of taking the quotient of the derivatives. We shall see that the satisfaction of the conditions of Theorem 7.12–A is sufficient to achieve this objective. The original result has been ascribed to the French mathematician, the Marquis de L'Hôpital (1661–1704). [Note that Cauchy was not born until 1789.]

Theorem 7.13–A (L'Hôpital's Rule). Suppose that f, g are functions differentiable in an interval surrounding the point a, and such that $f(a) = g(a) = 0$. Suppose also that Df, Dg do not vanish at the same point, and that

$$\lim_{x \to a} \frac{Df(x)}{Dg(x)} = \mu$$

where μ is supposed finite. Then, $\lim\limits_{x \to a} [f(x)/g(x)] = \mu$, also.

Proof. Since $\lim\limits_{x \to a} [Df(x)/Dg(x)] = \mu$, given $\varepsilon > 0$, there is a $\delta > 0$ such that, for all x satisfying $0 < |x - a| < \delta$, we have

$$\left| \frac{Df(x)}{Dg(x)} - \mu \right| < \varepsilon. \tag{2}$$

Suppose now that $0 < |h| < \delta$; then,

$$\frac{f(a+h)}{g(a+h)} = \frac{f(a+h) - f(a)}{g(a+h) - g(a)}$$

$$= \frac{Df(c)}{Dg(c)}$$

by Theorem 7.12–A, where c is between a and $a+h$. Inequality (2) implies that $Dg(c) \neq 0$; using (2), we obtain

$$\left| \frac{f(a+h)}{g(a+h)} - \mu \right| < \varepsilon$$

for all $|h| < \delta$,

$$\Rightarrow \lim_{x \to a} \frac{f(x)}{g(x)} = \mu. \qquad \blacklozenge$$

Corollary. Suppose that f, g are functions differentiable in an interval surrounding a, and such that $\lim_{x \to a} f(x)$ and $\lim_{x \to a} g(x)$ are infinite. If, in addition, Df and Dg do not vanish at the same point, and

$$\lim_{x \to a} \frac{Df(x)}{Dg(x)} = \mu,$$

where μ is finite, then

$$\lim_{x \to a} \frac{f(x)}{g(x)} = \mu.$$

The proof is left as an exercise for the reader.

We now illustrate the use of L'Hôpital's rule.

Example 7.13.1.   Evaluate

$$\lim_{x \to 0} \frac{\sin x - x}{x - \tan x}.$$

Solution.   Let us write

$$f(x) = \sin x - x, \qquad g(x) = x - \tan x;$$

then $f(0) = g(0) = 0$. Conditions of differentiability are satisfied, so we apply Theorem 7.13–A. Now,

$$\frac{Df(x)}{Dg(x)} = \frac{\cos x - 1}{1 - \sec^2 x}$$

and here $Df(0) = Dg(0) = 0$. There are two courses open to us: on the one hand, we can cancel the factor $(\cos x - 1)$ in top and bottom, so obtaining

$$\frac{\cos^2 x}{\cos x + 1}$$

and this equals $\frac{1}{2}$ at 0, by substitution.

So, by this means, we conclude that the required limit is $\frac{1}{2}$.

The alternative method is to consider Df and Dg as a new pair of functions fulfilling the conditions of Theorem 7.13–A. Write $Df = F$, $Dg = G$. Then, $F(0) = G(0) = 0$, and F, G are differentiable; apply Theorem 7.13–A to F/G:

$$\frac{DF(x)}{DG(x)} = \frac{-\sin x}{-2\sec^2 x \tan x}.$$

Here, again, $DF(0) = DG(0) = 0$, i.e. $D^2f(0) = D^2g(0) = 0$. So, we apply Theorem 7.13–A yet again to the quotient of the functions D^2f and D^2g. Both these functions satisfy the conditions of the theorem. We have

$$\frac{D^3f(x)}{D^3g(x)} = \frac{-\cos x}{-2\sec^4 x - 4\sec^2 x \tan^2 x}.$$

Now,

$$\lim_{x \to 0} \frac{D^3f(x)}{D^3g(x)} = \frac{-1}{-2} = \frac{1}{2}$$

and so, we again conclude that the original limit is $\frac{1}{2}$. ◆

Example 7.13.2. Evaluate

$$\lim_{x \to 0} \frac{1 - \cos x}{x^3}.$$

Solution. Here, we let $f(x) = 1 - \cos x$, $g(x) = x^3$; then, $f(0) = g(0) = 0$, and f, g are differentiable everywhere. We have

$$\frac{Df(x)}{Dg(x)} = \frac{\sin x}{3x^2}$$

$$\Rightarrow \lim_{x \to 0} \frac{Df(x)}{Dg(x)} = \lim_{x \to 0} \frac{\sin x}{3x^2}$$

$$= \left(\lim_{x \to 0} \frac{\sin x}{x}\right)\left(\lim_{x \to 0} \frac{1}{3x}\right) \qquad \text{[Theorem 6.6–B]}$$

$$= 1\infty$$

$$= \infty.$$

Hence, we conclude that the required limit is also ∞. ◆

This example shows that L'Hôpital's rule can be used in conjunction with the results of Chapter 6, to simplify the work if necessary.

Exercises

1. Let f be given by

$$f(x) = \begin{cases} -\frac{1}{3}x^3 & x \leqslant 0 \\ \frac{5}{2}x^2 - 4x & x > 0. \end{cases}$$

Where is f differentiable?

2. Let f be given by

$$f(x) = \begin{cases} x^2 + \dfrac{1}{x} + 6 & x \leqslant -1 \\ 3 - 3x & -1 < x \leqslant 0 \\ \sqrt{[1 + 8(x-1)^2]} & x > 0. \end{cases}$$

Where is f differentiable?

3. If $f(0) = 0$, and $f(x) = x^2 \sin 1/x$, for nonzero x, show that f has a derivative for all values of x, and that $Df(0) = 0$. Prove that Df is not, however, continuous at 0.

4. The function f is defined by setting, for $x > 0$,

$$f(x) = (1+x)\arctan \sqrt{x} - \sqrt{x}.$$

Find $Df(x)$.

5. The function f is defined for $-\frac{1}{2}\pi < x < \frac{1}{2}\pi$ by setting

$$f(x) = (\tan x + \sec x)^m.$$

Show that $Df(x) = m \sec x \cdot f(x)$.

6. Let f be defined in $(-\frac{1}{2}\pi, \frac{1}{2}\pi)$ by

$$f(x) = x + \tan x.$$

Show that f has an inverse function g, and that

$$Dg(y) = \frac{1}{2 + (y - g(y))^2}.$$

7. Show, using the definition, that if f is a constant function, then Df exists and is the zero function.

8. Show that if p is a polynomial function on R, then Dp exists everywhere on R.

9. Verify Rolle's theorem when $f(x) = e^x \sin x$, $a = 0$, $b = \pi$.

10. Verify Rolle's theorem when $f(x) = (x-a)^m(b-x)^n$; m, n positive integers.

11. Find, if possible, in the examples below, a number c such that $Df(c) = [f(b) - f(a)/b - a]$. If no such c can be found, discuss

which of the conditions in Theorem 7.7–A are violated. Even if there is such a point c, are the conditions of Theorem 7.7–A always satisfied?

(a) $f(x) = x(x-2)(x-4)$, $a = 1$, $b = 3$.

(b) $f(x) = x^{-2}$, $a = -1$, $b = 1$.

(c) $f(x) = x^{\frac{1}{3}}$, $a = -1$, $b = 1$.

12. Prove Corollary 2 of Theorem 7.7–A.

13. If f is a real-valued function which is differentiable at each point of a closed interval $[a, b]$, and $Df(a) < k < Df(b)$, show that there is a point c in (a, b) such that $Df(c) = k$. [**Note.** Df is not assumed to be continuous in $[a, b]$.]

14. f is a real-valued function which is differentiable at each point of $(0, 2)$. Suppose $|Df(x)| \leqslant 1$, for $0 < x < 2$. For $n = 1, 2, 3, \ldots$ define $a_n = f(1/n)$. Show that the sequence $\{a_n\}$ converges.

15. Prove Leibniz's theorem by induction.

16. (a) If $f(x) = \cos(ax+b)$, where a, b are real, find $D^n f(x)$.

(b) If $f(x) = (ax+b)^{-1}$, find $D^n f(x)$.

17. If $f(x) = (1-x^2)^{-1}$, find $D^n f(x)$.

18. If $f(x) = x^3 \cos x$, find $D^n f(x)$.

19. If $f(x) = e^{-x^2}$, show that

$$D^2 f(x) + 2x\, Df(x) + 2f(x) = 0.$$

Deduce that, for $n = 2, 3, \ldots$

$$D^{n+1} f(x) + 2x\, D^n f(x) + 2n\, D^{n-1} f(x) = 0.$$

20. If $f(x) = \arctan x$, show that

$$(1+x^2)D^2 f(x) + 2x\, Df(x) = 0.$$

Deduce that

$$(1+x^2)D^{n+2} f(x) + 2(n+1)x \cdot D^{n+1} f(x) + n(n+1)D^n f(x) = 0.$$

21. Find and classify the stationary points of the function given by

$$f(x) = \frac{(x-1)^2}{(x+1)^3}.$$

22. Find and classify the stationary points of the function given by

$$f(x) = \frac{(x+1)^5 x^4}{9x+1}.$$

23. Find and classify the stationary points of the function given by

$$f(x) = x - \sin x - \tan \alpha \cdot (1 - \cos x),$$

where $0 < \alpha < \pi/2$.

24. Show that the derivative of the function F given by

$$F(x) = e^x(x^2 - 6x + 12) - (x^2 + 6x + 12)$$

is never negative for any value of x, and show that

$$\frac{e^x(x-2)+x+2}{x^2(e^x-1)} < \frac{1}{6}$$

for all nonzero x.

25. Show that $2^6 \cdot 7! > 10^5$. Hence, compute $\sqrt{e}$ to four places of decimals.

26. Let f be a function with continuous derivatives of the first and second order. Suppose $f(c) = 0$, and that there is a half-open interval $I = [a, c)$ in which Df takes only positive values, while D^2f takes only negative values. Let a_0 be any point of I, and define the sequence of points $a_1, a_2, a_3, \ldots$ recursively by the equation

$$a_{n+1} = a_n - \frac{f(a_n)}{Df(a_n)} \qquad n = 0, 1, 2, \ldots$$

Show that the points $\{a_i\}$ all lie in the interval I, and that they form an increasing sequence with limit c.

27. If
    (i) $f(0) = 0$,
    (ii) f is continuous on $[0, h]$,
    (iii) Df is increasing in $(0, h)$,
    show that the function f/j is increasing in $(0, h)$.

28. If
    (i) $f(0) = g(0) = 0$,
    (ii) f and g are continuous on $[0, h]$,
    (iii) Df/Dg is increasing in $(0, h)$,
    show that the function f/g is increasing on $(0, h)$.

29. Show that $x/\sin x$ is increasing on $(0, \frac{1}{2}\pi)$.

30. Show that $x^2/2(1-\cos x)$ is increasing in $(0, \frac{1}{2}\pi)$.

31. Show that, if $x > 0$,
    (i) $\sin x - x < 0$,
    (ii) $\cos x - 1 + \frac{1}{2}x^2 > 0$,
    (iii) $\sin x - x + \frac{1}{6}x^3 > 0$.

32. Show that

$$\frac{\sin x}{x} > 1 - \frac{x}{\pi}$$

if $0 < x < \pi/2$.

33. Show that, if f is given by

$$f(x) = \sin \pi x - 4x(1-x),$$

then $f(x) < 0$ in the interval $0 < x < \frac{1}{2}$. [Use Example 7.6.1.]

34. In Theorem 7.8–B, the function F would vanish at the point a with any positive power of $(a+h-x)/h$. Define G therefore by

setting

$$G(x) = g(x) - \frac{(a+h-x)^p}{h^p} g(a), \qquad p \text{ a positive integer.}$$

Show that

$$f(a+h) = f(a) + h \cdot Df(a) + \ldots$$

$$+ \frac{h^{n-1}}{n-1!} D^{n-1}f(a) + \frac{h^n(1-\theta)^{n-p}}{p(n-1)!} D^n f(a+\theta h)$$

where $0 < \theta < 1$.

Note that, in Taylor's theorem, the point c satisfies $a < c < a+h$, so we can write $c = a + \theta h$ with $0 < \theta < 1$.

The term $[h^n(1-\theta)^{n-p}/p \cdot (n-1)!] D^n f(a+\theta h)$ is called **Taylor's remainder**. By putting $p = n$, we obtain **Lagrange's remainder**, as in Theorem 7.8–B. If we put $p = 1$, we obtain **Cauchy's remainder**.

35. Prove the corollary to Theorem 7.13–A.

36. Evaluate

$$\lim_{x \to 0+} x \ln x.$$

37. Evaluate

$$\lim_{x \to 0} \left(\frac{1}{\sin x} - \frac{1}{x} \right).$$

38. Evaluate

$$\lim_{x \to 0} \frac{e^x - 1 - x}{x^2}.$$

39. Evaluate

$$\lim_{x \to 0} \frac{1 - \cos x - \frac{1}{2}x^2}{x^4}.$$

[**Remark.** By using the power series expansions for exp and cos in Chapter 9, you should obtain a verification of the limits in Exercises 38 and 39.]

CHAPTER 8

Integration

8.1 The Integral of a Continuous Function on a Closed Interval

We remarked in the preface to Part Four that integration arose as a tool for finding areas. Let us consider, then, the problem of finding the "area under the curve" where the curve is the graph of a continuous positive function f (Fig. 8.1.1).

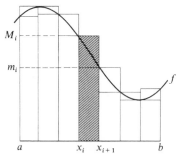

Fig. 8.1.1.

It is plain that if we divide $[a, b]$ into subintervals, and take the greatest value of f in each subinterval, we can form a set of rectangles whose total area contains the area under the curve f. Likewise, by taking the least value of f in each subinterval, we can form a set of rectangles whose total area is contained in the area under the curve f. By taking collections of subintervals of progressively smaller length, we can contain the area under f between estimates whose difference can be made as small as we please. So we obtain a number which represents the "area under f".

Our task is to formalise this idea and to extend it to functions which are not necessarily continuous and not necessarily positive. Let us begin by dispensing with the "positive" condition; for the moment, we retain the continuity as a guide to help us.

So, let f be a continuous function on $[a, b]$. We begin by defining the idea of a partition, also called a *division*.

Definition.   Let $P = \{x_0, x_1, \ldots, x_n\}$ be a set of points such that

$$a = x_0 < x_1 < \ldots < x_n = b.$$

Then, P is called a **partition** of $[a, b]$, into n subintervals.

Now, since f is continuous on $[a, b]$, it is bounded there, by Theorem 6.8–A. Write

$$m = \inf\{f(x) : a \leqslant x \leqslant b\}$$
$$M = \sup\{f(x) : a \leqslant x \leqslant b\}.$$

Then, $m \leqslant f(x) \leqslant M$. Also, f is bounded on each subinterval $[x_i, x_{i+1}]$, for $i = 0, 1, \ldots, n-1$. Let

$$m_i = \inf\{f(x) : x_i \leqslant x \leqslant x_{i+1}\}$$
$$M_i = \sup\{f(x) : x_i \leqslant x \leqslant x_{i+1}\}.$$

We now form the sums

$$U(f, P) = \sum_{i=0}^{n-1} M_i(x_{i+1} - x_i)$$
$$L(f, P) = \sum_{i=0}^{n-1} m_i(x_{i+1} - x_i).$$

Clearly, $L(f, P) \leqslant U(f, P)$, for any P.

Definition.   The sums $U(f, P)$ and $L(f, P)$ are called the **upper** and **lower sums** of f *corresponding to the partition* P, respectively.

The sum $U(f, P)$ evidently depends on the function f and the partition P; observe that each term in $U(f, P)$ corresponds to the area of the rectangle whose height is M_i and whose base is the interval $[x_i, x_{i+1}]$ (See Fig. 8.1.1).

Let $[x_j, x_{j+1}]$ be a subinterval of the partition P. If we insert another point of partition, say x' in this subinterval, then we may alter the upper and lower sums. If we write

$$M_{j1} = \sup\{f(x) : x_j \leqslant x \leqslant x'\}$$
$$M_{j2} = \sup\{f(x) : x' \leqslant x \leqslant x_{j+1}\},$$

then $U(f, P')$† contains the terms

$$M_{j1}(x' - x_j) + M_{j2}(x_{j+1} - x').$$

But, $M_{j1} \leqslant M_j$ and $M_{j2} \leqslant M_j$, clearly. Therefore,

$$M_{j1}(x' - x_j) + M_{j2}(x_{j+1} - x')$$
$$\leqslant M_j(x' - x_j) + M_j(x_{j+1} - x') = M_j(x_{j+1} - x_j).$$

†P' is the partition $\{x_0, x_1, \ldots, x_j, x', x_{j+1}, \ldots, x_n\}$.

Hence, it follows that

$$U(f, P') \leqslant U(f, P).$$

Thus, the insertion of an extra point of partition does not increase the upper sum. In Fig. 8.1.2 it *decreases* it by the amount of the shaded rectangle. In a similar way, the insertion of an extra point of partition does not decrease the lower sum. Indeed, the same is true if we insert k new points of partition, by repeating the argument.

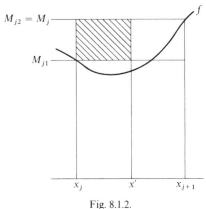

Fig. 8.1.2.

We next show how sums arising from different partitions compare.

Theorem 8.1–A.   Let P_1, P_2 be partitions of $[a, b]$. Then,

$$L(f, P_1) \leqslant U(f, P_2)$$
$$L(f, P_2) \leqslant U(f, P_1)$$

i.e. any lower sum does not exceed any upper sum.

Proof.   We use the idea just discussed in a clever way; let P_3 be the partition comprised of the points of both P_1 and P_2. We call P_3 a **refinement** of P_1 (and of P_2).

Since P_3 is obtained from P_1 by the insertion of points (from P_2), the preceding remarks show that

$$L(f, P_1) \leqslant L(f, P_3) \leqslant U(f, P_3) \leqslant U(f, P_1).$$

Likewise, we can regard P_3 as being obtained from P_2 by the insertion of points (this time, from P_1). So,

$$L(f, P_2) \leqslant L(f, P_3) \leqslant U(f, P_3) \leqslant U(f, P_2).$$

Combining these, we obtain

$$L(f, P_1) \leqslant U(f, P_3) \leqslant U(f, P_2)$$
$$L(f, P_2) \leqslant L(f, P_3) \leqslant U(f, P_1),$$

as required.   ◆

Our next result puts bounds on the size of the upper and lower sums.

Theorem 8.1–B.   Let P be a partition of $[a, b]$. Then,

$$m(b-a) \leqslant L(f, P) \leqslant U(f, P) \leqslant M(b-a).$$

Proof.   We have, for $i = 0, 1, \ldots, n-1$, $M_i \leqslant M$. Hence,

$$U(f, P) = \sum_{i=0}^{n-1} M_i(x_{i+1} - x_i)$$
$$\leqslant M \sum_{i=0}^{n-1} (x_{i+1} - x_i)$$
$$= M(b-a),$$

since $x_0 = a$, $x_n = b$. Similarly, since $m \leqslant m_i$,

$$L(f, P) \geqslant m(b-a),$$

and the theorem follows.   ◆

This result shows that the upper sums $\{U(f, P)\}$ are bounded below, by the constant $m(b-a)$. Hence, they have a greatest lower bound.

Definition.   Write $U \int_a^b f = \inf\{U(f, P)$, over all partitions $P\}$. Then, $U \int_a^b f$ is called the **upper integral** of f over $[a, b]$.

Exactly parallel, we have, since $\{L(f, P)\}$ is bounded above, by $M(b-a)$:

Definition.   Write $L \int_a^b f = \sup\{L(f, P)$, over all partitions $P\}$. Then, $L \int_a^b f$ is called the **lower integral** of f over $[a, b]$.

We naturally expect there to be an order relation between these numbers; it is no surprise to find

Theorem 8.1–C. $L \int_a^b f \leqslant U \int_a^b f.$

Proof.   Let $U(f, P_0)$ be any upper sum; by Theorem 8.1–A, no lower sum $L(f, P)$ can exceed $U(f, P_0)$. Hence, $U(f, P_0)$ is an upper bound of $\{L(f, P)\}$; in particular, $U(f, P_0)$ cannot be less than the least upper bound of $\{L(f, P)\}$. That is,

$$L \int_a^b f \leqslant U(f, P_0).$$

But now, $U(f, P_0)$ is any upper sum, and so the number $L \int_a^b f$, which is independent of P, is a lower bound of $\{U(f, P)\}$, the set of upper sums.

It therefore does not exceed the greatest lower bound of $\{U(f, P)\}$, which by definition is $U \int_a^b f$. So we have

$$L \int_a^b f \leqslant U \int_a^b f. \qquad \blacklozenge$$

It is now time to use the fact that f is continuous. Our intuition tells us that if f is continuous, then the upper and lower integrals (which correspond to limits of approximation by rectangles) are equal, and their common value is the area "under the curve" of Fig. 8.1.1. As yet we have not explicitly used the fact that f is *continuous*; Theorems 8.1–A, 8.1–B, and 8.1–C have all been proved under the hypothesis that f is *bounded* (which is a weaker condition). We shall see that this allows us to extend the scope of our discussion, in the next section.

Theorem 8.1–D. If f is continuous on $[a, b]$, then

$$L \int_a^b f = U \int_a^b f.$$

Proof. Since f is continuous on $[a, b]$, it is uniformly continuous there (Theorem 6.9–B). Hence (in fact, by Theorem 6.9–A) given any $\varepsilon > 0$, we can find a partition P of $[a, b]$ such that the oscillation of f in each subinterval of P does not exceed ε, i.e. such that

$$M_i - m_i < \varepsilon \qquad (i = 0, 1, \ldots, n-1),$$

by definition of m_i, M_i. Then,

$$U(f, P) - L(f, P) = \sum_{i=0}^{n-1} (M_i - m_i)(x_{i+1} - x_i)$$

$$< \varepsilon \sum_{i=0}^{n-1} (x_{i+1} - x_i)$$

$$= \varepsilon(b - a).$$

But by definition of upper and lower integral,

$$L(f, P) \leqslant L \int_a^b f \leqslant U \int_a^b f \leqslant U(f, P)$$

$$\Rightarrow U \int_a^b f - L \int_a^b f \leqslant U(f, P) - L(f, P)$$

$$< \varepsilon(b - a);$$

since ε is arbitrary, it follows that $U \int_a^b f - L \int_a^b f = 0$. $\qquad \blacklozenge$
In consequence of this theorem, we introduce a new terminology.

Definition. The common value of $L \int_a^b f$ and $U \int_a^b f$ is called the **integral** of f **from** a **to** b (or *the integral from a to b of f*), and is denoted by the symbol

$$\int_a^b f.$$

Note. The symbolism $\int_a^b f(x)\,dx$ is also used. We shall from time to time use this form, especially in situations where the function f is described by a formula involving the dummy x. The term "dx" in the form above indicates that x is to be considered as a dummy, with domain at least $[a, b]$. We employ $\int_a^b f$ in discussing the theory of integration, or when the function f has a special name e.g. sin, cos or ln. See Examples 8.6.1, 8.6.2 and the remark following Example 8.7.5.

Suppose f is continuous on $[a, b]$, and $[c, d]$ is a closed interval contained in $[a, b]$. Then,

$$\int_c^d f$$

denotes a certain number. We **define** the symbol $\int_d^c f$ by

$$\int_d^c f = -\int_c^d f;$$

further, if α is any point of $[a, b]$, we **define**

$$\int_\alpha^\alpha f = 0.$$

We take these equations as definitions. [However, note that if we divide $[c, d]$ by a partition P, we might think of $\int_d^c f$ as

$$\inf_P \sum_{i=0}^{n-1} M_i(x_i - x_{i+1})$$

$$= -\left(\inf_P \sum_{i=0}^{n-1} M_i(x_{i+1} - x_i)\right)$$

$$= -\inf_P U(f, P)$$

$$= -U\int_c^d f$$

$$= -\int_c^d f$$

so that our definition does appeal to the intuition.] We make another definition.

Definition. Let $P = \{x_0, \dots, x_n\}$ be a partition of $[a, b]$. The greatest of the differences $x_{i+1} - x_i$, $i = 0, 1, \dots, n-1$, is called the **norm**, or the **gauge**, of the partition P, sometimes denoted by $v(P)$.

If f is continuous on $[a, b]$, then, given $\varepsilon > 0$, there is a $\delta(\varepsilon) > 0$ such that for every partition P with $v(P) < \delta$,

$$M_i - m_i < \frac{\varepsilon}{b-a} \quad (i = 0, 1, \ldots, n-1).$$

$$\Rightarrow \; U(f, P) - L(f, P) < \varepsilon.$$

But since $L(f, P) \leqslant \int_a^b f \leqslant U(f, P)$, we have

$$\int_a^b f \; - \; L(f, P) < \varepsilon$$

provided only that $v(P)$ is sufficiently small.

This shows that we can approximate as closely as we please to $\int_a^b f$ by a lower sum, for a suitable partition P (see also Section 8.8).

We next prove a wider form of the following intuitive result. If f is continuous and positive on $[a, b]$, then the area under the curve is the same as a rectangle on base $[a, b]$ (Fig. 8.1.3).

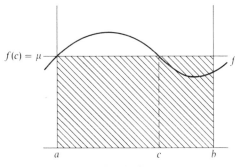

Fig. 8.1.3.

Theorem 8.1–E. Let f be continuous on $[a, b]$. Then, there is a point c, with $a \leqslant c \leqslant b$, such that

$$\int_a^b f = (b-a) f(c).$$

Proof. Since f is continuous, it is bounded; hence, we have

$$m \leqslant f(x) \leqslant M$$

where $m = \inf\{f(x): a \leqslant x \leqslant b\}, M = \sup\{f(x): a \leqslant x \leqslant b\}$. It follows that

$$m(b-a) \leqslant \int_a^b f \leqslant M(b-a)$$

using Theorem 8.1–B. Hence, there is a number μ, satisfying $m \leqslant \mu \leqslant M$ such that

$$\int_a^b f = \mu(b-a).$$

But by Theorem 6.8–D, since f is continuous, it takes every value between m and M, and in particular, takes the value μ. Hence, there is a point c of $[a, b]$ such that $f(c) = \mu$, and thus

$$\int_a^b f = (b-a)f(c). \qquad \blacklozenge$$

8.2 The Integral of a Bounded Function on a Closed Interval

In the last section, we set out to show that we could analytically find a number which represented the "area under a continuous curve". This task was completed in Theorem 8.1–D. However, as we then pointed out, it was only at this final stage that the full weight of the continuity of f was employed. The definitions and theorems preceding Theorem 8.1–D were made and proved under the weaker hypothesis that f is bounded. So we have, for example, the result that, for a bounded function,

$$L\int_a^b f \leqslant U\int_a^b f \qquad \text{(Theorem 8.1–C)}.$$

Equality can no longer be proved, in general. Nonetheless, we can divide the class of bounded functions into those for which equality does hold, and those for which there is strict inequality. We do this in an abstract way, since as yet we have no means of deciding which functions belong to which class. We therefore have the following definition.

Definition.　Let f be a bounded function on $[a, b]$, and define $L\int_a^b f$, $U\int_a^b f$ as in Section 8.1. We call the function f **integrable** over $[a, b]$ if

$$L\int_a^b f = U\int_a^b f.$$

Note.　Such a function is sometimes called **Riemann-integrable**, after the German mathematician Riemann, who developed the method.

Example 8.2.1.　If f is continuous on $[a, b]$, then f is integrable over $[a, b]$.
　　This is just a restatement of Theorem 8.1–D.
　　There are functions which are not integrable over $[a, b]$.

Example 8.2.2.   Let f be the function defined on $[0, 1]$ by setting

$$f(x) = \begin{cases} 0 & \text{if } x \text{ is rational} \\ 1 & \text{if } x \text{ is irrational.} \end{cases}$$

Then, f is not integrable over $[0, 1]$.

Proof.   We note first that f is bounded, for clearly,

$$0 \leqslant f(x) \leqslant 1 \quad \text{for all } x \text{ in } [0, 1].$$

If P is any partition of $[0, 1]$, then for any subinterval $[x_i, x_{i+1}]$ of P, we have (for $i = 0, 1, \ldots, n-1$)

$$m_i = 0 \quad \text{and} \quad M_i = 1;$$

this is a consequence of Theorems 2.6–C and 2.6–D. Hence,

$$U(f, P) = \sum_{i=0}^{n-1} (x_{i+1} - x_i) = 1, \qquad L(f, P) = 0;$$

thus,

$$L\int_0^1 f = \sup_P L(f, P) = 0,$$

$$U\int_0^1 f = \inf_P U(f, P) = 1;$$

the upper and lower integrals are not equal, and so f is not integrable over $[0, 1]$.   ◆

Having defined what an integrable function is, it would clearly be helpful to have a criterion for determining whether a given function is integrable. Riemann provided just such a criterion.

Theorem 8.2–A (Riemann).   Let f be bounded on $[a, b]$. Then, f is integrable over $[a, b]$ if and only if, given $\varepsilon > 0$, there is a partition P of $[a, b]$ such that

$$U(f, P) - L(f, P) < \varepsilon. \tag{1}$$

(The reader should observe the similarity to Cauchy's criterion for convergence in Theorem 4.5–A).

Proof.   (i) First, we show that the condition (1) is necessary. So, suppose f is integrable over $[a, b]$. Let $\varepsilon > 0$. Since

$$\int_a^b f = U\int_a^b f = \inf_P U(f, P),$$

there is a partition P_1 of $[a, b]$ such that

$$U(f, P_1) < \int_a^b f + \tfrac{1}{2}\varepsilon.$$

Likewise, since f is integrable, we have

$$\int_a^b f = L\int_a^b f = \sup_P L(f, P)$$

and so there is a partition P_2 such that

$$\int_a^b f - \tfrac{1}{2}\varepsilon < L(f, P_2).$$

Denote by P_3 the common refinement of P_1 and P_2 (as in the proof of Theorem 8.1–A). Then,

$$\int_a^b f - \tfrac{1}{2}\varepsilon < L(f, P_2) \leqslant L(f, P_3)$$
$$\leqslant U(f, P_3)$$
$$\leqslant U(f, P_1)$$
$$< \int_a^b f + \tfrac{1}{2}\varepsilon.$$

From this, we see that

$$U(f, P_3) - L(f, P_3) < \varepsilon.$$

(ii) To show the sufficiency, suppose that (1) is satisfied. Given $\varepsilon > 0$, there is a partition P with $U(f, P) - L(f, P) < \varepsilon$. But,

$$U\int_a^b f = \inf_P U(f, P)$$
$$\Rightarrow U\int_a^b f \leqslant U(f, P);$$

similarly, by the definition of $L\int_a^b f$, we have

$$L(f, P) \leqslant L\int_a^b f.$$

Hence,

$$U\int_a^b f - L\int_a^b f < \varepsilon.$$

This being the case for any $\varepsilon > 0$, it follows that

$$U\int_a^b f = L\int_a^b f,$$

that is, f is integrable over $[a, b]$.   ◆

Example 8.2.3. Let f be defined on $[0, 1]$ by

$$f(x) = \begin{cases} 1 & \text{if } x \neq \tfrac{1}{2} \\ 0 & \text{if } x = \tfrac{1}{2}. \end{cases}$$

Then, f is integrable over $[0, 1]$.

Proof. We first observe that f is a bounded function (Fig. 8.2.1). Let P be a partition of $[0, 1]$ such that the point $\tfrac{1}{2}$ belongs to the open interval (x_j, x_{j+1}). We have, in the usual notation,

$$m_i = M_i = 1, \qquad i = 0, 1, \ldots, n-1, \quad \text{and} \quad i \neq j.$$

$$m_j = 0, \qquad M_j = 1.$$

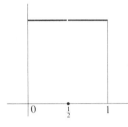

Fig. 8.2.1.

Let us calculate $U(f, P) - L(f, P) = \sum_{i=0}^{n-1} (M_i - m_i)(x_{i+1} - x_i)$; for $i \neq j$, $M_i = m_i$ and so these terms give a zero contribution to the sum. We are left with the term when $i = j$. Here, $M_j - m_j = 1$, and hence

$$U(f, P) - L(f, P) = x_{j+1} - x_j$$

which is clearly less than ε provided only that we choose x_j and x_{j+1} to satisfy $x_{j+1} - x_j < \varepsilon$. So, by Theorem 8.2-A, if we choose any partition P of $[0, 1]$ for which $x_j < \tfrac{1}{2} < x_{j+1}$ and $x_{j+1} - x_j < \varepsilon$, we have $U(f, P) - L(f, P) < \varepsilon$, and so f is integrable. To find the value of $\int_0^1 f$, we need only observe that for any partition P, $U(f, P) = 1$. Hence, $\int_0^1 f = 1$. ◆

We now ask what kind of functions are integrable? We have seen in Theorem 8.1–D that a function continuous on $[a, b]$ is integrable, and indeed, the method used in that proof showed that a continuous function satisfies Riemann's criterion. Example 8.2.3 shows that a particular bounded function with a single discontinuity is integrable, and it is clear that the method employed in this example can be extended to bounded functions which have a finite number of simple discontinuities. On the other hand, if we have too many discontinuities we may be in difficulties, as Example 8.2.2 shows. So the answer presumably lies between these extremes. We have the following result.

Theorem 8.2–B. Let f be a bounded function defined on the closed interval $[a, b]$. Suppose that, given $\eta > 0$, there is a set of subintervals of $[a, b]$ whose union has total length less than η, and contains all the points of discontinuity of f in $[a, b]$. Then, f is integrable over $[a, b]$.

Proof. Let ε be any positive real number. By hypothesis, we can enclose the discontinuities of f within a union of subintervals whose total length does not exceed $\varepsilon/[2(M - m)]$, where M, m are the bounds of f in $[a, b]$. The endpoints of these subintervals form a partition P_1 of $[a, b]$.

Next, let E denote the subset of $[a, b]$ obtained by removing from $[a, b]$ the interiors, but not the endpoints, of those subintervals which contain discontinuities of f. Then, E is a closed subset of $[a, b]$, since all the limit points of E will be in E. Since f is continuous on E, it will be uniformly continuous there (see Exercise 21 of Chapter 6).

Now, put $\eta = \varepsilon/[2(b-a)]$; then, there is a number $\delta > 0$ such that for all pairs of points x_1, x_2 of E satisfying $|x_1 - x_2| < \delta$, we have $|f(x_1) - f(x_2)| < \eta$. This is merely the definition of uniform continuity. Let P be a refinement of P_1 such that $v(P) < \delta$. Then,

$$U(f, P) - L(f, P) = \Sigma_i(M_i - m_i)(x_{i+1} - x_i)$$

where the sum Σ_i is made up of

Σ_1, being the sum over all those subintervals of P which contain discontinuities, and

Σ_2, being the sum over all the subintervals of P in E. Now,

$$\Sigma_1(M_i - m_i)(x_{i+1} - x_i) \leqslant (M - m)\Sigma_1(x_{i+1} - x_i) < \tfrac{1}{2}\varepsilon,$$

since $\Sigma_1(x_{i+1} - x_i)$ is just the total length of the subintervals of P containing discontinuities, and so does not exceed $\varepsilon/[2(M - m)]$. Further,

$$\Sigma_2(M_i - m_i)(x_{i+1} - x_i) \leqslant \eta\Sigma_2(x_{i+1} - x_i) < \tfrac{1}{2}\varepsilon,$$

since $\Sigma_2(x_{i+1} - x_i)$ is the total length of subintervals of P in E, and this clearly does not exceed $b - a$, since $E \subset [a, b]$. Thus,

$$U(f, P) - L(f, P) < \varepsilon,$$

and so by Theorem 8.2–A, f is integrable over $[a, b]$.   ◆

In the terminology of Chapter 6, Section 1, we can say that if f is a bounded function whose discontinuities have a *finite* number of limit points, then f is integrable over $[a, b]$ (see Exercise 36).

Theorem 8.2–C. Let f be a bounded function on $[a, b]$, with bounds m and M. If f is integrable over $[a, b]$, then

$$m(b-a) \leqslant \int_a^b f \leqslant M(b-a).$$

Proof. This is almost immediate, using Theorem 8.1–B. Details are left to the reader. ◆

Corollary. Let f be a bounded integrable function over $[a, b]$. If $f(x) \geqslant 0$ for all x in $[a, b]$, then $\int_a^b f \geqslant 0$.

Proof. $f(x) \geqslant 0$ for all x in $[a, b]$ $\Rightarrow$ $m \geqslant 0$. Result by Theorem 8.2–C. ◆

Although Theorem 8.2–C is true for bounded integrable functions f, we cannot go on to derive an analogous result to Theorem 8.1–E. We show, by example, that the conclusion of Theorem 8.1–E is false if the hypothesis "f is continuous" is weakened to "f is bounded, and integrable".

Example 8.2.4. Let f be the function defined by setting

$$f(x) = \begin{cases} 1+x & 0 \leqslant x < \frac{1}{2}, \frac{1}{2} < x \leqslant 1 \\ 0 & x = \frac{1}{2} \end{cases}$$

Then, f is integrable over $[0, 1]$, but there is no point c in $[0, 1]$ such that $\int_0^1 f = f(c)$ (Fig. 8.2.2).

Fig. 8.2.2.

Proof. f is bounded, and its single discontinuity can be contained in an interval of length less than η, as in Example 8.2.3. So, by Theorem 8.2–B, f is integrable. If we calculate $\int_0^1 f$, we find that its value is $\frac{3}{2}$. But there is no point of $[0, 1]$ at which f takes this value. The only likely candidate for the point c is the point $\frac{1}{2}$; but $f(\frac{1}{2}) = 0$. ◆

Note. In Example 8.2.3 on the other hand, there is a point c in $[0, 1]$ for which $\int_0^1 f = f(c)$. We can take c to be any value in $[0, 1]$ *except* $\frac{1}{2}$.

We conclude this section with an alternative criterion for integrability. This is due to the French mathematician Darboux, (1842–1917).

Theorem 8.2–D. Let f be a bounded function on the closed interval $[a, b]$. A necessary and sufficient condition that f be integrable over $[a, b]$ is that, for every $\varepsilon > 0$, there exist $\delta > 0$ such that for all partitions P with $v(P) < \delta$, we have

$$U(f, P) - L(f, P) < \varepsilon.$$

Proof. (i) The sufficiency is clear; if the condition is satisfied, then f is integrable, by Theorem 8.2–A.

(ii) The following proof of the necessity is fairly simple in conception, but the notation makes it appear more complicated than it is. Suppose f is integrable over $[a, b]$ and let ε be any positive number. By Theorem 8.2–A, there is a partition P_0 of $[a, b]$, say $P_0 = \{x_0, x_1, \ldots, x_n\}$ such that

$$U(f, P_0) - L(f, P_0) < \tfrac{1}{2}\varepsilon. \tag{1}$$

Let $P = \{y_0, y_1, \ldots, y_k\}$ be any other partition of $[a, b]$. Then, the subintervals of P can be divided into two types:

(α) those subintervals $[y_i, y_{i+1}]$ which lie entirely within a subinterval $[x_j, x_{j+1}]$ of P_0 i.e. $x_j < y_i < y_{i+1} < x_{j+1}$;

(β) those subintervals $[y_i, y_{i+1}]$ which contain a point x_j, as an interior, or as an end point, i.e. $y_i \leqslant x_j \leqslant y_{i+1}$.

We observe that there are at most $2n$ subintervals of type (β); for x_0 and x_n can belong to at most one each, while x_j $(1 \leqslant j \leqslant n-1)$ can be the common endpoint of two adjacent subintervals of P.

As usual, let m_j, M_j be the inf, sup of $f(x)$ in $[x_j, x_{j+1}]$, and write n_i, N_i for the inf, sup of $f(x)$ in $[y_i, y_{i+1}]$.

We begin by considering an interval of type (α); suppose

$$[y_i, y_{i+1}] \subset [x_j, x_{j+1}].$$

Then, clearly,

$$(N_i - n_i)(y_{i+1} - y_i) \leqslant (M_j - m_j)(y_{i+1} - y_i).$$

We now take the sum over all subintervals $[y_i, y_{i+1}]$ of type (α) *which lie in the particular subinterval* $[x_j, x_{j+1}]$; calling this sum Σ_1, we have

$$\Sigma_1(N_i - n_i)(y_{i+1} - y_i) \leqslant (M_j - m_j)\Sigma_1(y_{i+1} - y_i)$$
$$\leqslant (M_j - m_j)(x_{j+1} - x_j)$$

since all the subintervals $[y_i, y_{i+1}]$ are in $[x_j, x_{j+1}]$ and do not overlap each other.

Now, take the sum over all intervals $[x_j, x_{j+1}]$ of P_0 to obtain the total summation over all subintervals of type (α) in P:

$$\Sigma_\alpha(N_i - n_i)(y_{i+1} - y_i) \leqslant \sum_{j=0}^{j=n-1} (M_j - m_j)(x_{j+1} - x_j)$$
$$= U(f, P_0) - L(f, P_0)$$
$$< \tfrac{1}{2}\varepsilon, \text{ by (1)}.$$

Next, we consider intervals of type (β); we recall there are at most $2n$ of these. Since $N_i \leqslant M, m \leqslant n_i$, for $i = 0, 1, \ldots, k$, we have, for any subinterval of type (β),

$$(N_i - n_i)(y_{i+1} - y_i) \leqslant (M - m)(y_{i+1} - y_i)$$
$$\leqslant (M - m)v(P),$$

where $v(P)$ is the norm of the partition P. Hence, taking the sum over all subintervals of type (β), we have, at worst,

$$\Sigma_\beta (N_i - n_i)(y_{i+1} - y_i) \leqslant 2n(M - m)\, v(P);$$

now, $\Sigma_\alpha + \Sigma_\beta$ is just $U(f, P) - L(f, P)$, so that

$$U(f, P) - L(f, P) < \tfrac{1}{2}\varepsilon + 2n(M - m)v(P).$$

Let $\delta = \varepsilon/[4n(M - m)]$. Then, if $v(P) < \delta$, we have

$$U(f, P) - L(f, P) < \varepsilon,$$

as required. ◆

We note the following alternative formulation of Darboux's theorem.

Theorem 8.2–D(a). A necessary and sufficient condition that the bounded function f be integrable over $[a, b]$ is that, for every sequence of partitions $\{P_k\}$ of $[a, b]$ such that $\lim v(P_k) = 0$, we have

$$\lim\{U(f, P_k) - L(f, P_k)\} = 0.$$

We shall see an important application of this result in Section 8.8 of this chapter, in the calculation of certain limits. However, we now turn our attention to the collection of functions which are integrable over $[a, b]$ and examine the structure of this collection.

8.3 The Class $R[a, b]$

We begin by defining the symbol used above in the title.

Definition. We denote by $R[a, b]$ the class of all bounded integrable functions on the closed interval $[a, b]$.

If $C[a, b]$ is the class of all continuous functions on $[a, b]$, then by Theorem 8.1–D,

$$C[a, b] \subset R[a, b].$$

Our purpose in this section is to discuss the algebraic structure of $R[a, b]$. We shall show, for instance, that $R[a, b]$ is a vector space. In order to accomplish this, we require the following result.

Theorem 8.3–A. Let $f, g \in R[a, b]$; if P is a partition of $[a, b]$, then

(i) $U(f + g, P) \leqslant U(f, P) + U(g, P)$

(ii) $L(f, P) + L(g, P) \leqslant L(f + g, P)$.

Proof. (i) Suppose $P = \{x_0, \ldots, x_n\}$; define

$$M_i = \sup\{(f + g)\,(x) : x_i \leqslant x \leqslant x_{i+1}\}$$

$$M_i' = \sup\{f(x) : x_i \leqslant x \leqslant x_{i+1}\}$$

$$M_i'' = \sup\{g(x) : x_i \leqslant x \leqslant x_{i+1}\}.$$

Now, $(f + g)(x) = f(x) + g(x)$; but

$$f(x) \leqslant M_i', \qquad g(x) \leqslant M_i''$$

in $[x_i, x_{i+1}]$; hence,

$$(f + g)(x) \leqslant M_i' + M_i''$$

$$\Rightarrow M_i = \sup\{(f + g)(x) : x_i \leqslant x \leqslant x_{i+1}\} \leqslant M_i' + M_i''$$

by Exercise 9 of Chapter 2, and hence

$$U(f + g, P) = \sum_{i=0}^{n-1} M_i(x_{i+1} - x_i)$$

$$\leqslant \sum_{i=0}^{n-1} M_i'(x_{i+1} - x_i) + \sum_{i=0}^{n-1} M_i''(x_{i+1} - x_i)$$

$$= U(f, P) + U(g, P).$$

(ii) is similar.   ◆

Theorem 8.3–B. $R[a, b]$ is a vector space over the real numbers, i.e. if $f, g \in R[a, b]$, and α is any real number, then $f + g$ and αf belong to $R[a, b]$ also. Indeed,

(i) $\displaystyle\int_a^b f + g = \int_a^b f + \int_a^b g$

(ii) $\displaystyle\int_a^b \alpha f = \alpha \int_a^b f.$

Proof.   (i) Let $\varepsilon > 0$. Since f is integrable over $[a, b]$, there is (Theorem 8.2–A) a partition P_1 of $[a, b]$ such that

$$U(f, P_1) - L(f, P_1) < \tfrac{1}{2}\varepsilon;$$

since g is integrable over $[a, b]$, there is a partition P_2 such that

$$U(g, P_2) - L(g, P_2) < \tfrac{1}{2}\varepsilon.$$

Now let P_3 be a common refinement of P_1 and P_2. Then, by Theorem 8.3–A,

$$U(f + g, P_3) - L(f + g, P_3) \leqslant U(f, P_3) + U(g, P_3) - L(f, P_3) - L(g, P_3)$$

$$= U(f, P_3) - L(f, P_3) + U(g, P_3) - L(g, P_3)$$

$$< \tfrac{1}{2}\varepsilon + \tfrac{1}{2}\varepsilon.$$

So, by Theorem 8.2–A, $f + g$ belongs to $R[a, b]$. Also, if P is any partition,

$$L(f, P) + L(g, P) \leqslant \int_a^b f + \int_a^b g \leqslant U(f, P) + U(g, P);$$

furthermore, using Theorem 8.3–A again,

$$L(f, P) + L(g, P) \leqslant L(f + g, P)$$

$$\leqslant \int_a^b f + g$$

$$\leqslant U(f + g, P) \leqslant U(f, P) + U(g, P).$$

So both $\int_a^b f + g$ and $\int_a^b f + \int_a^b g$ lie between $U(f, P) + U(g, P)$ and $L(f, P) + L(g, P)$. But, given $\varepsilon > 0$, we can find a partition P such that

$$U(f, P) + U(g, P) - L(f, P) - L(g, P) < \varepsilon$$

as we did earlier in the proof. Hence,

$$\left| \int_a^b f + g - \int_a^b f - \int_a^b g \right| < \varepsilon.$$

Since ε is arbitrary, the result follows.

(ii) We consider the cases $\alpha \geq 0$, $\alpha < 0$ separately.

Case (a) $\alpha \geq 0$. Let $\varepsilon > 0$. There is a partition P of $[a, b]$ such that

$$U(f, P) - L(f, P) < \frac{\varepsilon}{\alpha}$$

since $f \in R[a, b]$. Now, if $\alpha \geq 0$,

$$\sup\{\alpha f(x) : x \in E\} = \alpha \sup\{f(x) : x \in E\},$$

$$\Rightarrow U(\alpha f, P) = \sum_{i=0}^{n-1} \alpha M_i(x_{i+1} - x_i)$$

$$= \alpha \sum_{i=0}^{n-1} M_i(x_{i+1} - x_i)$$

$$= \alpha U(f, P).$$

Similarly,

$$L(\alpha f, P) = \alpha L(f, P)$$

$$\Rightarrow U(\alpha f, P) - L(\alpha f, P) = \alpha(U(f, P) - L(f, P)) < \varepsilon.$$

$$\Rightarrow \alpha f \in R[a, b] \quad \text{by Theorem 8.2–A.}$$

Case (b) $\alpha < 0$. Again, if $\varepsilon > 0$, there is a partition P such that

$$U(f, P) - L(f, P) < \frac{\varepsilon}{-\alpha}.$$

Now, for $\alpha < 0$, by Exercise 11 of Chapter 2,

$$\sup\{\alpha f(x) : x \in E\} = \alpha \inf\{f(x) : x \in E\}$$

$$\inf\{\alpha f(x) : x \in E\} = \alpha \sup\{f(x) : x \in E\},$$

and hence,

$$U(\alpha f, P) = \alpha L(f, P)$$

$$L(\alpha f, P) = \alpha U(f, P)$$

$$\Leftrightarrow U(\alpha f, P) - L(\alpha f, P) = \alpha[L(f, P) - U(f, P)]$$

$$= -\alpha[U(f, P) - L(f, P)] < \varepsilon,$$

and so, again by Theorem 8.2–A, αf belongs to $R[a, b]$. In the same way as part (i), we can show that

$$\left| \int_a^b \alpha f - \alpha \int_a^b f \right| < \varepsilon,$$

which gives the required result.   ◆

Remark. We can define a mapping Φ of the vector space $R[a, b]$ into the set R of real numbers by setting, for each element f in $R[a, b]$,

$$\Phi(f) = \int_a^b f.$$

Theorem 8.3–B shows that if f, g belong to $R[a, b]$ and α is a scalar, then

$$\Phi(f + g) = \Phi(f) + \Phi(g)$$

$$\Phi(\alpha f) = \alpha \Phi(f).$$

Φ is therefore a linear transformation of $R[a, b]$ into R. In fact, scalar valued linear transformations are called **linear functionals**. The corollary to Theorem 8.2–C shows that if $f \geqslant 0$, then $\Phi(f) \geqslant 0$. In this case, we say the linear functional is *non-negative*. So we have the following conclusion: if Φ maps the vector space $R[a, b]$ into R, and is defined by

$$\Phi(f) = \int_a^b f, \quad \text{for all } f \in R[a, b],$$

then Φ is a non-negative linear functional on $R[a, b]$.

We may now ask about products of integrable functions. For we have seen in previous chapters that the sum, scalar multiple and product of continuous functions is again continuous, and that the derivative of the sum, scalar multiple and product of differentiable functions exists. Having shown that the sum and scalar multiple of integrable functions are integrable, it is only natural to ask if we can complete the treble for integrable functions also. We shall find it convenient to begin with a special case.

Theorem 8.3–C.   If $f \in R[a, b]$, so does f^2.

Proof. Since, by definition of the class $R[a,b]$, f is a bounded function, we have

$$|f(x)| \leqslant M, \qquad a \leqslant x \leqslant b.$$

As usual, let $\varepsilon > 0$. By Theorem 8.2–A, there is a partition P of $[a, b]$ such that

$$U(f, P) - L(f, P) < \frac{\varepsilon}{2M}.$$

Denote by N_i, n_i the supremum and infimum of $f^2(x)$ in $[x_i, x_{i+1}]$. Then, in the notation of Section 6.9,

$$N_i - n_i = \omega(f^2; x_i, x_{i+1})$$
$$= \sup\{|f^2(x) - f^2(y)| : x, y \in [x_i, x_{i+1}]\} \quad \text{(Verify!)}$$
$$= \sup\{|f(x) - f(y)||f(x) + f(y)| : x, y \in [x_i, x_{i+1}]\}$$
$$\leqslant 2M \sup\{|f(x) - f(y)| : x, y \in [x_i, x_{i+1}]\}$$
$$= 2M \omega(f; x_i, x_{i+1})$$
$$= 2M(M_i - m_i).$$

Hence,

$$U(f^2, P) - L(f^2, P) = \sum(N_i - n_i)(x_{i+1} - x_i)$$
$$\leqslant 2M \sum(M_i - m_i)(x_{i+1} - x_i)$$
$$= 2M[U(f, P) - L(f, P)] < \varepsilon.$$

By Theorem 8.2–A, this means f^2 is in $R[a, b]$.   ◆
This enables us to prove that $fg \in R[a, b]$ in a very simple way; indeed, all the hard work of the proof has already been done.

Theorem 8.3–D.   If $f, g \in R[a, b]$, then $fg \in R[a, b]$.

Proof. We have

$$fg = \tfrac{1}{2}((f + g)^2 - f^2 - g^2);$$

hence, by Theorems 8.3–C and 8.3–B, fg is in $R[a, b]$.   ◆
   We next show that if $f \in R[a, b]$, then $|f| \in R[a, b]$ also. To prove this in a simple way, we introduce two auxiliary functions. The reader should compare these with the device used in the second proof of Theorem 5.6–A.

Definition. Let f be any real valued function on a set E. Define f^+, f^- on E by setting

$$f^+(x) = \begin{cases} f(x) & \text{if } f(x) \geqslant 0 \\ 0 & \text{if } f(x) < 0 \end{cases}$$

$$f^-(x) = \begin{cases} 0 & \text{if } f(x) > 0 \\ -f(x) & \text{if } f(x) \leqslant 0 \end{cases}$$

f^+ is called the **positive part** of f, f^- the **negative part** of f. It is plain that, for all x,

$$f(x) = f^+(x) - f^-(x),$$
$$|f|(x) = |f(x)| = f^+(x) + f^-(x).$$

Also, if f is bounded, so are f^+, f^- and conversely. The reader should verify that if $f \in R[a, b]$, then so are f^+, f^- (see Exercise 2). This enables us to prove

Theorem 8.3–E.   If $f \in R[a, b]$, then $|f| \in R[a, b]$, and

$$\left| \int_a^b f \right| \le \int_a^b |f|.$$

Proof. By Exercise 2, f^+ and f^- are integrable, and hence, by Theorem 8.3–B, so is $f^+ + f^- = |f|$. Moreover,

$$\int_a^b |f| = \int_a^b f^+ + \int_a^b f^-$$

$$\ge \left| \int_a^b f^+ - \int_a^b f^- \right|$$

$$= \left| \int_a^b f \right|. \qquad \blacklozenge$$

We can also obtain this result by another method. We first have the following theorem.

Theorem 8.3–F.   If $f, g \in R[a, b]$, and for all x in $[a, b]$, $f(x) \le g(x)$, then

$$\int_a^b f \le \int_a^b g.$$

Proof.   We have, for all x in $[a, b]$, $g(x) - f(x) \ge 0$; hence, by the corollary to Theorem 8.2–C,

$$\int_a^b (g - f) \ge 0$$

$$\Rightarrow \int_a^b f \le \int_a^b g, \qquad \text{by Theorem 8.3–B.} \qquad \blacklozenge$$

Corollary.   If $f \in R[a, b]$, then $|\int_a^b f| \le \int_a^b |f|$.

Proof.   Let $|f| = g$; then, for all x in $[a, b]$,

$$-|f(x)| \le f(x) \le |f(x)|$$

$$\Rightarrow -\int_a^b |f| \le \int_a^b f \le \int_a^b |f| \qquad \text{(by Theorem 8.3–F)}$$

$$\Leftrightarrow \left| \int_a^b f \right| \le \int_a^b |f|, \qquad \text{by Theorem 2.4–A.} \qquad \blacklozenge$$

Theorem 8.3–F enables us to prove a result which is known as the *Second Mean Value Theorem for Integrals*. Observe that the difficulties which prevented us from extending Theorem 8.2–C to a result analogous to Theorem 8.1–E still apply; hence we have the hypothesis of continuity on f once more.

Theorem 8.3–G (Second Mean Value theorem). Let f be continuous on $[a, b]$, and g be a non-negative integrable function on $[a, b]$. Then, there is a point c of $[a, b]$ such that

$$\int_a^b fg = f(c) \int_a^b g.$$

Proof. Since f is continuous, we have for all x in $[a, b]$,

$$m \leqslant f(x) \leqslant M,$$

m and M being the least and greatest values of f in $[a, b]$, and so, since $g \geqslant 0$,

$$mg(x) \leqslant f(x)g(x) \leqslant Mg(x).$$

By Theorem 8.3–D, fg is integrable over $[a, b]$, so that

$$\int_a^b mg \leqslant \int_a^b fg \leqslant \int_a^b Mg \qquad \text{(Theorem 8.3–F)}$$

$$\Rightarrow m \int_a^b g \leqslant \int_a^b fg \leqslant M \int_a^b g \qquad \text{(Theorem 8.3–B)}$$

$$\Rightarrow \int_a^b fg = \mu \int_a^b g,$$

for some number μ satisfying $m \leqslant \mu \leqslant M$. But there is a point c in $[a, b]$ such that $\mu = f(c)$, in consequence of Theorem 6.8–D (which is where the continuity of f really comes in). Hence,

$$\int_a^b fg = f(c) \int_a^b g. \qquad \blacklozenge$$

Note. It is clear why the continuity of f is essential. But what of the condition that g be non-negative? Is this also necessary? At first sight, the answer would seem to be affirmative, in view of the following counterexample.

Example 8.3.1. Let $f(x) = g(x) = x$, and suppose that $a = -1$, $b = 1$. Then, the conclusion of Theorem 8.3–G is false in this case.

Proof. Here, f is continuous all right, but g is not non-negative. Now,

$$\int_a^b fg = \int_{-1}^1 x^2\, dx$$

$$= [\tfrac{1}{3}x^3]_{-1}^1 \quad \text{(assuming certain results from Section 8.6)}$$

$$= \tfrac{2}{3}.$$

On the other hand,

$$\int_b^b g = \int_{-1}^1 x\, dx = [\tfrac{1}{2}x^2]_{-1}^1 = 0.$$

Clearly, we cannot find a number $f(c)$ such that $f(c)$ times 0 is $\tfrac{2}{3}$. ◆

Theorem 8.3–G fails here because g changes sign in $[a, b]$. Thus, in the theorem, it is necessary that g be *of one sign* in $[a, b]$, and of course if g is non-negative, this is certainly the case.

Example 8.3.2. Let g be the constant function $g(x) = 1$ on $[a, b]$. Let f be continuous on $[a, b]$. Then, by Theorem 8.3–G,

$$\int_a^b f = \int_a^b fg = f(c) \int_a^b g,$$

$$= f(c) \int_a^b 1$$

$$= f(c) \cdot (b-a),$$

calculating $\int_a^b 1$ using upper sums, and this, of course, is just Theorem 8.1–E again, which is sometimes known as the First Mean Value theorem.

8.4 Additivity of the Integral

Suppose that f is integrable over the interval $[a, c]$, and also over the interval $[c, b]$. Then, $\int_a^c f$ and $\int_c^b f$ exist, as real numbers. It is plausible that f is then integrable over $[a, b]$, and that $\int_a^b f = \int_a^c f + \int_c^b f$. Conversely, if $f \in R[a, b]$, and $a < c < b$, then it is plausible that $f \in R[a, c]$ and $f \in R[c, b]$, and again, that $\int_a^c f + \int_c^b f = \int_a^b f$. It is this result that we now try to prove.

Theorem 8.4–A. Let $[a, b]$ be a closed interval, and let $a < c < b$.
  (i) If $f \in R[a, b]$, then $f \in R[a, c]$ and $f \in R[c, b]$;
  (ii) If $f \in R[a, c]$ and $f \in R[c, b]$, then $f \in R[a, b]$;
  (iii) If $f \in R[a, b]$, then

$$\int_a^b f = \int_a^c f + \int_c^b f.$$

Proof. (i) is left as an exercise for the reader (Exercise 1).

(ii) Let $\varepsilon > 0$. Then, there is a partition P_1 of $[a, c]$ such that

$$U(f, P_1) - L(f, P_1) < \tfrac{1}{2}\varepsilon, \quad \text{by Theorem 8.2–A.}$$

Further, there is a partition P_2 of $[c, b]$ such that

$$U(f, P_2) - L(f, P_2) < \tfrac{1}{2}\varepsilon.$$

Denote by P the partition of $[a, b]$ obtained by taking the subintervals of P_1 and P_2. Then,

$$U(f, P) = U(f, P_1) + U(f, P_2) \quad [\text{verify!}]$$

$$L(f, P) = L(f, P_1) + L(f, P_2)$$

$$\Rightarrow U(f, P) - L(f, P) < \varepsilon,$$

$$\Rightarrow f \in R[a, b], \quad \text{by Theorem 8.2–A.}$$

(iii) Suppose $f \in R[a, b]$. Let P, P_1, and P_2 be as in (ii). Then,

$$\int_a^b f \leqslant U(f, P)$$

$$\leqslant U(f, P_1) + U(f, P_2)$$

$$\Rightarrow \int_a^b f \leqslant \int_a^c f + \int_c^b f,$$

by Exercise 9 of Chapter 2 (applied to inf rather than sup). But now, if $f \in R[a, b]$, then $-f \in R[a, b]$ and so

$$-\int_a^b f \leqslant -\int_a^c f - \int_c^b f \quad \text{(using Theorem 8.3–B)}$$

$$\Leftrightarrow \int_a^b f \geqslant \int_a^c f + \int_c^b f,$$

which, together with the previous inequality, gives the result. ◆

8.5 The Fundamental Theorem of the Calculus

It is at this point that we rigorously prove the close relationship between the derivative and the integral. There are two important results in this section: Theorem 8.5–B, which specifies the relationship, and Theorem 8.5–C, which shows how we may evaluate an integral. This latter theorem is, no doubt, familiar; indeed, we have already used it in Example 8.3.1. It is therefore appropriate that we should justify our procedure.

In view of Theorem 8.4–A, if f is integrable over $[a, b]$, then it is integrable over any subinterval $[a, x]$, where $a < x \leqslant b$. We can therefore define a new function F whose domain is $[a, b]$, and whose range is in R, by setting

$$F(x) = \int_a^x f \qquad a < x \leqslant b$$

$$F(a) = 0.$$

The latter conforms to our previous definition that $\int_a^a f = 0$. In view of the fact that f is merely a function of class $R[a, b]$, it may come as a surprise to see that the function F has many desirable properties. The first of these is continuity.

Theorem 8.5–A.   The function F defined above is continuous on $[a, b]$.

Proof.   We shall prove that if $a < c < b$, then F is continuous at c. The verification that F is continuous at a and b requires adaptation for one sided limits, and is left to the reader.

Let h be a positive number such that $c+h$ lies in $[a, b]$. Then, we try to show that $F(c+h)-F(c) \to 0$ as $h \to 0$. We have

$$F(c+h)-F(c) = \int_a^{c+h} f - \int_a^c f$$

$$= \int_c^{c+h} f \quad \text{by Theorem 8.4–A;}$$

now, by Theorem 8.2–C, if m, M denote the bounds of f in $[a, b]$, we certainly have

$$mh \leqslant \int_c^{c+h} f \leqslant Mh$$

$$\Leftrightarrow mh \leqslant F(c+h)-F(c) \leqslant Mh.$$

If $h < 0$, and $c+h$ is in $[a, b]$, then

$$F(c)-F(c+h) = \int_{c+h}^c f$$

$$\Rightarrow -mh \leqslant F(c)-F(c+h) \leqslant -Mh.$$

So, let $K = \max\{|m|, |M|\}$; if h is any number for which $c+h$ is in $[a, b]$, we have

$$|F(c+h)-F(c)| \leqslant K|h|$$

$$\to 0 \quad \text{as } |h| \to 0,$$

and so F is continuous at c.   ◆

We now show that if we strengthen the condition on f to the hypothesis "f is continuous", then we improve the conclusion to "F is differentiable". This is the result we have been keeping up our sleeve since Section 7.1!

Theorem 8.5–B (Fundamental theorem of Calculus, first part). Let $f \in R[a, b]$, and suppose F is defined as above. If f is continuous at a point c of $[a, b]$, then F is differentiable at c; moreover,

$$DF(c) = f(c).$$

Proof. We shall construct the chord function of F at c, and show that the limit is $f(c)$. The reader should observe where the continuity of f is used.

Let ε be any positive real number. Then, there is a $\delta > 0$ such that for all h with $|h| < \delta$, we have

$$f(c) - \varepsilon < f(c+h) < f(c) + \varepsilon. \tag{1}$$

Suppose $0 < h_1 < \delta$. Then,

$$F(c + h_1) - F(c) = \int_c^{c+h_1} f \quad \text{(Theorem 8.4–A)}$$

$$\Rightarrow h_1\{f(c) - \varepsilon\} < F(c + h_1) - F(c) < h_1\{f(c) + \varepsilon\},$$

by (1) and Theorem 8.2–C,

$$\Rightarrow f(c) - \varepsilon < \frac{F(c + h_1) - F(c)}{h_1} < f(c) + \varepsilon$$

$$\Rightarrow \left| \frac{F(c + h_1) - F(c)}{h_1} - f(c) \right| < \varepsilon. \tag{2}$$

On the other hand, if $-\delta < h_2 < 0$,

$$F(c) - F(c + h_2) = \int_{c+h_2}^c f$$

$$\Rightarrow -h_2\{f(c) - \varepsilon\} < F(c) - F(c + h_2) < -h_2\{f(c) + \varepsilon\},$$

$$\Rightarrow f(c) - \varepsilon < \frac{F(c + h_2) - F(c)}{h_2} < f(c) + \varepsilon,$$

$$\Rightarrow \left| \frac{F(c + h_2) - F(c)}{h_2} - f(c) \right| < \varepsilon, \tag{3}$$

and so, for any h with $|h| < \delta$,

$$\left| \frac{F(c + h) - F(c)}{h} - f(c) \right| < \varepsilon,$$

$$\Rightarrow \lim_{h \to 0} \frac{F(c+h)-F(c)}{h} = f(c)$$

$$\Leftrightarrow DF(c) = f(c). \qquad \blacklozenge$$

We observe, from the definition of F, that $\int_a^b f = F(b)$. Thus, if we wish to evaluate $\int_a^b f$ for some continuous function f, all we have to do is to find F and evaluate it at the point b. To help us find F, we know by Theorem 8.5–B, that F satisfies the condition $DF = f$. So we might try to evaluate $\int_a^b f$ by looking for a function whose derivative is f. There is only one problem: if we find a function G such that $DG = f$, how do we know that G is the function F defined above? The simple answer to this is that we do not know, and the next theorem shows that we do not need to know. It suffices, in fact, to find any function G for which $f = DG$. This theorem is also referred to as the Fundamental Theorem of Calculus.

Theorem 8.5–C (Fundamental Theorem of Calculus, second part).

Let f be continuous on $[a, b]$, and let G be a function continuous on $[a, b]$, differentiable on (a, b) and satisfying $DG = f$ on (a, b). Then,

$$\int_a^b f = G(b) - G(a).$$

Proof. Let F be defined as before. By Theorems 8.5–A, 8.5–B, F is continuous on $[a, b]$, differentiable on (a, b), and

$$DF(x) = f(x) \qquad a < x < b.$$

Hence, for all x in (a, b),

$$DF(x) = DG(x) = f(x).$$

Therefore, by Corollary 2 of Theorem 7.7–A (the Mean Value theorem), there is a constant k such that, for $a \leqslant x \leqslant b$,

$$F(x) = G(x) + k.$$

But since $F(a) = 0$ by definition of F, we have

$$0 = G(a) + k$$

$$\Leftrightarrow G(a) = -k.$$

Thus,

$$\int_a^b f = F(b) = G(b) + k$$

$$= G(b) - G(a). \qquad \blacklozenge$$

Notation. We sometimes write $[G(x)]_a^b$ for $G(b) - G(a)$; this is to indicate that G is a function with $DG = f$, and that we evaluate it at a and b, and take the difference. See Examples 8.7.2 and 8.7.5.

Alternative Proof of Theorem 8.3–B when $f, g \in C[a, b]$.
Define F, G, H by setting for x in $[a, b]$,

$$F(x) = \int_a^x f, \qquad G(x) = \int_a^x g, \qquad H(x) = F(x) + G(x).$$

Now, H is continuous, and in (a, b),

$$DH = D(F + G) = DF + DG = f + g$$

by Theorem 8.5–B. So, by Theorem 8.5–C,

$$\int_a^b (f + g) = H(b) - H(a)$$

$$= F(b) + G(b) - F(a) - G(a)$$

$$= \int_a^b f + \int_a^b g. \qquad \blacklozenge$$

In consequence of Theorem 8.5–C, we make the following definition.

Definition. Let f be continuous on $[a, b]$ and let G be a function continuous on $[a, b]$, differentiable on (a, b) with $DG = f$ on (a, b). Then G is called an **antiderivative** of f. The term **primitive** is also used.

As a result of the second corollary to Theorem 7.7–A, any two antiderivatives of f differ only by a constant. The word "antiderivative" is used to suggest the reciprocity between the processes of differentiation and integration. Theorem 8.5–C shows how we can find the area under a curve (the historical reason for the integration process) by merely evaluating an antiderivative (which embodies the fact that integration and differentiation are inverse operations). It is worth pointing out that one can begin by *defining* integration as the process inverse to differentiation (i.e. begin by defining antiderivatives) and deduce that areas can be calculated. This approach is adopted in several textbooks.

8.6 Standard Antiderivatives

It is apparent that Theorem 8.5–C provides a much more direct and powerful way of evaluating integrals like $\int_a^b f$ than the method of calculating upper and lower sums. For example, the reader might care to attempt to calculate $U(f, P)$ when $f(x) = x^2$ and $P = \{0, x_1, \ldots, x_{n-1}, 1\}$; in fact, the sum $U(f, P)$ is easy to calculate only if we take P to be the partition of $[0, 1]$ into n equal subintervals $\{0, 1/n, 2/n, \ldots, 1\}$.

On the other hand, many functions have antiderivatives which are easy to find; for example, it is not difficult to see that $D(\frac{1}{3}x^3) = x^2$, so that $\frac{1}{3}x^3$ is an antiderivative of x^2. In this section, we tabulate the antiderivatives of some common functions. The justification for some of these will be given in Section 8.7, but for others, we must wait until Chapter 9.

In the following table, we list *an* antiderivative G; the reader should recall that, if k is a constant, then $G + k$ is also an antiderivative.

TABLE OF STANDARD ANTIDERIVATIVES

	function f	antiderivative G such that $DG = f$
	$f(x) = x^n \quad (n \neq -1)$	$G(x) = \dfrac{x^{n+1}}{n+1} \quad (n \neq -1)$
†	$f(x) = x^{-1}$	$G(x) = \ln|x|$
†	$f(x) = e^x$	$G(x) = e^x$
†	$f(x) = \cos x$	$G(x) = \sin x$
†	$f(x) = \sin x$	$G(x) = -\cos x$
*	$f(x) = \tan x$	$G(x) = -\ln|\cos x|$
*	$f(x) = \cot x$	$G(x) = \ln|\sin x|$
†	$f(x) = \sec^2 x$	$G(x) = \tan x$
†	$f(x) = \operatorname{cosec}^2 x$	$G(x) = -\cot x$
†	$f(x) = a^x \quad (a > 0, a \neq 1)$	$G(x) = \dfrac{a^x}{\ln a} \quad (a > 0, a \neq 1)$
†	$f(x) = \sinh x$	$G(x) = \cosh x$
†	$f(x) = \cosh x$	$G(x) = \sinh x$
*	$f(x) = \tanh x$	$G(x) = \ln \cosh x$
*	$f(x) = \coth x$	$G(x) = \ln|\sinh x|$
*	$f(x) = \operatorname{sech} x$	$G(x) = \arctan \sinh x$
†	$f(x) = \operatorname{sech}^2 x$	$G(x) = \tanh x$
†	$f(x) = \operatorname{cosech}^2 x$	$G(x) = -\coth x$
†*	$f(x) = \dfrac{1}{\sqrt{(a^2 - x^2)}} \quad x \neq \pm a$	$G(x) = \dfrac{1}{a}\arcsin\dfrac{x}{a} \quad x \neq \pm a$

TABLE OF STANDARD ANTIDERIVATIVES—*continued*

function f	antiderivative G such that $DG = f$	
†* $f(x) = \dfrac{1}{x^2 + a^2}$	$G(x) = \dfrac{1}{a}\arctan\dfrac{x}{a}$	
* $f(x) = \dfrac{1}{x^2 - a^2}$ $x \neq \pm a$	$G(x) = \dfrac{1}{2a}\ln\left|\dfrac{x-a}{x+a}\right|$	$x \neq \pm a$

Those entries in the table marked † are justified by results in Chapter 9. Those marked * can be deduced using the techniques of substitution described in the next section.

Example 8.6.1. Evaluate $\int_0^{\frac{1}{2}\pi} \cos$.
Solution. By the table of antiderivatives, $D\sin = \cos$. Hence, by Theorem 8.5–C,

$$\int_0^{\frac{1}{2}\pi} \cos = \sin\tfrac{1}{2}\pi - \sin 0$$
$$= 1. \qquad \blacklozenge$$

Example 8.6.2. Evaluate $\int_0^1 1/(1+x^2)\,dx$.
Solution. Again, by the table above, we see that

$$D\arctan x = \frac{1}{1+x^2} \quad (a = 1)$$

and so the required integral is

$$\arctan 1 - \arctan 0$$
$$= \tfrac{1}{4}\pi. \qquad \blacklozenge$$

Of course, many integrals that we encounter are not so simple. However, there are two important techniques which help us to evaluate complicated integrals. These are integration by parts, and integration by substitution. We deal with these in the next section.

8.7 Techniques of Integration

The idea behind the techniques of this section is to transform the integral we require, $\int_a^b f$, if it is not a standard type, into a simpler form which is a standard type or a combination of standard types. The first of these techniques makes use of the product rule for derivatives (Theorem 7.3–A). It is used to evaluate integrals of the form $\int_a^b f \cdot Dg$.

Theorem 8.7–A (Integration by parts). Let f, g be functions which have continuous derivatives on (a, b). Then,

$$\int_a^b f \cdot Dg = f(b)g(b) - f(a)g(a) - \int_a^b g \cdot Df.$$

Proof. The proof is exceedingly simple. We note that $D(fg)$ exists and is given (Theorem 7.3–A) by

$$D(fg) = f \cdot Dg + g \cdot Df.$$

Hence, fg is an antiderivative of $f \cdot Dg + g \cdot Df$. By Theorem 8.5–C,

$$\int_a^b (f \cdot Dg + g \cdot Df) = fg(b) - fg(a);$$

thus, we have, by Theorem 8.3–B,

$$\int_a^b f \cdot Dg + \int_a^b g \cdot Df = f(b)g(b) - f(a)g(a),$$

whence the result follows.   ◆

Note. We observe that we still have to find $\int_a^b g \cdot Df$. The point of using this technique is to have $\int_a^b g \cdot Df$ simpler than $\int_a^b f \cdot Dg$!

Example 8.7.1.   Evaluate $\int_0^1 x\, e^x\, dx$.

Solution.   We write $x\, e^x$ as $f \cdot Dg$. We therefore have to decide which will be f and which Dg. Suppose we take $f(x) = x$, $Dg(x) = e^x$. Then, noting that an antiderivative for e^x (Dg) is e^x itself, it follows by Theorem 8.7–A that

$$\int_0^1 xe^x\, dx = f(1)g(1) - f(0)g(0) - \int_0^1 e^x\, dx$$

$$= e - \int_0^1 e^x\, dx$$

$$= e - [e^1 - e^0]$$

$$= 1.$$ ◆

Note.   Observe what happens if we take $f(x) = e^x$, $Dg(x) = x$ in this example. An antiderivative g of the identity function is $\frac{1}{2}x^2$, according to the table in Section 8.6. So, we obtain

$$\int_0^1 x\, e^x\, dx = e \cdot \tfrac{1}{2} - e^0 \cdot 0 - \int_0^1 \tfrac{1}{2}x^2\, e^x\, dx$$

$$= \tfrac{1}{2}e - \tfrac{1}{2}\int_0^1 x^2\, e^x\, dx.$$

The integral on the right-hand side is even worse than the one with which we started! So this is certainly not the way to go about integrating by parts. By taking $f(x) = x$, $Dg(x) = e^x$, as in Example 8.7.1, we obtain the *simpler* integral $\int_0^1 e^x\, dx$.

Example 8.7.2. Evaluate $\int_0^1 x^2 e^x \, dx$.
Again, we write the integrand as $f \cdot Dg$. This time, we let $f(x) = x^2$, and $Dg(x) = e^x$. Then, by Theorem 8.7–A,

$$\int_0^1 x^2 e^x \, dx = [x^2 e^x]_0^1 - \int_0^1 2x e^x \, dx$$

$$= e - 2 \int_0^1 x e^x \, dx.$$

The integral on the right-hand side can be evaluated by Example 8.7.1, so that the required integral is $e - 2$. But, the reader should notice that in this present example, we are effectively applying the technique of integration by parts twice. ◆

This sort of repetition of the technique is used to calculate integrals involving exponential and trigonometric functions. The reader should pay particular attention to the following application of Theorem 8.7–A.

Example 8.7.3. Evaluate $\int_0^{\frac{1}{4}\pi} e^x \sin x \, dx$.

Solution. Let $I = \int_0^{\frac{1}{4}\pi} e^x \sin x \, dx$; write $f(x) = e^x$, $Dg(x) = \sin x$. Then,

$$I = -e^{\frac{1}{4}\pi} \cos \frac{\pi}{4} + e^0 \cos 0 + \int_0^{\frac{1}{4}\pi} e^x \cos x \, dx. \tag{1}$$

We now use Theorem 8.7–A on $\int_0^{\frac{1}{4}\pi} e^x \cos x \, dx$:
let $f_1(x) = e^x$, $Dg_1(x) = \cos x$; then,

$$\int_0^{\frac{1}{4}\pi} e^x \cos x \, dx = e^{\frac{1}{4}\pi} \sin \frac{\pi}{4} - e^0 \sin 0 - \int_0^{\frac{1}{4}\pi} e^x \sin x \, dx$$

$$= e^{\frac{1}{4}\pi} \sin \frac{\pi}{4} - I.$$

If we substitute this in (1), we obtain an equation for I, namely,

$$I = -e^{\frac{1}{4}\pi} \cos \frac{\pi}{4} + 1 + e^{\frac{1}{4}\pi} \sin \frac{\pi}{4} - I$$

$$\Rightarrow 2I = 1$$

$$\Rightarrow I = \tfrac{1}{2}.$$

Here, upon integrating by parts twice, we retrieve the original integral and have a simple equation to solve for it. ◆

We now continue with a second kind of technique for evaluating integrals. This method depends upon the chain rule (Theorem 7.4–A).

Theorem 8.7–B (Integration by Substitution). Let g be a function such that Dg is continuous on $E = [\alpha, \beta]$, and let f be continuous on $g(E)$. Suppose $a = g(\alpha)$, $b = g(\beta)$. Then,

$$\int_a^b f = \int_\alpha^\beta (f \circ g) \cdot Dg.$$

Proof. Define F by setting, for each x in $g(E)$,

$$F(x) = \int_a^x f.$$

Now, Dg is continuous on $[\alpha, \beta]$ and $f \circ g$ is continuous on $[\alpha, \beta]$, by Theorem 6.7–D. So, we can define G on $[\alpha, \beta]$ by

$$G(t) = \int_\alpha^t f \circ g \cdot Dg.$$

The integral on the right exists, by Theorem 8.1–D. By Theorem 8.5–B,

$$DG(t) = (f \circ g)(t) \cdot Dg(t). \tag{2}$$

On the other hand, consider the function $F \circ g$ defined on $[\alpha, \beta]$. By Theorem 7.4–A (The Chain rule),

$$D(F \circ g) = DF \circ g \cdot Dg$$
$$= f \circ g \cdot Dg \tag{3}$$

since, again by Theorem 8.5–B, $DF = f$. By (2) and (3), therefore,

$$DG(t) = D(F \circ g)(t) \quad \text{for all } t \text{ in } [\alpha, \beta]$$
$$\Leftrightarrow G(t) - (F \circ g)(t) = k,$$

for all t in $[\alpha, \beta]$, where k is a constant. Now, $G(\alpha) = 0$, by the definition of G. Also, $F \circ g(\alpha) = F(g(\alpha)) = F(a) = 0$, and so it follows that $k = 0$. Thus, for all t in $[\alpha, \beta]$,

$$G(t) = (F \circ g)(t).$$

In particular, putting $t = \beta$,

$$\int_\alpha^\beta f \circ g \cdot Dg = G(\beta)$$
$$= (F \circ g)(\beta)$$
$$= F(g(\beta))$$
$$= F(b)$$
$$= \int_a^b f. \qquad \blacklozenge$$

Once more, the idea of using this technique is to simplify the original integral. Theorem 8.7–B can be used in two ways. We show how some of the antiderivatives of Section 8.6 are obtained.

Example 8.7.4.   Prove that $\int_0^x \tan = -\ln|\cos x|$.

Proof.   Let f be given by

$$f(y) = \frac{1}{y}$$

and g by

$$g(t) = \cos t.$$

Then,

$$Dg(t) = -\sin t,$$

and hence

$$f \circ g(t) . Dg(t) = f(\cos t) . (-\sin t)$$

$$= -\frac{\sin t}{\cos t}$$

$$= -\tan t.$$

By Theorem 8.7–B, then,

$$\int_0^x \tan = \int_1^{\cos x} -\frac{1}{y} dy$$

$$= -\ln|\cos x| + \ln 1$$

$$= -\ln|\cos x|. \qquad \blacklozenge$$

In this example, we write the *given* integral in the form

$$\int_\alpha^\beta f \circ g . Dg;$$

Theorem 8.5–B then assures us that this is $\int_{g(\alpha)}^{g(\beta)} f$. The next example is different.

Example 8.7.5.   Prove that, if $0 < x < \pi/2$,

$$\int_0^x \frac{1}{y^2 + a^2} dy = \frac{1}{a} \arctan \frac{x}{a}.$$

Proof.   Here, let

$$f(y) = \frac{1}{y^2 + a^2};$$

let g be the function given by

$$g(\theta) = a \tan \theta;$$

then,

$$Dg(\theta) = a \sec^2 \theta,$$

and $f \circ g$ is given by

$$f \circ g(\theta) = \frac{1}{a^2 \tan^2 \theta + a^2}$$

$$= \frac{1}{a^2 \sec^2 \theta}.$$

By Theorem 8.7–B,

$$\int_0^x f = \int_\alpha^\beta (f \circ g) \cdot Dg$$

where $g(\alpha) = 0$, $g(\beta) = x$. Hence, $\alpha = g^{-1}(0) = \arctan 0 = 0$, and $\beta = g^{-1}(x) = \arctan x/a$. Thus,

$$\int_0^x f = \int_0^{\arctan x/a} \underbrace{\frac{1}{a^2 \sec^2 \theta}}_{(f \circ g)(\theta)} \cdot \underbrace{a \sec^2 \theta}_{Dg(\theta)} \, d\theta$$

$$= \int_0^{\arctan x/a} \frac{1}{a} \, d\theta$$

$$= \frac{1}{a} \arctan \frac{x}{a}. \qquad \blacklozenge$$

This is a true example of integration by substitution. For, in this case, we *substitute the function*, $a \tan \theta$, of the *new* dummy θ, for the original dummy, y. We then obtain an integral of a function of θ. The symbol "$d\theta$" indicates that θ is to be considered as a dummy, and that any other letters occurring in the integral represent constants. Thus,

$$\int_a^b f(x) \, dx = \int_\alpha^\beta (f \circ g)(\theta) \cdot Dg(\theta) \, d\theta$$

indicates that, on the left-hand side, x is a dummy (with domain $[a, b]$), while on the right-hand side, θ is a dummy (with domain $[\alpha, \beta]$). See the note on page 254.

We finally mention a third method of integration, namely, integration by partial fractions. We illustrate this by an example.

Example 8.7.6. If $x \neq \pm a$, find $\int_0^y 1/(x^2 - a^2) \, dx$.

Solution.   Using the technique of partial fractions, we can write

$$\frac{1}{x^2 - a^2} = \frac{A}{x-a} + \frac{B}{x+a}$$

from which we deduce that $2aA = 1$, $2aB = -1$. So, by Theorem 8.3–B,

$$\int_0^y \frac{1}{x^2 - a^2}\, dx = \frac{1}{2a}[\ln|x-a|]_0^y - \frac{1}{2a}[\ln|x+a|]_0^y$$

since $\ln|x-a|$ is an antiderivative for $1/(x-a)$, and $\ln|x+a|$ is an antiderivative for $1/(x+a)$,

$$= \frac{1}{2a}[\ln|y-a| - \ln|a| - \ln|y+a| + \ln|a|]$$

$$= \frac{1}{2a}\ln\left|\frac{y-a}{y+a}\right|,$$

as required.   ◆

To conclude this section, we illustrate the use of the method of integration by parts to give another proof of Taylor's Theorem (see Theorem 7.8–B).

Theorem 8.7–C (Taylor).   Let $f, Df, \ldots, D^n f$ be continuous in an interval surrounding the point a. Then, if x is a point of this interval, we have

$$f(x) = f(a) + (x-a)Df(a) + \ldots + \frac{(x-a)^{n-1}}{n-1!}D^{n-1}f(a)$$

$$+ \frac{1}{(n-1)!}\int_a^x (x-t)^{n-1}D^n f(t)\, dt. \tag{4}$$

Proof.   We use the method of induction. The result is true for $n = 1$ since $f(x) = f(a) + \int_a^x Df = f(a) + [f(x) - f(a)] = f(x)$.
Assume the formula (4) for $n = 1, 2, \ldots, k$; consider

$$\frac{1}{(k-1)!}\int_a^x (x-t)^{k-1}D^k f(t)\, dt = \frac{1}{(k-1)!}\int_a^x \alpha \cdot D\beta$$

where $\alpha(t) = D^k f(t)$ and $D\beta(t) = (x-t)^{k-1}$.
Using Theorem 8.7–A, and noting that $\beta(t) = -(1/k)(x-t)^k$ by Section 8.6, we have

$$\frac{1}{(k-1)!}\int_a^x (x-t)^{k-1}D^k f(t)\, dt = -\frac{1}{k!}[(x-t)^k D^k f(t)]_a^x$$

$$+ \frac{1}{k!}\int_a^x (x-t)^k D^{k+1}f(t)\, dt$$

$$= \frac{1}{k!}(x-a)^k D^k f(a)$$

$$+ \frac{1}{k!}\int_a^x (x-t)^k D^{k+1}f(t)\, dt,$$

Hence,

$$f(x) = f(a)+\ldots+\frac{(x-a)^k}{k!}D^k f(a)+\frac{1}{k!}\int_a^x (x-t)^k D^{k+1}f(t)\, dt,$$

which is (4) with $n = k+1$.

We have thus shown that equation (4) with $n = k$ implies (4) with $n = k+1$. Since the case $n = 1$ is true, it follows that (4) holds for all values of n.   ◆

8.8 The Integral as a Limit

In Section 8.2, we proved a necessary and sufficient condition that a bounded function f, defined on $[a, b]$, be integrable over $[a, b]$, namely, that for every sequence $\{P_k\}$ of partitions for which $v(P_k) \to 0$, we should have

$$\lim\{U(f, P_k)-L(f, P_k)\} = 0.$$

It is clear that, if this condition is satisfied, then

$$\int_a^b f = \lim U(f, P_k) = \lim L(f, P_k).$$

Our purpose in this section is to show that, instead of using the sequence $\{U(f, P_k)\}$, we can, in fact, use another sequence, which has the advantage that we have a large measure of control over its construction. This sequence is a sequence of Riemann sums; we begin by stating exactly what sort of an object a Riemann sum is.

Definition.   Let f be defined and bounded in $[a, b]$, and let $\{P_k\}$ be a sequence of partitions of $[a, b]$ such that $\lim v(P_k) = 0$. Consider a particular partition P_k; from each subinterval $[x_i^{(k)}, x_{i+1}^{(k)}]$, choose a point $\xi_i^{(k)}$, and form the sum

$$\sum_i f(\xi_i^{(k)})(x_{i+1}^{(k)} - x_i^{(k)}).$$

This sum is called a **Riemann sum** of f corresponding to the partition P_k (and the points $\{\xi_i^{(k)}\}$).

The theorem we now prove shows that the integral of f over $[a, b]$ is a limit of Riemann sums. Thus, we are no longer restricted to the numbers m_i, M_i; we are free to choose any value ξ_i of f we like from the subinterval $[x_i, x_{i+1}]$.

Theorem 8.8–A. Let the notation be as in the definition above. Then,

(i) If $f \in R[a, b]$, then for every sequence of partitions $\{P_k\}$ with $v(P_k) \to 0$ and every choice of points $\xi_i^{(k)}$, the corresponding sequence of Riemann sums converges, with limit $\int_a^b f$.

(ii) If there is a real number I such that, for every sequence $\{P_k\}$ of partitions and every choice of points $\xi_i^{(k)}$, the corresponding sequence of Riemann sums converges with the limit I, then $f \in R[a, b]$, and

$$I = \int_a^b f.$$

Proof. (i) Let $\{P_k\}$ be a sequence of partitions with $\lim v(P_k) = 0$. Let $\xi^{(k)}$ be points chosen from the subintervals $[x_i^{(k)}, x_{i+1}^{(k)}]$. Suppose $\varepsilon > 0$. By Theorem 8.2–D(a), there is an integer n_0 such that for all $k > n_0$,

$$U(f, P_k) - L(f, P_k) < \varepsilon.$$

For every subinterval of the partition P_k, we have

$$m_i^{(k)}(x_{i+1}^{(k)} - x_i^{(k)}) \leqslant f(\xi_i^{(k)})(x_{i+1}^{(k)} - x_i^{(k)}) \leqslant M_i^{(k)}(x_{i+1}^{(k)} - x_i^{(k)})$$

(since in any subinterval, f lies between its bounds in that interval),

$$\Rightarrow L(f, P_k) \leqslant \sum_i f(\xi_i^{(k)})(x_{i+1}^{(k)} - x_i^{(k)}) \leqslant U(f, P_k).$$

But, if $f \in R[a, b]$,

$$L(f, P_k) \leqslant \int_a^b f \leqslant U(f, P_k).$$

Hence, for all $k > n_0$,

$$\left| \int_a^b f - \sum_i f(\xi_i^{(k)})(x_{i+1}^{(k)} - x_i^{(k)}) \right| < \varepsilon,$$

and (i) follows.

(ii) Let $\{P_k\}$ be any sequence of partitions of $[a, b]$ such that $\lim v(P_k) = 0$. Let $\varepsilon > 0$. In each subinterval $[x_i^{(k)}, x_{i+1}^{(k)}]$ of P_k, there is a point $\xi_i^{(k)}$ such that

$$m_i^{(k)} \leqslant f(\xi_i^{(k)}) \leqslant m_i^{(k)} + \frac{\varepsilon}{4(b-a)}$$

$$\Rightarrow L(f, P_k) \leqslant \sum_i f(\xi_i^{(k)})(x_{i+1}^{(k)} - x_i^{(k)}) < L(f, P_k) + \tfrac{1}{4}\varepsilon$$

$$\Rightarrow |L(f, P_k) - \sum_i f(\xi_i^{(k)})(x_{i+1}^{(k)} - x_i^{(k)})| < \tfrac{1}{4}\varepsilon.$$

By hypothesis, there is an integer n_1 such that, for all $k > n_1$,

$$|I - \sum_i f(\xi_i^{(k)})(x_{i+1}^{(k)} - x_i^{(k)})| < \tfrac{1}{4}\varepsilon$$

$$\Rightarrow |L(f, P_k) - I| < \tfrac{1}{2}\varepsilon \quad \text{for all } k > n_1.$$

By a similar argument, we can find an integer n_2 such that for all $k > n_2$,

$$|U(f, P_k) - I| < \tfrac{1}{2}\varepsilon.$$

Hence, if $k > \max(n_1, n_2)$, we have

$$U(f, P_k) - L(f, P_k) < \varepsilon,$$

which means that $f \in R[a, b]$ by Theorem 8.2–A, and by (i) it follows that $I = \lim U(f, P_k) = \int_a^b f$. ◆

This result has applications in the calculations of certain limits.

Example 8.8.1.   Evaluate

$$\lim_{n \to \infty} \sum_{r=1}^{n} \frac{n}{n^2 + r^2}.$$

Solution.   We try to express the summation as a Riemann sum. Let us write $r = i + 1$, so that the sum becomes

$$\sum_{i=0}^{n-1} \frac{n}{n^2 + (i+1)^2}. \tag{1}$$

We now try to write the general term in the sum as $f(\xi_i)(x_{i+1} - x_i)$; if we do this, (1) certainly has the form of a Riemann sum. First,

$$\frac{n}{n^2 + (i+1)^2} = \frac{1}{1 + \left(\dfrac{i+1}{n}\right)^2} \cdot \frac{1}{n}$$

To write this in the required form, we take $1 / \{1 + [(i+1)/n]^2\}$ as $f(\xi_i)$, and $1/n$ as $(x_{i+1} - x_i)$. If we write $x_i = i/n$, then it is plain that $x_{i+1} - x_i = 1/n$, for $i = 0, 1, \ldots, n-1$. Also, if we take f to be the function given by

$$f(x) = \frac{1}{1 + x^2},$$

it is again evident that

$$\frac{1}{1 + \left(\dfrac{i+1}{n}\right)^2} = f(x_{i+1}).$$

Thus, we have

$$\frac{n}{n^2 + (i+1)^2} = f(x_{i+1})(x_{i+1} - x_i) \qquad \text{i.e. } \xi_i = x_{i+1}.$$

Furthermore,

$$x_0 = \frac{0}{n} = 0, \qquad x_n = \frac{n}{n} = 1.$$

Each subinterval of $[0, 1]$ has length $1/n$, so the norm $v(P_n)$ of this partition is $1/n$, which tends to zero, by Example 4.1.5. Therefore, since the function f above is integrable, it follows by Theorem 8.8–A that

$$\lim_{n \to \infty} \sum_{r=1}^{n} \frac{n}{n^2 + r^2} = \int_0^1 f$$

$$= \int_0^1 \frac{1}{1 + x^2} \, dx$$

$$= \arctan 1 - \arctan 0,$$

by Section 8.6 and Theorem 8.5–C,

$$= \frac{\pi}{4}. \qquad \blacklozenge$$

Theorem 8.8–A is also valuable if we wish to calculate the value of an integral which is not a simple or standard function. For, if we know that the function f to be integrated *is* integrable (e.g. if it is continuous or has finitely many discontinuities), we can then choose a sequence $\{P_k\}$ of partitions, with $\lim v(P_k) = 0$, in such a way as to make life as simple as possible. We illustrate this by an example.

Example 8.8.2.   Evaluate $\int_0^1 x^3 \, dx$.

Solution.   Suppose that we are unaware that $\frac{1}{4}x^4$ is an antiderivative of x^3, and that we try to calculate the integral using Riemann sums. Since f, given by $f(x) = x^3$, is integrable over $[0, 1]$, $f \in R[0, 1]$ and so we can use Theorem 8.8–A. We choose a partition P_n of $[0, 1]$ into n equal subintervals, of length $1/n$. Thus,

$$P_n = \left\{ 0, \frac{1}{n}, \ldots, \frac{n}{n} = 1 \right\}$$

and clearly, $v(P_n) \to 0$. We choose for $\xi_i^{(n)}$ the upper endpoint of the interval $\{i/n, [(i+1)/n]\}$; this makes the calculation easier. The corresponding Riemann sum is

$$\sum_{i=0}^{n=1} \left(\frac{i+1}{n} \right)^3 \frac{1}{n}$$

$$= \frac{1}{n^4} \sum_{r=1}^{n} r^3 \qquad (r = i+1)$$

$$= \frac{1}{n^4}\left(\frac{n(n+1)}{2}\right)^2 \qquad \text{(sum of the cubes of } 1, \ldots, n)$$

$$= \frac{1}{4}\left(1 + \frac{1}{n}\right)^2$$

$$\to \tfrac{1}{4}.$$

Hence,

$$\int_0^1 x^3 \, dx = \tfrac{1}{4}. \qquad \qquad \blacklozenge$$

Note. The reader may care to form the upper and lower sums for the function $f(x) = x^3$, using a partition P which is not divided into equal subintervals. He will see that the calculation of these will be very difficult, except in the special case when P has equal subintervals. Theorem 8.8–A assures us that we come to no harm by taking such a partition.

8.9 Improper Integrals

So far, we have concerned ourselves with the integral of a function f, bounded and defined on a closed interval $[a, b]$. It is now time to widen the scope of our investigation, and to consider such integrals as $\int_0^1 (1/x) \, dx$, where the function to be integrated is not bounded (indeed, is not defined) in $[0, 1]$, and $\int_0^\infty e^{-x} \, dx$, where the interval over which we integrate is not bounded.

We rely heavily on the results of the preceding sections, and use the ideas we have established as a springboard for the new ones.

Suppose, first of all, that $f \in R[\alpha, b]$, for every α satisfying $a < \alpha \leqslant b$. Then, $\int_\alpha^b f$ is some real number, depending on α. We can therefore define a function φ, with domain $(a, b]$, given by

$$\varphi(\alpha) = \int_\alpha^b f, \qquad \text{for each } \alpha \text{ in } (a, b].$$

We then make the following definition.

Definition. If φ is defined as above, and $\lim_{\alpha \to a+} \varphi(\alpha)$ exists, then we say that this limit is the **improper integral** *from a to b of f*, and write

$$\lim_{\alpha \to a+} \varphi(\alpha) = \int_a^b f.$$

We say also that f is **improperly integrable** over (a, b). If $\lim_{\alpha \to a+} \varphi(\alpha)$ does not exist, or is ∞ or $-\infty$, then we say that $\int_a^b f$ does not exist (occasionally, that $\int_a^b f$ is divergent, but see below).

Remark. The reader should observe that this definition is consistent with the definition of $\int_a^b f$ when f is continuous on $[a, b]$. For then,

$$\varphi(\alpha) = \int_\alpha^b f$$

$$= F(b) - F(\alpha) \qquad \text{(by Theorem 8.5–C)}$$

$$\Rightarrow \lim_{\alpha \to a+} \varphi(\alpha) = F(b) - \lim_{\alpha \to a+} F(\alpha)$$

$$= F(b) - F(a) \qquad \text{(Theorem 6.7–A),}$$

since, by Theorem 8.5–A, F is continuous on $[a, b]$,

$$= F(b) \qquad \text{(since } F(a) = 0\text{, by definition of } F)$$

$$= \int_a^b f.$$

Example 8.9.1. Evaluate $\int_0^1 (1/\sqrt{x})\,dx$.

Solution. This is an improper integral of the type mentioned, since $f(x) = 1/\sqrt{x}$ is continuous in $[\alpha, 1]$ for $0 < \alpha \leqslant 1$. Writing

$$\varphi(\alpha) = \int_\alpha^1 \frac{1}{\sqrt{x}}\,dx,$$

we have, by Section 8.6,

$$\varphi(\alpha) = 2[\sqrt{x}]_\alpha^1$$

$$= 2 - 2\sqrt{\alpha}$$

$$\Rightarrow \lim_{\alpha \to 0+} \varphi(\alpha) = 2,$$

$$\Rightarrow \int_0^1 \frac{1}{\sqrt{x}}\,dx \text{ exists, and has the value 2.} \qquad \blacklozenge$$

A similar situation arises if $f \in R[a, \beta]$, for all β satisfying $a \leqslant \beta < b$.

Definition. Define a function ψ on $[a, b)$ by setting

$$\psi(\beta) = \int_a^\beta f, \qquad \text{for all } \beta \text{ in } [a, b).$$

Then, if $\lim_{\beta \to b-} \psi(\beta)$ exists, this limit is called the **(improper) integral from** a to b of f, and is denoted by $\int_a^b f$. If $\lim_{\beta \to b-} \psi(\beta)$ does not exist, we say that $\int_a^b f$ does not exist. Again, this is consistent with the definition when $f \in R[a, b]$.

Example 8.9.2. Show that $\int_0^1 1/\sqrt{(1-x^2)}\,dx = \frac{1}{2}\pi$.

Proof. For $0 \leqslant \beta < 1$, let

$$\psi(\beta) = \int_0^\beta \frac{1}{\sqrt{(1-x^2)}}\, dx$$

$\Rightarrow \psi(\beta) = \arcsin \beta - \arcsin 0$ (by Section 8.6 and Theorem 8.5–C)

$\qquad\quad = \arcsin \beta$ (see Section 9.8)

$\Rightarrow \lim\limits_{\beta \to 1^-} \psi(\beta) = \arcsin 1$ (by Theorem 9.8–D)

$$= \frac{\pi}{2}. \qquad\qquad ◆$$

At this point, it is convenient to introduce a new word to describe such points as a and b above.

Definition.   A point at which f is not defined, or a point c such that $\lim\limits_{x \to c+} f(x)$ or $\lim\limits_{x \to c-} f(x)$ does not exist or is infinite, is called a **singularity** of f.

We now show how more complicated cases of discontinuity can be reduced to a combination of those above. Suppose now that a and b are singularities of f, but that $f \in R[\alpha, \beta]$ for all α, β satisfying $a < \alpha < \beta < b$. Let c be any point of (a, b). Then,

if $\qquad\qquad\qquad \int_a^c f$ exists i.e. if $\lim\limits_{\alpha \to a+} \int_\alpha^c f$ exists,

and if $\qquad\qquad\quad \int_c^b f$ exists i.e. if $\lim\limits_{\beta \to b-} \int_c^\beta f$ exists,

then we define $\int_a^b f$ to be the number given by

$$\int_a^b f = \int_a^c f + \int_c^b f.$$

At first sight, it looks as if this definition of $\int_a^b f$ depends on the choice of the point c. But this is not so; if d is in (a, b), say with $c < d$, then we can write, for $a < \alpha < c < d < \beta < b$,

$$\int_\alpha^c f + \int_c^\beta f = \int_\alpha^c f + \left[\int_c^d f + \int_d^\beta f\right] \qquad \text{(by Theorem 8.4–A)}$$

$$= \left[\int_\alpha^c f + \int_c^d f\right] + \int_d^\beta f$$

$$= \int_\alpha^d f + \int_d^\beta f \qquad\qquad \text{(also by Theorem 8.4–A)}$$

If we now take the limit as $\alpha \to a+$ and $\beta \to b-$, we have

$$\int_a^c f + \int_c^b f = \int_a^d f + \int_d^b f = \int_a^b f.$$

Example 8.9.3.   Evaluate $\int_0^1 1/\sqrt{[x(1-x)]}\, dx$.

Solution.   We observe that 0 and 1 are both singularities, but that $1/\sqrt{[x(1-x)]}$ is bounded (indeed, continuous) in any interval of the form $[\alpha, 1-\delta]$, where $\alpha > 0, \delta > 0$. We write

$$\int_0^1 f = \int_0^{\frac{1}{2}} f + \int_{\frac{1}{2}}^1 f.$$

Now,

$$\int_0^{\frac{1}{2}} f = \lim_{\alpha \to 0+} \int_\alpha^{\frac{1}{2}} \frac{1}{\sqrt{[x(1-x)]}} dx$$

$$= \lim_{\alpha \to 0+} (\arcsin 0 - \arcsin (2\alpha - 1))\dagger$$

$$= -\arcsin(-1)$$

$$= \frac{\pi}{2};$$

$$\int_{\frac{1}{2}}^1 f = \lim_{\beta \to 1-} \int_{\frac{1}{2}}^\beta \frac{1 \cdot}{\sqrt{[x(1-x)]}} dx$$

$$= \lim_{\beta \to 1-} (\arcsin (2\beta - 1) - \arcsin 0)\dagger$$

$$= \arcsin 1$$

$$= \frac{\pi}{2};$$

hence, adding, we have the result.   ◆

Next, if $a < d < b$, where d, and possibly a or b, is a singularity of f, and if $\int_a^d f, \int_d^b f$ exist as improper integrals, then we define

$$\int_a^b f = \int_a^d f + \int_d^b f.$$

We now show that Theorem 8.4–A generalises for improper integrals.

Theorem 8.9–A.   If $\int_a^b f$ is an improper integral, and $a < c < b$, then

$$\int_a^b f = \int_a^c f + \int_c^b f.$$

† Write $x(1-x) = (\frac{1}{2})^2 - (\frac{1}{2} - x)^2$, and use the substitution $1 - 2x = \sin \theta$.

Proof. Suppose, for example, that f has singularities at a, b and at a point $d \neq c$ between a and b, say with $d < c$. By definition,

$$\int_a^b f = \int_a^d f + \int_d^b f,$$

each term on the right being an improper integral. Further,

$$\int_d^b f = \lim_{\delta \to d+} \int_\delta^c f + \lim_{\beta \to b-} \int_c^\beta \quad \text{(by definition)}$$

$$= \int_d^c f + \int_c^b f.$$

Hence,

$$\int_a^b f = \int_a^d f + \int_d^c f + \int_c^b f$$

$$= \int_a^c f + \int_c^b f,$$

since $\int_a^d f + \int_d^c f = \int_a^c f$ by the remark preceding this theorem.   ◆

We now give some sufficient conditions for the existence of improper integrals (Theorems 8.9–C, 8.9–D). We require a preliminary result.

Theorem 8.9–B.   Let $f \in R[\alpha, b]$ for all α satisfying $a < \alpha \leqslant b$. If, to each $\varepsilon > 0$, there corresponds a $\delta > 0$ such that

$$\left| \int_{\alpha_1}^{\alpha_2} f \right| < \varepsilon,$$

for all pairs of numbers α_1, α_2 satisfying $a < \alpha_i < a + \delta$ $(i = 1, 2)$, then $\lim_{\alpha \to a+} \int_\alpha^b f$ exists.

Proof.   Define φ by setting

$$\varphi(\alpha) = \int_\alpha^b f.$$

Then,

$$\int_{\alpha_1}^{\alpha_2} f = \varphi(\alpha_1) - \varphi(\alpha_2),$$

and the result follows by applying Theorem 6.6–I.   ◆

This Cauchy type result is not very useful in practice. Of much more powerful application is the following test.

Theorem 8.9–C.   Suppose $f \in R[\alpha, b]$ for all α such that $a < \alpha \leqslant b$. If, for all x in $(a, b]$,

$$|f(x)| < \frac{c}{(x-a)^\mu}$$

where c is a positive constant and $0 < \mu < 1$, then $\int_a^b f$ exists as an improper integral.

Proof. Let $\alpha_1 < \alpha_2$. Then, by Theorem 8.3–F (Corollary),

$$\left| \int_{\alpha_1}^{\alpha_2} f \right| \leq \int_{\alpha_1}^{\alpha_2} \frac{c}{(x-a)^\mu}\, dx$$

$$= \left[\frac{c(x-a)^{1-\mu}}{1-\mu} \right]_{\alpha_1}^{\alpha_2}$$

$$< \frac{c(\alpha_2 - a)^{1-\mu}}{1-\mu} \qquad \text{since } \alpha_1 - a > 0$$

$$< \frac{c\delta^{1-\mu}}{1-\mu}$$

in the notation of Theorem 8.9–B, and this can be made smaller than any given ε by choosing δ suitably. By Theorem 8.9–B, therefore, the result is established.   ◆

Completely analogous is the following result, for a singularity at b.

Theorem 8.9–D.   Suppose $f \in R[a, \beta]$ for all β such that $a \leq \beta < b$. If, for all x in $[a, b)$,

$$|f(x)| < \frac{c}{(b-x)^\mu}$$

where c is a positive constant and $0 < \mu < 1$, then $\int_a^b f$ exists as an improper integral.

The proof is left to the reader.

Example 8.9.4.   If $p > 0$, $q > 0$, then

$$\int_0^1 x^{p-1}(1-x)^{q-1}\, dx$$

exists.

Proof. We again write $\int_0^1$ as $\int_0^{\frac{1}{2}} + \int_{\frac{1}{2}}^1$, and apply Theorems 8.9–C, 8.9–D. Consider

$$\int_0^{\frac{1}{2}} x^{p-1}(1-x)^{q-1}\, dx\,;$$

if $p \geq 1$, the function $x^{p-1}(1-x)^{q-1}$ is continuous and so belongs to $R[0, \frac{1}{2}]$. If $p < 1$,

$$|f(x)| = |x^{p-1}(1-x)^{q-1}|$$

$$< \frac{c}{x^{1-p}}$$

where c is any constant exceeding $\max\{(1-x)^{q-1} : 0 \leqslant x \leqslant \frac{1}{2}\}$. Since $0 < 1-p < 1$ when $0 < p < 1$, the integral under consideration exists, by Theorem 8.9–C. Likewise, if $q \geqslant 1$, the function to be integrated over $[\frac{1}{2}, 1]$ is continuous, and so is in $R[\frac{1}{2}, 1]$. If $0 < q < 1$,

$$|x^{p-1}(1-x)^{q-1}| < \frac{c}{(1-x)^{1-q}}$$

where $c > \max\{x^{p-1} : \frac{1}{2} \leqslant x \leqslant 1\}$. Since $0 < q < 1 \Rightarrow 0 < 1-q < 1$,

$$\int_{\frac{1}{2}}^{1} x^{p-1}(1-x)^{q-1}\, dx$$

exists by Theorem 8.9–D, and the result follows.   ◆

Another type of improper integral is that in which the range of integration is infinite. However, the methods used above are easily extended to cover this case also.

Definition.   Suppose that $\int_a^b f = \varphi(b)$ is defined for all $b > a$. Then, if $\lim\limits_{b \to \infty} \varphi(b)$ exists, as a real number, this limit is denoted by

$$\int_a^{\infty} f.$$

We also say, in this case, that $\int_a^{\infty} f$ **converges**.

Likewise, if $\int_a^b f = \psi(a)$ is defined for all $a < b$, and $\lim\limits_{a \to -\infty} \psi(a)$ exists, then this limit is denoted by

$$\int_{-\infty}^{b} f.$$

If both $\int_{-\infty}^{a} f, \int_a^{\infty} f$ are convergent, then their sum is denoted by

$$\int_{-\infty}^{\infty} f.$$

Note.   This sum is independent of the choice of a. For, if $c > a$,

$$\int_a^{\infty} f = \lim_{b \to \infty} \int_a^b f$$

$$= \lim_{b \to \infty} \left(\int_a^c f + \int_c^b f \right)$$

$$= \int_a^c f + \lim_{b \to \infty} \int_c^b f$$

$$= \int_a^c f + \int_c^{\infty} f.$$

On the other hand,

$$\int_{-\infty}^{a} f = \lim_{d \to -\infty} \int_{d}^{a} f$$

$$= \lim_{d \to -\infty} \left(\int_{d}^{c} f + \int_{c}^{a} f \right)$$

$$= \lim_{d \to -\infty} \int_{d}^{c} f + \int_{c}^{a} f$$

$$= \int_{-\infty}^{c} f + \int_{c}^{a} f.$$

Adding, we obtain

$$\int_{-\infty}^{a} f + \int_{a}^{\infty} f = \int_{-\infty}^{c} f + \int_{c}^{a} f + \int_{a}^{c} f + \int_{c}^{\infty} f$$

$$= \int_{-\infty}^{c} f + \int_{c}^{\infty} f.$$

We can again formulate a test for convergence of infinite integrals.

Theorem 8.9–E.   If the (improper) integral $\int_{a}^{b} f$ is defined for all $b > a$, and

$$|f(x)| < \frac{c}{x^{1+p}}$$

for all sufficiently large x, where $c > 0$, $p > 0$ are constants, then $\int_{a}^{\infty} f$ converges.

Proof.   Let $\varepsilon > 0$, and suppose that $x_2 > x_1$. If the inequality above is satisfied for $x > x_0$, and $x_1 > x_0$, then we have

$$\left| \int_{x_1}^{x_2} f \right| \leq \int_{x_1}^{x_2} \frac{c}{x^{1+p}} dx$$

$$= \left[-\frac{c}{px^p} \right]_{x_1}^{x_2}$$

$$\leq \frac{c}{px_1^p}$$

$$< \varepsilon$$

if $x_1 > (c/p\varepsilon)^{1/p}$.
Write $A = \max (x_0, (c/p\varepsilon)^{1/p})$; then,

$$\left| \int_{x_1}^{x_2} f \right| < \varepsilon \quad \text{if } x_2 > x_1 > A,$$

and if we now set $\varphi(x) = \int_a^x f$, and apply Theorem 6.6–I adapted for limits at ∞, the result follows.   ◆

Example 8.9.5.   If $t > 0$, then $\int_0^\infty x^{t-1} e^{-x} dx$ converges.

Proof.   Here, we have an infinite integral with a singularity at 0 if $t < 1$. Consider

$$\varphi(b) = \int_0^b x^{t-1} e^{-x} dx;$$

we first of all show that $\varphi(b)$ is defined for $b > 0$. Now, $x^{t-1} e^{-x}$ is continuous on $[0, b]$ if $t \geqslant 1$, and if $t < 1$ (N.B. $t > 0$!),

$$|x^{t-1} e^{-x}| < x^{t-1}$$

and so $\int_0^b x^{t-1} e^{-x} dx$ exists, by Theorem 8.9–C with $c = 1$. Next,

$$x^2(x^{t-1} e^{-x}) = x^{t+1} e^{-x}$$

$$\rightarrow 0 \quad \text{as } x \rightarrow \infty \quad \text{(see Theorem 9.2–G).}$$

This means

$$x^{t-1} e^{-x} < \frac{1}{x^2} \quad \text{if } x > x_0;$$

apply Theorem 8.9–E with $c = p = 1$, and the result follows.   ◆

Definition.   Define a function Γ by setting, for each $t > 0$,

$$\Gamma(t) = \int_0^\infty x^{t-1} e^{-x} dx.$$

This function is called the **Gamma function**, and it has interesting properties, as well as wide applications (see Exercise 37).

Theorem 8.9–E is reminiscent of the Comparison Test for series (Theorem 5.4–B). We compare $f(x)$ with the function value c/x^{1+p}, which can be directly shown to be improperly integrable over $[a, \infty)$. We can extend this to any function known to be integrable over $[a, \infty)$.

Theorem 8.9–F (Comparison test for Integrals).   Let f, g be real-valued functions defined on the set $E = \{x \in R : x \geqslant a\}$, and integrable over every subinterval $[a, b]$ of E. If, for every x in E,

$$0 \leqslant f(x) \leqslant g(x),$$

and $\int_a^\infty g$ converges, then $\int_a^\infty f$ converges.

Proof.   Suppose $\int_a^\infty g = \mu$. Then, for each point b of E,

$$\int_a^b f \leqslant \int_a^b g \leqslant \int_a^\infty g = \mu.$$

Thus, the function φ given by

$$\varphi(b) = \int_a^b f$$

is bounded above. Moreover, since f is non-negative, φ is non-decreasing, as a consequence of Corollary 1 of Theorem 8.2–C (suitably generalised, if necessary), and hence, by Theorem 6.6–G, $\lim_{b \to \infty} \varphi(b)$ exists; that is, $\int_a^\infty f$ is convergent.   ◆

Corollary.   Under the conditions of Theorem 8.9–F, if $\int_a^\infty f$ is divergent, then $\int_a^\infty g$ is also divergent.

Proof. If $\int_a^\infty g$ converges, so does $\int_a^\infty f$ by Theorem 8.9–F, a contradiction.   ◆

We can use this result to establish another test for the convergence of a series Σa_n.†

Theorem 8.9–G.   Let f be a positive, nonincreasing function defined on $\{x \in R : x \geqslant 1\}$ and integrable over every subinterval $[1, b]$. Then, the series $\Sigma f(n)$ is convergent if and only if $\int_1^\infty f$ is convergent. In this case,

$$0 \leqslant \Sigma f(n) - \int_1^\infty f \leqslant f(1).$$

Proof. Write $a_n = f(n)$; consider the interval $[r, r+1]$. Since f is nonincreasing, we have, for all x in $[r, r+1]$,

$$f(r+1) \leqslant f(x) \leqslant f(r)$$

$$\Leftrightarrow a_{r+1} \leqslant f(x) \leqslant a_r. \tag{1}$$

Define the functions L, U of $\{x \in R : x \geqslant 1\}$ by setting

$$L(x) = a_{r+1}, \quad (r < x \leqslant r+1) \qquad U(x) = a_r, \quad (r \leqslant x < r+1).$$

Then, for all $x \geqslant 1$,

$$0 \leqslant L(x) \leqslant f(x) \leqslant U(x).$$

(i) Suppose $\int_1^\infty f$ converges; then, by Theorem 8.9–F, $\int_1^\infty L$ is convergent. That is, $\lim_{b \to \infty} \int_1^b L$ exists; in particular, if n is any integer, $\lim_{n \to \infty} \int_1^n L$ exists. But,

$$\int_1^n L = \int_1^2 L + \int_2^3 L + \ldots + \int_{n-1}^n L$$

$$= a_2 + a_3 + \ldots + a_n$$

$$= A_n - a_1;$$

hence, $\lim A_n$ exists, i.e. Σa_n converges.

---

† This test is sometimes known as the **Cauchy–Maclaurin Integral Test** for series.

(ii) Suppose that Σa_n converges; then, $\lim A_n$ exists. But,

$$A_n = a_1 + a_2 + \ldots + a_n$$

$$= \int_1^2 U + \int_2^3 U + \ldots + \int_n^{n+1} U$$

$$= \int_1^{n+1} U$$

$$\Rightarrow \lim \int_1^n U \text{ exists, say with value } \mu.$$

Let b be any real number exceeding 1; if $[b]$ denotes the greatest integer not exceeding b, then clearly $[b] \leqslant b < [b] + 1$. Since $U(x) \geqslant 0$,

$$\int_1^{[b]} U \leqslant \int_1^b U \leqslant \int_1^{[b]+1} U$$

$$\Rightarrow \mu \leqslant \lim_{b \to \infty} \int_1^b U \leqslant \mu$$

$$\Rightarrow \int_1^\infty U \text{ converges}$$

$$\Rightarrow \int_1^\infty f \text{ converges, by Theorem 8.9–F.}$$

Finally, if Σa_n converges, it is clear that $\Sigma a_n \geqslant 0$ since the terms are all non-negative; further, by (1),

$$a_{r+1} \leqslant \int_r^{r+1} f$$

and so, for $n = 2, 3, 4, \ldots$

$$a_1 + a_2 + \ldots + a_n - \int_1^n f$$

$$= a_1 - \left(\int_1^2 f - a_2 \right) - \ldots - \left(\int_{n-1}^n f - a_n \right) \leqslant a_1.$$

Hence,

$$A_n - \int_1^n f \leqslant f(1)$$

$$\Rightarrow \lim A_n - \lim \int_1^n f \leqslant f(1)$$

$$\text{i.e. } \Sigma f(n) - \int_1^\infty f \leqslant f(1).$$

On the other hand, also by (1),

$$\int_r^{r+1} f \leqslant a_r$$

and so

$$A_n - \int_1^{n+1} f = \left(a_1 - \int_1^2 f \right) + \left(a_2 - \int_2^3 f \right) + \dots$$

$$+ \left(a_n - \int_n^{n+1} f \right) \geqslant 0$$

$$\Rightarrow \Sigma f(n) - \int_1^\infty f \geqslant 0. \qquad \blacklozenge$$

Example 8.9.6.   Discuss the series

$$\sum_{n=1}^\infty \frac{1}{n^s}, \qquad s > 0.$$

Consider the function given by

$$f(x) = \frac{1}{x^s}, \qquad \text{for all } x \geqslant 1.$$

Then, f is positive nonincreasing, and continuous.

$$\int_1^\infty f = \lim_{b \to \infty} \int_1^b f$$

$$= \lim_{b \to \infty} \int_1^b x^{-s} \, dx$$

$$= \lim_{b \to \infty} \left[\frac{b^{1-s} - 1}{1-s} \right] \qquad (s \neq 1).$$

If $0 < s < 1$, then $b^{1-s} \to \infty$, and so $\int_1^\infty f$ diverges, whence $\Sigma 1/n^s$ diverges, by Theorem 8.9–G. If $s > 1$, then $b^{1-s} \to 0$, and so $\int_1^\infty f$ converges. By Theorem 8.9–G, $\Sigma 1/n^s$ converges also. Finally, if $s = 1$, we note that

$$\int_1^b \frac{1}{x} \, dx = \ln |b|$$

$$\to \infty,$$

and so $\Sigma 1/n$ is divergent. $\qquad \blacklozenge$

Corollary.   The last remark of Example 8.9.6 shows how we can find an estimate for

$$1+\frac{1}{2}+\frac{1}{3}+\dots+\frac{1}{n};$$

for, by the methods of Theorem 8.9–G,

$$1+\frac{1}{2}+\dots+\frac{1}{n}-\int_1^n\frac{1}{x}\,dx\leqslant 1;$$

hence,

$$1+\frac{1}{2}+\dots+\frac{1}{n}\leqslant \ln n+1.$$

In fact, the difference between $1+\dots+1/n$ and $\ln n$ approaches a limit as $n\to\infty$. The value of this limit is approximately $0\cdot5772\dots$ and is denoted by γ. It is called **Euler's constant** after Leonhard Euler (Switzerland, 1707–1783).

Example 8.9.7.   Show that $\Sigma\,1/(n\ln n)$ diverges.

Proof.   Define g by setting, for $x\geqslant 2$,

$$g(x)=\frac{1}{x\ln x}.$$

Note that g has a singularity at 1. g is positive, continuous, and non-increasing. If $b>2$,

$$\int_2^b\frac{1}{x\ln x}\,dx=\ln\ln b-\ln\ln 2$$

$$\to\infty\quad\text{as }b\to\infty.$$

By Theorem 8.9–G, $\Sigma\,1/(n\ln n)$ diverges.   ◆
We have seen some aspects of the relationship between infinite integrals and series. There are other analogous results for infinite integrals to those established for series, which we will leave the reader to discover for himself. However, an analogue of Theorem 5.2–D is hardly to be expected, in view of the example immediately following Example 6.2.1. We now show there is no such analogue.

Example 8.9.8.   If $\int_1^\infty f$ converges, then it does *not* follow that $\lim_{x\to\infty} f(x)=0$.

Proof.   Consider the function f given by

$$
f(x) = \begin{cases}
n^2 x - n^3 + 1 & \text{if } n - \dfrac{1}{n^2} \leqslant x \leqslant n \\[2ex]
-n^2 x + n^3 + 1 & \text{if } n \leqslant x \leqslant n + \dfrac{1}{n^2} \\[2ex]
0 & \text{if } n + \dfrac{1}{n^2} \leqslant x \leqslant n + 1 - \dfrac{1}{(n+1)^2}.
\end{cases}
$$

The graph of f looks like that of Fig. 8.9.1.

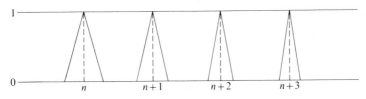

Fig. 8.9.1.

The area of each triangle is easily calculated. The height is unity, in every case, and the base of the triangle centred on n has length $2/n^2$. So the triangle on the point n has area $1/n^2$. Since $\Sigma\, 1/n^2$ converges, it follows that $\int_1^\infty f$ converges (though not by Theorem 8.9–G!). But $\lim\limits_{x \to \infty} f(x)$ does not exist. ◆

We finally mention that the techniques of integration by parts and by substitution can be generalised in an obvious way for improper integrals. We illustrate this with examples.

Example 8.9.9.   Evaluate $\int_0^1 x \ln x \, dx$.

Solution.   The point 0 is a singularity. So, if $0 < \alpha < 1$, consider

$$
\int_\alpha^1 x \ln x \, dx = \left[\frac{1}{2} x^2 \ln x \right]_\alpha^1 - \frac{1}{2} \int_\alpha^1 x^2 \cdot \frac{1}{x} \, dx
$$

$$
= -\frac{1}{2}\alpha^2 \ln \alpha - \frac{1}{2} \int_\alpha^1 x \, dx
$$

$$
= -\tfrac{1}{2}\alpha^2 \ln \alpha - \tfrac{1}{2}(\tfrac{1}{2} - \tfrac{1}{2}\alpha^2).
$$

Now, $\alpha^2 \ln \alpha \to 0$ as $\alpha \to 0+$, by Theorem 9.3–E, and so

$$
\int_0^1 x \ln x \, dx = \lim_{\alpha \to 0+} \int_\alpha^1 x \ln x \, dx
$$

$$
= -\tfrac{1}{4}.
$$

◆

Example 8.9.10. Find for what values of p $\int_1^\infty (\sin x)/x^p \, dx$ converges.

Solution. If we write

$$f(x) = \frac{\sin x}{x^p},$$

then for $x > 1$,

$$|f(x)| \leqslant \frac{1}{x^p}$$

and so $\int_1^\infty f$ converges if $p > 1$. However, we can do better than this; let us consider

$$\int_1^b \frac{\sin x}{x^p} \, dx$$

and integrate by parts.
Then,

$$\int_1^b \frac{\sin x}{x^p} \, dx = \left[-\frac{\cos x}{x^{p+1}} \right]_1^b - p \int_1^b \frac{\cos x}{x^{p+1}} \, dx$$

$$= -\frac{\cos b}{b^p} + \frac{\cos 1}{1} - p \int_1^b \frac{\cos x}{x^{p+1}} \, dx.$$

Now,

$$\left| \frac{\cos b}{b^p} \right| \leqslant \frac{1}{b^p}$$

$$\to 0 \quad \text{as } b \to \infty \text{ if } p > 0;$$

cos 1 is finite, and since

$$\left| \frac{\cos x}{x^{p+1}} \right| \leqslant \frac{1}{x^{p+1}} \qquad \text{for all } x,$$

it follows by Theorem 8.9–E that

$$\int_1^\infty \frac{\cos x}{x^{p+1}} \, dx$$

converges for $p > 0$. Hence, $\int_1^\infty (\sin x)/x^p \, dx$ converges if $p > 0$. ◆

Remark. The reader should observe that we cannot integrate by parts a second time to improve the inequality for p. This is the case because the term $1/b^p \to 0$ if, and only if, $p > 0$.

Example 8.9.11. Evaluate $\int_0^\infty 1/[(1+x)\sqrt{x}] \, dx$.

Solution.   Here, we have singularities at 0 and at ∞. Let

$$\varphi(b) = \int_0^b \frac{1}{(1+x)\sqrt{x}}\, dx.$$

This is itself an improper integral defined by

$$\lim_{\alpha \to 0+} \psi(\alpha) = \lim_{\alpha \to 0+} \int_\alpha^b \frac{1}{(1+x)\sqrt{x}}\, dx.$$

We make the substitution $x(t) = t^2$. Then, $Dx(t) = 2t$, and

$$\psi(\alpha) = \int_{\sqrt{\alpha}}^{\sqrt{b}} \frac{1}{(1+t^2)t} \cdot 2t\, dt$$

$$= \int_{\sqrt{\alpha}}^{\sqrt{b}} \frac{2}{1+t^2}\, dt$$

$$= 2\,(\arctan \sqrt{b} - \arctan \sqrt{\alpha})$$

$$\Rightarrow \lim_{\alpha \to 0+} \psi(\alpha) = \varphi(b) = 2 \arctan \sqrt{b}$$

$$\Rightarrow \lim_{b \to \infty} \varphi(b) = \int_0^\infty \frac{1}{(1+x)\sqrt{x}}\, dx$$

$$= 2 \cdot \frac{\pi}{2}$$

$$= \pi. \qquad \blacklozenge$$

Exercises

1. Deduce, from Theorem 8.2–A, that if $a \leqslant c < d \leqslant b$, and $f \in R[a, b]$, then $f \in R[c, d]$.
2. Show that if $f \in R[a, b]$, then f^+ and f^- also belong to $R[a, b]$.
3. Define f on $[0, 1]$ as follows:

$$f(0) = 0$$

$$f(x) = \frac{1}{2^n} \quad \text{if} \quad \frac{1}{2^{n+1}} < x \leqslant \frac{1}{2^n} \qquad n = 0, 1, 2, \ldots$$

   Show that $\int_0^1 f$ is defined.
4. Let f be continuous and non-negative in $[a, b]$. If $f(x)$ is not zero for all x in $[a, b]$, prove that $\int_a^b f > 0$. Show, by an example, that the result may be false if f is not continuous.
5. Let f be continuous and nondecreasing in $[0, 1]$. Define F by

$$F(x) = \frac{1}{x} \int_0^x f, \qquad 0 < x < 1.$$

   Prove that F is nondecreasing in $(0, 1)$.

6. Show that, if n is a positive integer,

$$0 < \int_0^{\pi/2} \sin^n < \int_0^{\pi/2} \sin^{n-1}.$$

7. Prove that $\int_0^1 x \arctan x \, dx = \frac{1}{4}\pi - \frac{1}{2}$.

8. Evaluate $\int_1^2 1/[x(1+x^4)] \, dx$ by the substitution $t = g(x) = x^4$.

9. Evaluate

$$\int_0^{\frac{1}{4}\pi} \frac{1}{a^2 \cos^2 x + b^2 \sin^2 x} \, dx$$

by the substitution $t = g(x) = \tan x$.

10. Evaluate

$$\int_0^{\frac{1}{4}\pi} \frac{x \sin x \cos x}{a^2 \cos^2 x + b^2 \sin^2 x} \, dx.$$

(Integrate by parts and use Exercise 9).

11. Evaluate

(i) $\displaystyle\int_0^1 \frac{1}{4a^2 + x^2} \, dx$

(ii) $\displaystyle\int_0^1 \frac{1}{4a^2 + x^2} \, da.$

(Be careful!).

12. Suppose that

$$I_n = \int_0^{\frac{1}{2}\pi} \sin^n;$$

prove that

$$nI_n = (n-1)I_{n-2} \qquad (n = 2, 3, \ldots)$$

(Write $\sin = -D \cos$, and integrate by parts).

13. Show that

$$I_{2n+1} = \frac{2 . 4 \ldots 2n}{3 . 5 \ldots 2n+1}$$

$$I_{2n} = \frac{1 . 3 \ldots 2n-1}{2 . 4 \ldots 2n} \cdot \frac{\pi}{2}.$$

14. Prove that if f is continuous in the closed interval $[-a, a]$, and is an *even* function, then

$$\int_{-a}^a f = 2 \int_0^a f.$$

15. Prove that if f is continuous on $[-a, a]$, and is an *odd* function,

$$\int_{-a}^{a} f = 0.$$

16. Suppose that f is continuous on $[0, \pi]$, and in this interval,

$$f(x) = f(\pi - x).$$

Prove that $\int_0^\pi f = 2\int_0^{\frac{1}{2}\pi} f$.

17. Evaluate

$$\int_0^\pi \frac{x \sin x}{1 + \cos^2 x} dx.$$

(Use Exercise 16).

18. If $I(m, n) = \int_0^1 x^m (1-x)^n \, dx$, where m, n are positive integers, show that

$$(m+n+1)I(m, n) = nI(m, n-1)$$

and deduce that

$$I(m, n) = \frac{m!n!}{(m+n+1)!}.$$

19. Prove that

(i) $\displaystyle\sum_{r=1}^{n} \frac{2}{2n+2r-1} \to \ln 2$ as $n \to \infty$

(ii) $\displaystyle\frac{1}{n^p} \sum_{r=1}^{n} r^{p-1} \to \frac{1}{p}$ as $n \to \infty$, where $p > 0$ is constant.

(iii) $\displaystyle\sum_{r=1}^{n} \frac{1}{\sqrt{(n^2 + r^2)}} \to \ln(1 + \sqrt{2})$ as $n \to \infty$.

20. Suppose that f is positive and continuous on $[a, b]$. If M denotes the maximum value of f on $[a, b]$, show that

$$M = \lim \left(\int_a^b f^n \right)^{1/n}.$$

21. Show that the following integrals exist:

(i) $\displaystyle\int_0^1 \frac{\sqrt{x}}{\sin x} dx$; (ii) $\displaystyle\int_0^1 \sin x \ln(1-x) \, dx$;

(iii) $\displaystyle\int_1^\infty \frac{\cos x + \sin x}{(x+1)(x+2)} dx.$

22. Show that $\int_1^\infty (\cos x)/x^p \, dx$ exists, if $p > 0$.

23. Show that $\int_0^\infty (\cos x)/x^p \, dx$ exists, if $0 < p < 1$.
24. Show that $\int_0^\infty (\sin x)/x^p \, dx$ exists, if $0 < p < 2$.
25. Show that $\int_0^\infty x^{p-1}/(1+x) \, dx$ exists, if $0 < p < 1$.
26. Prove that

$$\int_0^\infty \left(\frac{\sin x}{x}\right)^2 dx = \int_0^\infty \frac{\sin x}{x} \, dx.$$

(Integrate by parts.)
27. Show that

$$\int_a^b \frac{1}{(x-a)^p} \, dx, \qquad \int_a^b \frac{1}{(b-x)^p} \, dx$$

do not exist if p is a constant such that $p \geqslant 1$.
28. The function f is continuous on $[a, b]$ for all $b > a$. If

$$f(x) > \frac{1}{x}$$

for all $x > x_0$, show that $\int_a^\infty f$ does not exist.
29. Evaluate

$$\int_0^{\frac{1}{2}\pi} \frac{1}{a^2 \cos^2 x + b^2 \sin^2 x} \, dx.$$

(Compare this with Exercise 9.)
30. If p, q are positive constants, show that

$$\int_0^\infty \frac{x^{p-1}}{(1+x)^{p+q}} \, dx = \int_0^1 t^{p-1}(1-t)^{q-1} \, dt.$$

[Use the substitution $x = x(t) = t/(1-t)$].
31. Discuss the convergence of

$$\sum_{n=2}^\infty \frac{1}{n(\ln n)^2}.$$

32. Discuss the convergence of

(i) $\displaystyle\sum_{n=2}^\infty \frac{1}{n(\ln n)^p}$ (ii) $\displaystyle\sum_{n=3}^\infty \frac{1}{n \ln n(\ln \ln n)^p}$

(iii) $\displaystyle\sum_{n=3}^\infty \frac{1}{n^r(\ln n)^q(\ln \ln n)^p}$

where $p > 0, q > 0, r > 0$.
33. Show that if $\int_{-\infty}^\infty f$ exists, then the value of this integral is

$$\lim_{b \to \infty} \int_{-b}^b f.$$

Show, by considering the function given by $f(x) = x^3$, that the converse is not true i.e. that $\lim\limits_{b \to \infty} \int_{-b}^{b} x^3 \, dx$ exists, but $\int_{-\infty}^{\infty} x^3 \, dx$ is not defined.

The limit $\lim\limits_{b \to \infty} \int_{-b}^{b} f$, which may exist although $\int_{-\infty}^{\infty} f$ does not, has got a special name. It is called the **Cauchy Principal Value** of $\int_{-\infty}^{\infty} f$.

34. Suppose that f is unbounded only at the point c of $[a, b]$. Then, we can define $\int_{a}^{b} f$ as

$$\lim_{\varepsilon \to 0+} \int_{a}^{c-\varepsilon} f + \lim_{\delta \to 0+} \int_{c+\delta}^{b} f,$$

provided this limit exists. It may happen that this limit does not exist, as $\varepsilon \to 0$, $\delta \to 0$ independently. However, taking $\delta = \varepsilon$, we may find that

$$\lim_{\varepsilon \to 0+} \int_{a}^{c-\varepsilon} f + \lim_{\varepsilon \to 0+} \int_{c+\varepsilon}^{b} f$$

exists. This is called the **Cauchy Principal Value** of $\int_{a}^{b} f$.

Show that

$$\int_{0}^{3} \frac{1}{(x-1)^5} \, dx$$

does not exist, but has a principal value of $\frac{15}{64}$.

35. Does $\int_{0}^{4} 1/(3-x)$ exist? Does it have a principal value?

36. Prove the following result, using Theorem 8.2-B: "If f is bounded on $[a, b]$, and the discontinuities of f have only a finite number of limit points, then $f \in R[a, b]$". Show how the function of Example 8.2.2 violates this condition.

37. Prove that $\Gamma(n+1) = n\Gamma(n)$, and deduce that if n is a positive integer, then $\Gamma(n) = n!$ Show that the right-hand side of Exercise 30 can be written in the form

$$\frac{\Gamma(p)\Gamma(q)}{\Gamma(p+q)}.$$

CHAPTER 9

The Elementary Functions

9.1 Introduction

Our purpose in this chapter is to derive what are known as the "elementary" functions. We meet these from our earliest encounters with calculus; they include such functions as sin, cos, ln, the exponential function and the hyperbolic functions.

For these, our starting point will be a series, defined for each real number x, and we shall show that this series exhibits various desirable characteristics. For example, it will be convergent for each x, and so define a function; this function will be continuous and differentiable, and have convenient algebraic properties e.g. $f(x+y) = f(x) \cdot f(y)$. From this single series, we shall derive the various other "elementary" functions named above.

Some of the functions we have already met in Chapter 3 are classed as **elementary**. By *elementary* we mean, roughly speaking, that these are the basic functions from which other functions are built.

The *constant functions* on R will be classed as elementary; so will the *identity function* on R. For simplicity, we shall also classify as elementary, functions which can be formed from these by algebraic operations. Thus, the functions j_n given by $j_n(x) = x^n$ (for $x \in R$, $n \in N$), the *polynomial functions* and the *rational functions* will be classed as elementary.

9.2 The Exponential Function

Suppose $f: R \to R$ is a continuous function with derivatives of all orders, and suppose that f has a Maclaurin series given by

$$f(x) = f(0) + xDf(0) + \frac{1}{2!}x^2 D^2 f(0) + \ldots$$

where

$$\frac{x^n}{n!} D^n f(\theta x) \to 0 \qquad (0 < \theta < 1).$$

The expansion (1) is valid for all values of x such that the series

$$\sum_{n=0}^{\infty} \frac{x^n}{n!} D^n f(0)$$

converges, and the value of the sum will be, in this case, $f(x)$ [but see Section 7.8].

Suppose further that f is a function which satisfies the condition $Df(x) = f(x)$ for all $x \in R$. Then, the series (1) has the especially simple form

$$f(0)\left\{1 + x + \frac{x^2}{2!} + \ldots\right\}.$$

Suppose, for simplicity, that the function f also satisfies the condition $f(0) = 1$. (If $f(0) \neq 0$, we can arrange to divide by the appropriate scalar factor). Then the function f, continuous with derivatives of all orders, satisfying $Df = f$ and $f(0) = 1$ has the Maclaurin Series

$$1 + x + \frac{x^2}{2!} + \ldots \tag{2}$$

Conversely, we may ask : given the series (2), does it define a function? Is this function unique? What properties does it have? We begin with the following result.

Theorem 9.2–A. Let x be a real number. Then, the series (2) is absolutely convergent for all values of x.

Proof. The general term of the series (2) is

$$u_n = \frac{x^{n-1}}{(n-1)!}.$$

Clearly, if $x = 0$, the series (2) converges, with sum 1. If $x \neq 0$, then

$$\left|\frac{u_{n+1}}{u_n}\right| = \frac{|x|}{n}$$

$$\to 0$$

for all x, and so $\Sigma|u_n|$ converges by Theorem 5.4–G, for all x. $\blacklozenge$

Note. Though this does not concern us in this book, the series

$$\sum_{n=0}^{\infty} \frac{z^n}{n!}$$

is convergent for all complex numbers z.

Definition. The series

$$\sum_{n=0}^{\infty} \frac{x^n}{n!}$$

is absolutely convergent for all values of $x \in R$. Denote the sum of the series by $E(x)$.

We now investigate the properties of the function E.

Theorem 9.2–B.   Let $x_1, x_2 \in R$. Then,

$$E(x_1 + x_2) = E(x_1) . E(x_2).$$

Proof.   We have

$$E(x_1) = 1 + x_1 + \frac{x_1^2}{2!} + \dots$$

$$E(x_2) = 1 + x_2 + \frac{x_2^2}{2!} + \dots;$$

since both series converge absolutely, so does their Cauchy product, to the number $E(x_1) . E(x_2)$ by Theorem 5.9–B. Hence,

$$E(x_1)E(x_2) = w_0 + w_1 + w_2 + \dots,$$

where

$$w_n = \sum_{k=0}^{n} \frac{x_1^k}{k!} \frac{x_2^{n-k}}{(n-k)!}$$

$$= \frac{1}{n!} \sum_{k=0}^{n} \frac{n!}{k!(n-k)!} x_1^k x_2^{n-k}$$

$$= \frac{1}{n!} \sum_{k=0}^{n} \binom{n}{k} x_1^k x_2^{n-k}$$

$$= \frac{1}{n!}(x_1 + x_2)^n \qquad \text{(by the Binomial Theorem).}$$

So,

$$E(x_1) . E(x_2) = \sum_{n=0}^{\infty} \frac{(x_1 + x_2)^n}{n!}$$

$$= E(x_1 + x_2). \qquad \blacklozenge$$

Remark.   The property $E(0) = 1$ can be deduced from Theorem 9.2–B, although it is already evident by putting $x = 0$ in (2).

We next show that the function E coincides with its derivative.

Theorem 9.2–C.   For all $x \in R$, $DE(x) = E(x)$.

Proof.   Suppose $h \neq 0$, and form the chord function:

$$\frac{E(x+h) - E(x)}{h} = \frac{E(x) . E(h) - E(x)}{h} \qquad \text{(by Theorem 9.2–B)}$$

$$= E(x) \left\{ \frac{E(h) - 1}{h} \right\}.$$

Now,

$$E(h) - 1 = h + \frac{h^2}{2!} + \frac{h^3}{3!} + \dots \qquad \text{(by (2))}$$

$$\Rightarrow \frac{E(h) - 1}{h} = 1 + \frac{h}{2!} + \frac{h^2}{3!} + \dots$$

$$\Rightarrow \left| \frac{E(h) - 1}{h} - 1 \right| \leqslant \frac{|h|}{2!} + \frac{|h|^2}{3!} + \dots$$

$$\leqslant \frac{|h|}{2} + \frac{|h|^2}{2} + \dots$$

$$= \frac{|h|}{2(1 - |h|)}$$

$$\to 0 \qquad \text{as } |h| \to 0$$

$$\Rightarrow \lim_{h \to 0} \frac{E(h) - 1}{h} = 1$$

$$\Rightarrow DE(x) = \lim_{h \to 0} \frac{E(x+h) - E(x)}{h} = E(x). \qquad \blacklozenge$$

We now ask how many functions like E there can be. The answer is given in the next theorem.

Theorem 9.2–D. The function E has the properties $E(0) = 1$, $DE = E$. If F also satisfies $F(0) = 1$, $DF = F$, then $F = E$. In short, the function E is unique.

Proof. Consider the function Q given by

$$Q(x) = F(x) . E(-x);$$

then, for all $x \in R$,

$$DQ(x) = DF(x) . E(-x) - F(x) . DE(-x) \qquad \text{(Theorem 7.4–A)}$$

$$= F(x)E(-x) - F(x) . E(-x) \qquad \text{(by hypothesis)}$$

$$= 0$$

$$\Leftrightarrow Q(x) \quad \text{is a constant function}$$

$$\Rightarrow Q(x) = Q(0), \qquad \forall \, x \in R,$$

$$\Rightarrow F(x)E(-x) = 1. \qquad (3)$$

Then,

$$F(x) = F(x) . E(x - x)$$

$$= \{F(x)E(-x)\} . E(x) \qquad \text{(by Theorem 9.2–B)}$$

$$= E(x) \qquad \text{by (3).} \qquad \blacklozenge$$

Note on the proof.   Why choose $Q(x) = F(x)E(-x)$, you say? The answer is given in the last three lines of the proof; $E(x-x) = E(0) = 1$ on the one hand, and is $E(-x) \cdot E(x)$ on the other. So it will follow that $F = E$ if we can show $F(x)E(-x)$ to be constant. The proof is thus reconstructed by a reverse argument, and set down as a direct argument.

Definition.   The unique function E which satisfies the conditions $DE = E$, $E(0) = 1$ and $E(x+y) = E(x) \cdot E(y)$ for all x, y in R is called the **exponential function**. It is usually denoted by exp.

Remark.   The function exp defined above has the series (2) as its Maclaurin Series.

Definition.   We denote the real number exp 1 by the letter e. It can be shown that $e \sim 2 \cdot 71828 \ldots$

Theorem 9.2–E.   For every $x \in R$, $\exp(x) = e^x$.

Proof.   Firstly, $1 = \exp(0) = \exp(1-1) = \exp 1 \cdot \exp(-1) = e \cdot \exp(-1)$. Hence, we have $\exp(-1) = 1/e = e^{-1}$. Next, let $n \in N$;

$$\exp n = \exp(1+1+ \ldots +1) \qquad (n \text{ terms})$$

$$= (\exp 1)^n \qquad\qquad (\text{by Theorem 9.2–B})$$

$$= e^n.$$

Using the first part of the proof, it follows that $\exp(n) = e^n$, $\forall\ n \in Z$. If now $q \in Z$, then

$$q \cdot 1/q = 1 \ \Rightarrow\ \exp(q \cdot 1/q) = \exp 1$$

$$\Rightarrow\ \exp(1/q+1/q+ \ldots +1/q) = e \qquad (q \text{ terms})$$

$$\Rightarrow\ (\exp 1/q)^q = e$$

$$\Rightarrow\ \exp 1/q = e^{1/q} \qquad (\text{defined since } e > 0).$$

It follows that if $x \in Q$, i.e. $x = p/q$ with p, $q \in Z$, then $\exp x = e^x$. Finally, if $x \in R$, it can be shown that $\exp(x) = e^x$, by using the fact that every real number is the limit of a sequence of rationals. This is left as an exercise.   ◆

Theorem 9.2–F.   The function exp is increasing (and hence is $(1, 1)$). Its range is $R^+ = \{x \in R : x > 0\}$.

Proof.   Clearly, if $x \geqslant 0$, $\exp(x) \geqslant 1$, by considering the series (2). Next,

$$\exp(-x) = 1/\exp x.$$

$$\Rightarrow\ \exp(-x) > 0, \qquad \text{since } \exp x > 0.$$

So, for all x, $\exp x > 0$.

Since $D(\exp) = \exp$, it follows that $D(\exp x) > 0$ for all $x \in R$; so, by Corollary 3 of Theorem 7.7–A, exp is increasing.

Next, if $x > 0$, $\exp x > 1 + x$

$$\Rightarrow \lim_{x \to \infty} \exp x = \infty.$$

Again, since $\exp(-x) = 1/\exp x$, we have

$$\lim_{x \to -\infty} \exp x = 0.$$

Finally, exp is continuous, for all $x \in R$, by Theorem 9.2–C and Theorem 7.2–A, and so takes every positive real number as a function value (Theorem 6.8–D, Corollary 2) i.e.

$$\mathscr{R}(\exp) = \{x \in R : x > 0\} = R^+. \qquad \blacklozenge$$

We next compare the growth rate of exp with the power functions.

Theorem 9.2–G. Let $n \in N$; then

(i) $\displaystyle \lim_{x \to \infty} \frac{\exp x}{x^n} = \infty$;

(ii) $\displaystyle \lim_{x \to -\infty} \frac{\exp x}{x^n} = 0.$

Proof. (i) we have

$$\exp x = 1 + x + \frac{x^2}{2!} + \ldots + \frac{x^{n+1}}{(n+1)!} + \ldots$$

$$\Rightarrow \exp x > \frac{x^{n+1}}{(n+1)!} \quad \text{if } x > 0, \qquad \text{for any } n \in N$$

$$\Rightarrow \frac{\exp x}{x^n} > \frac{x}{(n+1)!} \quad \text{if } x > 0, \qquad \text{for any } n \in N.$$

$$\Rightarrow \lim_{x \to \infty} \frac{\exp x}{x^n} \geqslant \frac{1}{(n+1)!} \lim_{x \to \infty} x.$$

Since $\lim_{x \to \infty} x = \infty$, (i) follows. Thus, exp increases more rapidly than any power of x.

(ii) We have

$$\exp(-x) = \frac{1}{\exp x} \quad \text{for all } x > 0,$$

$$\Rightarrow \frac{\exp(-x)}{(-x)^n} = \frac{1}{(-x)^n \exp x} \quad \forall\, x > 0, \forall\, n \in N.$$

Now, $\lim_{x \to \infty} \exp x = \infty$, and $\lim_{x \to \infty} (-x)^n = \pm\infty$, according as n is even or odd. So $1/[(-x)^n \exp x] \to 0$, which proves (ii). This shows that as $x \to -\infty$, exp decays more slowly than powers of x. ◆

Corollary. Theorem 9.2–G holds for any real number $n \geqslant 0$. The graph of the function exp is shown in Fig. 9.2.1.

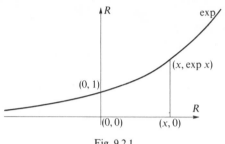

Fig. 9.2.1.

9.3 The Logarithmic Function

By Theorem 9.2–F, the function exp is a $(1, 1)$ function of R with range R^+. So, by Section 3.7, there is an inverse function $\lambda : R^+ \to R$.

Definition. The **logarithmic function** is the function λ of R^+, with range R, which is the inverse function of exp. It will be denoted by ln.†

Theorem 9.3–A. For all $x \in R$, $\quad \ln(\exp x) = x$;

for all $y \in R^+$, $\quad \exp(\ln y) = y$.

Proof. This follows from the definition and Theorem 3.7–A. ◆
We now investigate the properties of the function ln.

Theorem 9.3–B. The function ln is continuous and differentiable, for all $x \in R^+$. Further,

$$D(\ln x) = \frac{1}{x}, \quad \forall \, x \in R^+.$$

Proof. The function exp is never zero, and so $D(\exp) = \exp$ is also never zero, and is defined for all $x \in R$. We may therefore appeal to Theorem 7.5–A. Then, $D \ln$ exists, for every $x \in R^+$. So ln is differentiable on R^+ and so, by Theorem 7.2–A, is continuous for all $x \in R^+$. Finally, let $x \in R^+$; since exp has range R^+, there is a point $\xi \in R$ such that $\exp \xi = x$. By Theorem 7.5–A again,

$$D \ln x = \frac{1}{D \exp \xi}$$

† See footnote on page 317.

$$= \frac{1}{\exp \xi}$$

$$= \frac{1}{x}. \qquad \blacklozenge$$

Theorem 9.3–C. For all $x, y \in R^+$, $\ln xy = \ln x + \ln y$.

Proof. By Theorem 9.3–A, $x = \exp(\ln x)$, $y = \exp(\ln y)$; so,

$$xy = \exp(\ln x) . \exp(\ln y)$$

$$= \exp(\ln x + \ln y) \qquad \text{(Theorem 9.2–B)}$$

$$\Leftrightarrow \ln xy = \ln x + \ln y, \qquad \text{using Theorem 9.3–A again.} \qquad \blacklozenge$$

Theorem 9.3–D. $\ln e = 1$; $\ln 1 = 0$; $\lim\limits_{x \to \infty} \ln x = \infty$; $\lim\limits_{x \to 0+} \ln x = -\infty$.

Proof. We have

$$e = \exp 1 \;\Rightarrow\; \ln e = \ln(\exp 1) = 1 \qquad \text{by Theorem 9.3–A};$$

$$1 = \exp 0 \;\Rightarrow\; \ln 1 = \ln(\exp 0) = 0 \qquad \text{by Theorem 9.3–A}.$$

To show $\lim\limits_{x \to \infty} \ln x = \infty$, consider the function $\ln \circ \exp$. Now, by Theorem 6.7–D, if a is a point of R, and $b = \lim \exp x$, then

$$\lim_{x \to b} \ln x = \lim_{x \to a} \ln(\exp x)$$

$$= \lim_{x \to a} x$$

$$= a.$$

Let $a \to +\infty$, and the result follows by a remark in Theorem 9.2–F. The last part is similar. $\qquad \blacklozenge$

We next show that the growth rate of $\ln x$ as $x \to \infty$ is slower than any power of x, but as $x \to 0+$, $\ln x$ decays more rapidly than any power of x.

Theorem 9.3–E. If $n \in N$,

(i) $\lim\limits_{x \to \infty} \dfrac{\ln x}{x^n} = 0$; $\qquad$ (ii) $\lim\limits_{x \to 0+} \dfrac{\ln x}{x^n} = -\infty$.

Proof. If $x \geqslant 1$, then

$$x^n \geqslant x \;\Rightarrow\; \frac{\ln x}{x^n} \leqslant \frac{\ln x}{x}.$$

Now,

$$x = \exp(\ln x)$$

$$\Rightarrow \frac{\ln x}{x} = \frac{j}{\exp}(\ln x)$$

where j is the identity function on R^+. Thus,

$$\lim_{x \to \infty} \frac{\ln x}{x} = \lim_{x \to \infty} \frac{j}{\exp}(\ln x)$$

$$= \lim_{x \to \infty} \frac{x}{\exp x} \qquad \text{(by Theorem 6.7–D)}$$

$$= 0 \qquad \text{(by Theorem 9.2–G).}$$

The second half is similar.   ◆

9.4 Associated Exponential and Logarithmic Functions

In Section 9.2, we saw that the exponential function can be written in the form $\exp x = e^x$, where e is a real number, approximately $2{\cdot}72$. Clearly, for each positive real a, we can define a function Q_a given by $Q_a(x) = a^x$. For example, we have known for a long time functions like $f(x) = 2^x$. It is easy to define if $x \in Z$, and we extend the definition in an obvious way to Q, and then to R. The function Q_2 is illustrated in Fig. 9.4.1.

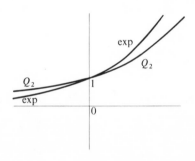

Fig. 9.4.1.

Definition.   Let $a > 0$. The function $Q_a : R \to R$ given by

$$Q_a(x) = a^x$$

is called the **exponential mapping with base** a.

The function exp is of course, just Q_e. But the functions Q_a and exp are closely related.

Theorem 9.4–A.   For all x, $Q_a(x) = \exp(x \ln a)$.

Proof.   Since $a > 0, a \in \mathscr{R}(\exp) \Rightarrow \exists\, k$ such that $a = \exp k = e^k$; then, $a^x = e^{kx}$ (by Theorems 9.2–B, 9.2–E) $= \exp(xk) = \exp(x \ln a)$, since $a = \exp k \Leftrightarrow k = \ln a$. Thus, $Q_a(x) = \exp(x \ln a)$.   ◆

Theorem 9.4–B. For all x, y, and each $a > 0$,

$$Q_a(x) \cdot Q_a(y) = Q_a(x+y)$$

$$Q_a(-x) = \frac{1}{Q_a(x)}$$

$$\{Q_a(x)\}^y = Q_a(xy).$$

The proofs are left to the reader.

Theorem 9.4–C. Q_a is differentiable, and

$$DQ_a(x) = \ln a \cdot Q_a(x).$$

Proof. We have

$$Q_a(x) = \exp(x \ln a)$$

$$\Rightarrow DQ_a(x) = D(\exp(x \ln a)) \cdot D(x \ln a) \qquad \text{(by Theorem 7.4–A)}$$

$$= \exp(x \ln a) \cdot \ln a$$

$$= \ln a \cdot Q_a(x). \qquad \blacklozenge$$

Theorem 9.4–D. Q_a is a $(1, 1)$ continuous function of R with range R^+. The proof is left to the reader.

Definition. By Theorem 9.4–D, Q_a has an inverse function defined on R^+ and taking values in R. This is called the **logarithmic mapping with base** a. It is denoted by $\log_a$. $\log_e$ is the function of Section 9.3.†

Example 9.4.1. The most important logarithmic mapping with base different from e is $\log_{10}$ i.e. $a = 10$. This is widely used in technology.

Theorem 9.4–E. If $a > 0$,

(i) $\log_a x = \ln x \cdot \log_a e = \dfrac{\ln x}{\ln a}$

(ii) $D \log_a x = \dfrac{1}{x \ln a} = \dfrac{\log_a e}{x}.$

Proof. (i) Let $\log_a x = y$; then,

$$x = Q_a(y), \qquad \text{by definition}$$

$$= \exp(y \ln a) \qquad \text{by Theorem 9.4–A}$$

$$\Rightarrow \ln x = y \ln a \qquad \text{since } \ln \circ \exp x = x$$

$$\Rightarrow \cdot y = \frac{\ln x}{\ln a}. \tag{1}$$

---

† $\log_e$ is denoted by ln, standing for **logarithm Napierian**, or **logarithm natural**, after the Scottish mathematician, John Napier (1550–1617).

Now, in particular, taking $x = e$,

$$\log_a e = \frac{1}{\ln a} \qquad \text{by (1)}$$

$$\Rightarrow y = \ln x . \log_a e$$

$$\Leftrightarrow \log_a x = \ln x . \log_a e.$$

This proves (i).

(ii)
$$\log_a x = \frac{\ln x}{\ln a}$$

$$\Rightarrow D \log_a x = D\left(\frac{\ln x}{\ln a}\right)$$

$$= \frac{1}{x \ln a}$$

$$= \frac{\log_a e}{x} \qquad \text{by (1).} \qquad \blacklozenge$$

Theorem 9.4–E gives a recipe for changing bases. It shows how the functions $\log_a$ and ln are related. From this we can deduce how $\log_a$ and $\log_b$ $(a > 0, b > 0)$ are related, by using their common relation with ln (see Exercise 4).

9.5 The Hyperbolic Functions

We began, in Section 9.2, by considering the Maclaurin series of a function f, and imposing conditions on f. Consider

$$\exp x = 1 + x + \frac{x^2}{2!} + \frac{x^3}{3!} + \dots .$$

Here, we assumed

$$f(0) = Df(0) = D^2f(0) = \dots = 1.$$

In this section we shall look at different restrictions. In the Maclaurin series

$$f(x) = f(0) + xDf(0) + \frac{x^2}{2!} D^2f(0) + \dots$$

we might suppose f to be even, i.e. $f(-x) = f(x)$, for all x. This would imply that $Df(0) = D^3f(0) = D^5f(0) = \dots = 0$ (this is easy to verify). Suppose that f is not only even, but has the additional property that $f(0) = D^2f(0) = D^4f(0) = \dots$ and suppose the common value is

1. Then, f has the Maclaurin series

$$f(x) = 1 + \frac{x^2}{2!} + \frac{x^4}{4!} + \ldots.$$

This series is absolutely convergent for all x (easily verified).

Definition.   The series

$$\sum_{n=0}^{\infty} \frac{x^{2n}}{2n!}$$

is absolutely convergent for all x. For each x, we denote its sum by cosh x. Then, cosh is a function of R into R. It is called the **hyperbolic cosine**.

Theorem 9.5–A.   For all x, cosh $x = \frac{1}{2}(\exp x + \exp(-x))$.

Proof. This is a trivial consequence of the definition, using the Maclaurin series for $\exp x$ and $\exp(-x)$.

We may consider the function φ which is an odd function i.e. $\varphi(-x) = -\varphi(x)$; then this implies that in the Maclaurin series for φ, $\varphi(0) = D^2\varphi(0) = D^4\varphi(0) = \ldots = 0$. If we suppose further that $D\varphi(0) = D^3\varphi(0) = \ldots = 1$, then φ has the Maclaurin series

$$\varphi(x) = x + \frac{x^3}{3!} + \frac{x^5}{5!} + \ldots$$

$$= \frac{1}{2}\{\exp x - \exp(-x)\}.$$

Definition.   The series

$$\sum_{n=0}^{\infty} \frac{x^{2n+1}}{2n+1!}$$

is absolutely convergent for all x. For each x, denote its sum by sinh x. Then sinh is a function of R into R. It is called the **hyperbolic sine**.

We now try to investigate the properties of sinh and cosh. We can examine their derivatives, and their relation to each other. We shall sum up the results in the following theorem.

Theorem 9.5–B.   (i) cosh $0 = 1$, sinh $0 = 0$,
  (ii) $D \cosh x = \sinh x$, $D \sinh x = \cosh x$
  (iii) $\cosh^2 x - \sinh^2 x = 1$.

Proof.   (i) follows immediately from the equations

$$\cosh x = \frac{1}{2}(\exp x + \exp(-x)),$$

$$\sinh x = \frac{1}{2}(\exp x - \exp(-x)).$$

(ii) By Theorem 7.3–A

$$D \cosh x = \tfrac{1}{2}D(\exp x + \exp(-x))$$
$$= \tfrac{1}{2}(\exp x - \exp(-x))$$
$$= \sinh x,$$

and similarly, $D \sinh x = \cosh x$.

(iii) This is immediate, using the equations in (i). ◆

Definition.   We can define a function of R into R by setting

$$\tanh x = \frac{\sinh x}{\cosh x}, \qquad \forall\, x \in R.$$

Then, tanh is called the **hyperbolic tangent**. It is an odd function.

Theorem 9.5–C. $D \tanh x = 1/(\cosh^2 x)$.

Proof.   This follows from Theorems 9.5–B and 7.3–A. ◆

Theorem 9.5–D.   The function sinh is increasing, for all x; the function cosh is increasing in $\{x \in R : x \geqslant 0\}$, decreasing in $\{x \in R : x \leqslant 0\}$; tanh is increasing, for all x.
Also,

$$\mathcal{R}(\sinh) = R,$$
$$\mathcal{R}(\cosh) = \{x \in R : x \geqslant 1\}$$
$$\mathcal{R}(\tanh) = \{x \in R : -1 < x < 1\}.$$

Proof.   We have

$$\cosh x = 1 + \frac{x^2}{2!} + \frac{x^4}{4!} + \dots.$$

Hence,

$$\cosh x \geqslant 1, \qquad \forall\, x \in R$$

$$\Rightarrow D \sinh x > 0, \qquad \forall\, x \in R$$

$$\Rightarrow \text{sinh is increasing (by Corollary 3 of Theorem 7.7–A)}.$$

Next, $\sinh x = \tfrac{1}{2}\{\exp x - \exp(-x)\}$;

$$x > 0 \Rightarrow \exp x > 1\, \&\, \exp(-x) < 1 \Rightarrow \sinh x > 0$$
$$\Rightarrow \cosh \text{ increasing}.$$

$$x < 0 \Rightarrow \exp x < 1\, \&\, \exp(-x) > 1 \Rightarrow \sinh x < 0$$
$$\Rightarrow \cosh \text{ decreasing}.$$

Since $\cosh 0 = 1 < \cosh x, \forall\ x > 0$, cosh is increasing in $\{x \in R : x \geqslant 0\}$ and similarly, is decreasing in $\{x \in R : x \leqslant 0\}$.

We have $D \tanh x = 1/(\cosh^2 x) > 0$, since $\cosh x \neq 0$ for all $x \in R$. So tanh is increasing for all $x \in R$.

To investigate the ranges, we note that all the functions are continuous on R.

Now, $\sinh x = \frac{1}{2}(\exp x - \exp(-x))$

$$\Rightarrow \lim_{x \to \infty} \sinh x = \infty, \qquad \text{by Theorem 9.2-G with } n = 0,$$

and $\lim_{x \to -\infty} \sinh x = -\infty$, since sinh is odd; hence, $\mathscr{R}(\sinh) = R$, by Theorem 6.8–D, Corollary 2. Next, $\cosh x = \frac{1}{2}(\exp x + \exp(-x))$

$$\Rightarrow \lim_{x \to \infty} \cosh x = \infty \qquad \text{(Theorem 9.2-G with } n = 0)$$

and

$$\lim_{x \to -\infty} \cosh x = \infty.$$

Since cosh is increasing and continuous in $[0, \infty)$, decreasing and continuous in $(-\infty, 0]$, it follows that $\mathscr{R}(\cosh) = [1, \infty)$.

Finally, we have

$$\tanh x = \frac{\exp x - \exp(-x)}{\exp x + \exp(-x)}$$

Now,

$$\tanh x = \frac{1 - \exp(-2x)}{1 + \exp(-2x)} = \frac{\exp(2x) - 1}{\exp(2x) + 1};$$

the first is obtained by multiplying top and bottom by $\exp(-x)$, the second by multiplying top and bottom by $\exp x$. Then,

$$\lim_{x \to \infty} \tanh x = 1 \qquad \text{using the first form,}$$

$$\lim_{x \to -\infty} \tanh x = -1 \qquad \text{using the second form;}$$

since tanh is continuous and increasing, it follows by Theorem 6.8–D, Corollary 2 that $\mathscr{R}(\tanh) = (-1, 1)$. ◆

We finally mention three more functions obtainable from sinh and cosh. We leave the investigation of their properties to the reader.

Definition. The function φ defined by $\varphi(x) = 1/(\sinh x)\ (x \neq 0)$ is called the **hyperbolic cosecant**; it is denoted by cosech.

Definition. The function ψ defined by $\psi(x) = 1/(\cosh x)$, all $x \in R$, is called the **hyperbolic secant**; it is denoted by sech.

Definition. The function tanh is a continuous $(1, 1)$ mapping of $(x \neq 0)$ is called the **hyperbolic cotangent**; it is denoted by coth.

The functions sinh and cosh, and the various associated functions, are called "hyperbolic" because the points $\{(a \cosh t, b \sinh t) : t \in R\}$ define a hyperbola in $R \times R$, viz $\{(x, y) \in R \times R : (x^2/a^2) - (y^2/b^2) = 1\}$.

9.6 The Inverse Hyperbolic Functions

The function sinh was shown to be a $(1, 1)$ mapping of R, with range R. Hence it has an inverse function, whose domain is also R.

Definition. The inverse function of sinh, defined on R, is denoted by **argsinh**. Thus, if we have sinh $x = y$, then $x = $ argsinh y.

Theorem 9.6–A. argsinh is continuous and increasing on R. Further, for each $x \in R$,

$$D \text{ argsinh } x = \frac{1}{\sqrt{(1+x^2)}}.$$

Proof. argsinh is continuous and increasing, by Theorem 6.10–D and Exercise 34 of Chapter 3. By Theorem 7.5–A,

$$D \text{ argsinh } x = \frac{1}{D \sinh y} \qquad [\exists\, y \in R \text{ s.t. } x = \sinh y]$$

$$= \frac{1}{\cosh y}$$

$$= \frac{1}{\sqrt{(1+\sinh^2 y)}} \qquad \begin{array}{l}\text{(choosing the positive root since}\\ \cosh y \geqslant 1)\end{array}$$

$$= \frac{1}{\sqrt{(1+x^2)}}. \qquad\qquad\qquad \blacklozenge$$

The function cosh is not $(1, 1)$ on its domain. It is, however, $(1, 1)$ on the subset $\{x \in R : x \geqslant 0\}$; the range of cosh on this subset is the set $\{y \in R : y \geqslant 1\}$.

Definition. Let $y \in \{y \in R : y \geqslant 1\}$. Then, we can find a unique $x \geqslant 0$ such that cosh $x = y$. Hence, we can define a function on $\{y \in R : y \geqslant 1\}$ with range $\{x \in R : x \geqslant 0\}$. This function is denoted **argcosh**; argcosh $y = x \Leftrightarrow x \geqslant 0$, $y \geqslant 1$ and cosh $x = y$.

Theorem 9.6–B. argcosh is continuous and increasing; further, for each $x > 1$,

$$D \text{ argcosh } x = \frac{1}{\sqrt{(x^2-1)}}.$$

The proof is similar to that of Theorem 9.6–A.

Definition. The function tanh is a continuous $(1, 1)$ mapping of R with range $\{x \in R : -1 < x < 1\}$. Hence, we can define an inverse function on $\{x \in R : -1 < x < 1\}$ with range R. This inverse function is denoted by **argtanh**.

Theorem 9.6–C. argtanh is continuous and increasing; for each $x \in \{x \in R : -1 < x < 1\}$,

$$D \operatorname{argtanh} x = \frac{1}{(1-x^2)}.$$

The proof is again left to the reader.

9.7 The Circular Functions

We have so far investigated the functions whose Maclaurin series have been

$$1 + x + \frac{x^2}{2!} + \frac{x^3}{3!} + \dots,$$

$$1 + \frac{x^2}{2!} + \frac{x^4}{4!} + \frac{x^6}{6!} + \dots,$$

$$x + \frac{x^3}{3!} + \frac{x^5}{5!} + \dots;$$

that is, for $x \geqslant 0$, each series has been a series of constant sign; indeed, for the latter two, this is true for $x < 0$ also. Suppose we now look at the corresponding alternating series; it is clear that the series

$$1 - x + \frac{x^2}{2!} - \frac{x^3}{3!} + \dots$$

converges absolutely, for all x, to $\exp(-x)$. However, what of the series

$$1 - \frac{x^2}{2!} + \frac{x^4}{4!} - \dots \tag{1}$$

and

$$x - \frac{x^3}{3!} + \frac{x^5}{5!} - \dots? \tag{2}$$

The first is certainly not $\cosh(-x)$ [which is even], the second is evidently not $\sinh(-x)$, for sinh is odd. So, the series (1) and (2) represent two new functions, for it is clear that both (1) and (2) converge absolutely, for all x.

Denote the sum of the series (1) by $C(x)$, that of (2) by $S(x)$. In view of (1), (2) we might expect C and S to be differentiable, with

$$C(0) = -D^2C(0) = D^4C(0) = \ldots = 1$$
$$DC(0) = D^3C(0) = D^5C(0) = \ldots = 0$$
$$S(0) = D^2S(0) = D^4S(0) = \ldots = 0$$
$$DS(0) = -D^3S(0) = D^5S(0) = \ldots = 1$$

by the Maclaurin Expansion. Indeed, by formally differentiating the series (1) and (2), we might expect that $DS(x) = C(x)$, $DC(x) = -S(x)$. We prove that this is so.

Theorem 9.7–A.   For all $x \in R$,

$$DS(x) = C(x);$$
$$DC(x) = -S(x).$$

Proof.   The series

$$(x+h) - \frac{(x+h)^3}{3!} + \frac{(x+h)^5}{5!} - \ldots \quad \text{and} \quad x - \frac{x^3}{3!} + \frac{x^5}{5!} - \ldots$$

are absolutely convergent. Hence, by Theorem 5.2–C,

$$S(x+h) - S(x) = (x+h) - x - \frac{(x+h)^3 - x^3}{3!} + \frac{(x+h)^5 - x^5}{5!} - \ldots$$

$$= h - \frac{1}{3!}\{3x^2h + h^2y_1\} + \frac{1}{5!}\{5x^4h + h^2y_2\} - \ldots$$

where y_k is a finite sum of terms of the form cx^rh^s, c being a real number.

$$\left[\text{In fact, } y_k = \sum_{p=2}^{2k+1} \binom{2k+1}{p} x^{2k+1-p}h^{p-2}\right].$$

Hence,

$$\frac{S(x+h) - S(x)}{h} = 1 - \frac{1}{3!}\{3x^2 + hy_1\} + \frac{1}{5!}\{5x^4 + hy_2\} - \ldots$$

$$= \left\{1 - \frac{x^2}{2!} + \frac{x^4}{4!} - \ldots\right\} - h\left\{\frac{y_1}{3!} - \frac{y_2}{5!} + \ldots\right\}$$

rearranging, since we have absolute convergence (Theorem 5.6–B). Now, if h is sufficiently small,

$$|y_k| < \binom{2k+1}{2}|x|^{2k-1} + \binom{2k+1}{3}|x|^{2k-1}$$

i.e. $|y_k|$ does not exceed the leading term (independent of h) plus the second term multiplied by $|x/h|$. So,

$$|y_k| < \binom{2k+2}{3}|x|^{2k-1}$$

$$\Rightarrow \frac{y_1}{3!} - \frac{y_2}{5!} + \frac{y_3}{7!} - \cdots < \sum_{k=1}^{\infty} \frac{2k+2}{6} \cdot \frac{|x|^{2k-1}}{(2k-1)!} \cdots$$

The series on the right converges, for all x, by the Ratio Test. Hence,

$$\frac{S(x+h) - S(x)}{h} = C(x) - hA,$$

say, where

$$\frac{y_1}{3!} - \frac{y_2}{5!} + \cdots = A.$$

If we now take the limit at zero, we have

$$DS(x) = C(x).$$

The second part is similar.   ◆

Theorem 9.7–B. For all $x, y \in R$,

$$C(x+y) = C(x)C(y) - S(x)S(y)$$

$$S(x+y) = S(x)C(y) + C(x)S(y).$$

Proof. We look at the Taylor Series for $C(x)$; then

$$C(x+y) = C(x) + yDC(x) + \frac{y^2}{2!}D^2C(x) + \cdots$$

$$= C(x) - yS(x) - \frac{y^2}{2!}C(x) + \cdots \qquad \text{(by Theorem 9.7–A)}$$

$$= C(x)\left\{1 - \frac{y^2}{2!} + \frac{y^4}{4!} - \cdots\right\} - S(x)\left\{y - \frac{y^3}{3!} + \frac{y^5}{5!} - \cdots\right\},$$

since the Taylor Series is absolutely convergent,

$$= C(x)C(y) - S(x)S(y).$$

The proof for $S(x+y)$ is similar.   ◆

Corollary 1. Let $y = x$; $C(2x) = C^2(x) - S^2(x)$, $S(2x) = 2S(x)C(x)$. Let $y = -x$; $C(0) = 1 = C^2(x) + S^2(x)$.

Corollary 2. For all x, $-1 \leqslant C(x) \leqslant 1$, $-1 \leqslant S(x) \leqslant 1$.

Proof. By Corollary 1, $C^2(x) + S^2(x) = 1$; since $C^2(x) \geqslant 0$, $S^2(x) \geqslant 0$, it follows that $C^2(x) \leqslant 1$, $S^2(x) \leqslant 1$. Hence the result.   ◆

Theorem 9.7–C.

$$\lim_{x \to 0} \frac{S(x)}{x} = 1; \qquad \lim_{x \to 0} \frac{1 - C(x)}{x^2} = \frac{1}{2}.$$

Proof. This can be proved by using the Maclaurin Series, or by using L'Hôpital's Rule (Theorem 7.13–A). Since $S(0) = 0$, we have

$$\lim_{x \to 0} \frac{S(x)}{x} = \lim_{x \to 0} \frac{DS(x)}{1} = \lim_{x \to 0} C(x) = 1.$$

Again,

$$1 - C(0) = 0 \;\Rightarrow\; \lim_{x \to 0} \frac{1 - C(x)}{x^2} = \lim_{x \to 0} \frac{-DC(x)}{2x}$$

$$= \lim_{x \to 0} \frac{S(x)}{2x}$$

$$= \tfrac{1}{2},$$

by the preceding part.   ◆

We have so far shown that that there are functions S and C such that $DS = C$, $S(0) = 0$, $DC = -S$, $C(0) = 1$. How many such functions are there? We assume that there is another pair C_1, S_1 with the same properties.

Theorem 9.7–D. If C_1, S_1 is a pair of functions with the same properties as C, S, then $C_1 = C$, $S_1 = S$.

Proof. Consider the function F given by

$$F(x) = (C(x) - C_1(x))^2 + (S(x) - S_1(x))^2.$$

Then,

$$DF(x) = 2(C(x) - C_1(x))(-S(x) + S_1(x)) + 2(S(x) - S_1(x))(C(x) - C_1(x))$$

$$= 0$$

$$\Rightarrow \; F(x) \text{ is a constant.}$$

$$F(0) = 0 \;\Rightarrow\; F(x) = 0 \qquad \text{for all } x$$

$$\Rightarrow \; \left. \begin{array}{l} C(x) - C_1(x) = 0 \\ S(x) - S_1(x) = 0 \end{array} \right\} \qquad \text{for all } x.$$

Hence the functions C, S are unique.   ◆

Definition. The function C which satisfies $DC = -S$, $C(0) = 1$ is called the **cosine function**. It is usually written as **cos**.

Definition. The function S which satisfies $DS = C$, $S(0) = 0$ is called the **sine function**. It is usually written as **sin**.

We further examine the function sin.

Theorem 9.7–E.   (i) If $0 < x \leqslant 2$, $\sin x > 0$;
(ii) $\sin 1 > 1/\sqrt{2}$;
(iii) $\sin 4 < 0$.

Proof.   (i) We look at the Taylor Series for sin;

$$\sin x = x\left(1 - \frac{x^2}{6}\right) + \frac{x^5}{5!}\left(1 - \frac{x^2}{42}\right) + \dots.$$

If $0 < x \leqslant 2$, all the terms are positive, proving (i);
(ii) by the series above, for $0 < x \leqslant 2$,

$$\sin x > x\left(1 - \frac{x^2}{6}\right)$$

$$\Rightarrow \sin 1 > \frac{5}{6} > \frac{1}{\sqrt{2}}.$$

(iii) By the Corollary 1 of Theorem 9.7–B, it follows that

$$\sin 4 = 2 \sin 2 \cos 2;$$

also, in consequence of the corollary,

$$\cos 2x = 1 - 2 \sin^2 x$$

$$\Rightarrow \cos 2 = 1 - 2 \sin^2 1$$

$$< 0, \qquad \text{by (ii)}$$

$$\Rightarrow \sin 4 < 0, \qquad \text{since } \sin 2 > 0. \qquad \blacklozenge$$

Theorem 9.7–F.   There is a unique real number ξ, such that $2 < \xi < 4$ and $\sin \xi = 0$.

Proof.   sin is continuous; by Theorem 9.7–E, $\sin 2 > 0$, $\sin 4 < 0$; hence, by Theorem 6.8–C, there is a point ξ, $2 < \xi < 4$, such that $\sin \xi = 0$. If ξ_1 also satisfies $2 < \xi_1 < 4$, $\sin \xi_1 = 0$, then

$$\sin(\xi - \xi_1) = \sin \xi \cos \xi_1 - \cos \xi \sin \xi_1 = 0.$$

But $|\xi - \xi_1| < 2$, since both of ξ, ξ_1 lie between 2 and 4, and by Theorem 9.7–E(i), $\sin(\xi - \xi_1) > 0$ if $0 < |\xi - \xi_1| \leqslant 2$. So $\xi = \xi_1$ i.e. ξ is unique. $\blacklozenge$

Definition.   The least positive real number x such that $\sin x$ is zero is denoted by the Greek letter π. From the theorem above, $2 < \pi < 4$. Let us now see what we can deduce from this.

Theorem 9.7–G.   We have (i) $\sin \frac{1}{2}\pi = 1$, $\cos \frac{1}{2}\pi = 0$;
(ii) $\cos \pi = -1$;
(iii) $\sin(x + 2\pi) = \sin x$;
(iv) $\cos(x + 2\pi) = \cos x$.

Proof.   (i) By definition of π,

$$\sin x > 0 \quad \text{for} \quad 0 < x < \pi;$$

also,

$$0 = \sin \pi = 2 \sin \tfrac{1}{2}\pi \cos \tfrac{1}{2}\pi \qquad \text{(by Corollary 1 of Theorem 9.7–B)}$$

$$\Rightarrow \cos \tfrac{1}{2}\pi = 0 \qquad \text{since } \sin \tfrac{1}{2}\pi > 0.$$

Next, since

$$1 = \sin^2 \tfrac{1}{2}\pi + \cos^2 \tfrac{1}{2}\pi, \quad \text{we have} \quad \sin^2 \tfrac{1}{2}\pi = 1$$

$$\Rightarrow \sin \tfrac{1}{2}\pi = \pm 1$$

$$\Rightarrow \sin \tfrac{1}{2}\pi = +1 \qquad \text{(since } \sin \tfrac{1}{2}\pi > 0\text{)}.$$

(ii) $\cos \pi = \cos^2 \tfrac{1}{2}\pi - \sin^2 \tfrac{1}{2}\pi$, by Corollary 1 of Theorem 9.7–B.

$$\Rightarrow \cos \pi = -1 \qquad \text{by part (i)}.$$

(iii) Firstly,

$$\sin 2\pi = 2 \sin \pi \cos \pi \qquad \text{(Corollary 1, Theorem 9.7–B)}$$

$$= 0; \qquad \text{(definition of } \pi\text{)}$$

$$\cos 2\pi = \cos^2 \pi - \sin^2 \pi$$

$$= 1 \qquad \text{by (ii)}.$$

Hence,

$$\sin(x + 2\pi) = \sin x \cos 2\pi + \cos x . \sin 2\pi$$

$$= \sin x.$$

(iv) $\cos(x + 2\pi) = \cos x \cos 2\pi - \sin x \sin 2\pi$

$$= \cos x, \qquad \text{by (iii)}. \qquad \blacklozenge$$

Corollary.   By repeating the argument of (iii) and (iv), we can show that $\sin n\pi = 0$, $\cos 2n\pi = 1$, $\cos(2n-1)\pi = -1$, for all $n \in Z$; also, $\sin(x + 2n\pi) = \sin x$, $\cos(x + 2n\pi) = \cos x$.

The functions sin and cos, in view of this theorem, repeat themselves after any interval of length 2π. This has a special name.

Definition.   If f is a function defined on R, with the property that $f(x + \alpha) = f(x)$, for some real number α, and all $x \in R$, then f is called **periodic**, and the number α is called its **period**. If f has period α, then it has period $k\alpha$, where $k \in N$. This is easy to deduce.

Thus, sin and cos are periodic; their period is 2π (see Fig. 9.7.2, page 331).

Theorem 9.7–H.   The function sin is increasing in $\{x \in R : -\pi/2 < x < \pi/2\}$; the function cos is decreasing in $\{x \in R : 0 < x < \pi\}$.

Proof. Suppose $0 < x < \pi$. Then, $D \cos x = -\sin x$; by definition of π, $-\sin x < 0 \Rightarrow \cos$ is decreasing, by Corollary 3 of Theorem 7.7.–A.

Next, cos decreasing in $(0, \pi)$

$$\Rightarrow \cos \text{ decreasing in } \left(0, \frac{\pi}{2}\right)$$

$$\Rightarrow \cos x > 0 \quad \text{if} \quad 0 < x < \frac{\pi}{2}, \qquad \text{since } \cos \frac{\pi}{2} = 0.$$

Further, cos is an even function

$$\Rightarrow \cos x > 0 \quad \text{if} \quad -\frac{\pi}{2} < x < 0$$

$$\Rightarrow \cos x > 0 \quad \text{if} \quad -\frac{\pi}{2} < x < \frac{\pi}{2}.$$

Therefore, $D \sin x > 0$ if $-\pi/2 < x < \pi/2 \Rightarrow \sin$ is increasing in $(-\pi/2, \pi/2)$.

Finally, we observe that

$$\sin\left(-\frac{\pi}{2}\right) = -\sin \frac{\pi}{2} = -1.$$

So sin takes values in $[-1, 1]$; by a similar argument, so does cos. ◆

To conclude this section, we define four associated circular functions. Their graphs are illustrated in Figs. 9.7.1 and 9.7.2 (see page 331).

Definition. The function **tan** is the function defined by setting,

$$\text{for all } x \in R, \qquad x \neq \frac{2n+1}{2}\pi,$$

$$\tan x = \frac{\sin x}{\cos x}.$$

Theorem 9.7–I. The function tan is continuous in each interval of the form $\{x \in R : (2n-1)\pi/2 < x < (2n+1)\pi/2\}$ and is increasing in this interval; $\tan 0 = 0$; tan is an odd function and is periodic with period π; tan is differentiable at all points $x \neq (2n+1)\pi/2$, and

$$D \tan x = \frac{1}{\cos^2 x};$$

also, $\lim\limits_{x \to (2n-1)\pi/2 +} \tan x = -\infty$; $\lim\limits_{x \to (2n+1)\pi/2 -} \tan x = \infty$; the range of tan is R.

The verification of these statements is left to the reader.

Definition. The function **cosec** is defined by setting, for all $x \neq n\pi$,

$$\operatorname{cosec} x = \frac{1}{\sin x}.$$

Theorem 9.7–J. The function cosec is continuous and differentiable in each interval $\{x \in R : n\pi < x < (n+1)\pi\}$, and

$$D \operatorname{cosec} x = -\frac{\cos x}{\sin^2 x} \qquad (x \neq n\pi).$$

Also,

$$\lim_{x \to 2n\pi +} \operatorname{cosec} x = \lim_{x \to (2n+1)\pi -} \operatorname{cosec} x = \infty \,;$$

$$\lim_{x \to (2n+1)\pi +} \operatorname{cosec} x = \lim_{x \to (2n+2)\pi -} \operatorname{cosec} x = -\infty \,;$$

and, for all $x \neq n\pi$, we have $|\operatorname{cosec} x| \geqslant 1$.
Again, details are left to the reader.

Definition. The function **sec** is defined by setting, for all $x \neq (2n+1)\pi/2$,

$$\sec x = \frac{1}{\cos x}.$$

Theorem 9.7–K. The function sec is continuous and differentiable in each interval $\{x \in R : (2n-1)\pi/2 < x < (2n+1)\pi/2\}$, and

$$D \sec x = \frac{\sin x}{\cos^2 x} \qquad (x \neq (2n+1)\pi/2).$$

For all $x \neq (2n+1)\pi/2$, $|\sec x| \geqslant 1$; also,

$$\lim_{x \to (4n-1)\pi/2 +} \sec x = \lim_{x \to (4n+1)\pi/2 -} \sec x = \infty \,;$$

$$\lim_{x \to (4n+1)\pi/2 +} \sec x = \lim_{x \to (4n+3)\pi/2 -} \sec x = -\infty.$$

Definition. The function **cot** is defined by setting, for all $x \neq n\pi$,

$$\cot x = \frac{\cos x}{\sin x}.$$

Note. For all $x \neq \frac{1}{2}n\pi$, $\cot x = 1/(\tan x)$.

Theorem 9.7–L. The function cot is continuous and differentiable in each interval $\{x \in R : n\pi < x < (n+1)\pi\}$, and

$$D \cot x = -\frac{1}{\sin^2 x} = -\operatorname{cosec}^2 x \qquad (x \neq n\pi);$$

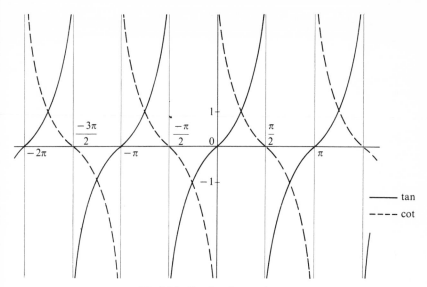

Fig. 9.7.1. Graphs of tan and cot.

——— tan
- - - - cot

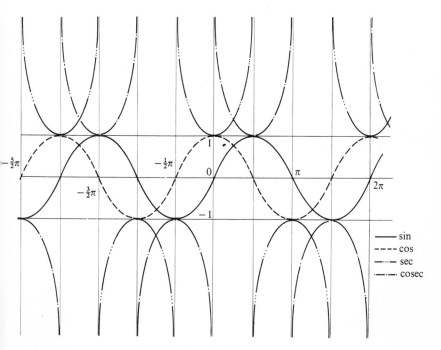

Fig. 9.7.2. Graphs of sin, cos, sec, cosec.

——— sin
- - - - cos
— ··· — sec
— · — · cosec

cot is an odd function, decreasing in each interval $\{n\pi < x < (n+1)\pi\}$, with

$$\lim_{x \to n\pi +} \cot x = \infty, \qquad \lim_{x \to n\pi -} \cot x = -\infty.$$

The details are left to the reader.

The graphs of the four derived circular functions are given above. For comparison, the graphs of sin, and cos, are also given.

9.8 The Inverse Circular Functions

The functions sin, cos, and tan described in Section 9.7 are not $(1, 1)$. For, as we saw in the Corollary to Theorem 9.7–G, sin and cos are periodic with period 2π i.e. $\sin(2n\pi + x) = \sin x$, $\cos(2n\pi + x) = \cos x$. The function tan is periodic with period π (Theorem 9.7–I). Therefore, as things stand, there is no possibility of defining an inverse function. But, if we consider restrictions of the functions sin, cos and tan, then this does become possible.

It might seem enough, in view of the fact that sin has period 2π, to consider the restriction of sin, say to $(-\pi, \pi)$; but even this is too much; for

$$\sin(\pi - x) = \sin \pi \cos x - \cos \pi \sin x$$

$$= \sin x.$$

Hence, if $0 < x < \pi/2$, $\exists\, y$ such that $\pi/2 < y < \pi$ and $\sin x = \sin y$, where $y \neq x$; so sin is not $(1, 1)$ in $(-\pi, \pi)$. Now, (Theorem 9.7–H) we have seen that $\mathscr{R}(\sin) = \{x \in R : -1 \leqslant x \leqslant 1\}$, so we look at the smallest interval in which each point of the range is attained. By Theorem 9.7–H, this is $[-\pi/2, \pi/2]$. We therefore introduce the following definitions.

Definition. Denote by **Sin** (using the upper case S) the restriction of the function sin to the interval $P = [-\pi/2, \pi/2]$. Thus, Sin $= \sin/P$, is the notation of Section 3.3.

Theorem 9.8–A. The function Sin is a $(1, 1)$ function of P with range $[-1, 1]$. It is continuous on P and differentiable throughout $(-\pi/2, \pi/2)$.

Proof. This follows immediately from the definition and the properties of sin.   ◆

Definition. Denote by **Cos** (using upper case C) the restriction of cos to the interval $Q = [0, \pi]$.

Theorem 9.8–B. The function Cos is a $(1, 1)$ function of Q with range $[-1, 1]$. It is continuous on Q and differentiable throughout $(0, \pi)$.

Proof. This follows from the definition and the properties of cos.   ◆

The tan function is slightly less complicated. It has period π, but it is strictly increasing and continuous in each interval $((2n-1)\pi/2, (2n+1)\pi/2)$, by Theorem 9.7–I.

Definition. Denote by **Tan** the restriction of the function tan to the interval $P_1 = (-\pi/2, \pi/2)$.

Theorem 9.8–C. The function Tan is a $(1, 1)$ function of P_1 with range R. It is continuous and differentiable on P_1.

Proof. Again, use the definition and properties of tan. ◆
We are now in a position to define inverse functions.

Definition. By Theorem 9.8–A, the function Sin has an inverse function, defined on $[-1, 1]$, and with range P. We denote this inverse function by **arcsin**. Thus,

$$\mathscr{D}(\arcsin) = [-1, 1], \qquad \mathscr{R}(\arcsin) = [-\pi/2, \pi/2].$$

Note. We use lower case letters throughout arcsin; but we reiterate that arcsin is the inverse function of Sin, not of sin.

Theorem 9.8–D. arcsin is continuous on $[-1, 1]$, and differentiable on $(-1, 1)$, with

$$D \arcsin x = \frac{1}{\sqrt{(1-x^2)}}, \qquad \forall\, x \in (-1, 1).$$

Proof. arcsin enjoys the properties of Sin, by Theorems 6.10–D and 7.5–A. In particular, by Theorem 7.5–A,

$$D \arcsin x = \frac{1}{D \operatorname{Sin} y} \qquad (\text{given } x, \exists\, y \in P \text{ s.t. } x = \operatorname{Sin} y)$$

$$= \frac{1}{\cos y}$$

$$= \frac{1}{\sqrt{(1 - \operatorname{Sin}^2 y)}} \qquad (\text{choosing the appropriate square root})$$

$$= \frac{1}{\sqrt{(1 - x^2)}}. \qquad\qquad ◆$$

Definition. By Theorem 9.8–B, the function Cos has an inverse function, defined on $[-1, 1]$ with range Q. We denote this inverse function by **arccos**. Thus,

$$\mathscr{D}(\arccos) = [-1, 1], \qquad \mathscr{R}(\arccos) = [0, \pi].$$

We have

$$y = \arccos x \;\Leftrightarrow\; x = \operatorname{Cos} y.$$

Theorem 9.8–E.   arccos is continuous and decreasing on $[-1, 1]$, and is differentiable on $(-1, 1)$; for $x \in (-1, 1)$,

$$D \arccos x = -\frac{1}{\sqrt{(1-x^2)}}.$$

Proof.   Similar to Theorem 9.8–D.   ◆

Definition.   By Theorem 9.8–C, the function Tan has an inverse function, defined on R with range $(-\pi/2, \pi/2)$. We denote this inverse function by **arctan**. Then,

$$\mathscr{D}(\arctan) = R, \qquad \mathscr{R}(\arctan) = (-\pi/2, \pi/2).$$

We have

$$y = \arctan x \Leftrightarrow x = \operatorname{Tan} y.$$

Theorem 9.8–F.   arctan is continuous, increasing, and differentiable, on R, with

$$D \arctan x = \frac{1}{1+x^2}, \qquad \forall\, x \in R.$$

Proof.   Similar to Theorem 9.8–D.   ◆

We illustrate the graphs of arcsin, arccos and arctan below (Figs. 9.8.1, 9.8.2, 9.8.3).

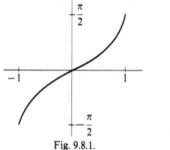

Fig. 9.8.1.
Graph of arcsin.

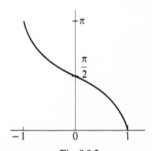

Fig. 9.8.2.
Graph of arccos.

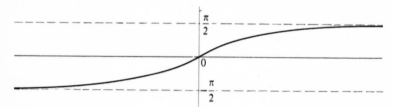

Fig. 9.8.3.
Graph of arctan.

Exercises

1. Complete the proof of Theorem 9.2–E.
2. Prove Theorem 9.4–B.
3. Prove Theorem 9.4–D.
4. Give a recipe for changing the function $\log_a$ from base a to base b.
5. Investigate the properties of the functions cosech, sech, and coth.
6. Prove Theorem 9.6–B.
7. Prove Theorem 9.6–C.
8. Prove Theorem 9.7–I.
9. Prove Theorem 9.7–J.
10. Prove Theorem 9.7–K.
11. Prove Theorem 9.7–L.
12. Prove Theorem 9.8–E.
13. Prove Theorem 9.8–F.

Biography

ABEL, Neils Henrik, b. Findoe (Norway) 1802, d. Arendal (Norway) 1829.

ARCHIMEDES, b. Syracuse 287 B.C., d. Syracuse 212 B.C.

BOLZANO, Bernhard, b. in Bohemia 1781, d. in Bohemia 1848.

CANTOR, Georg, b. Petrograd 1845, d. Halle 1918.

CAUCHY, Augustin-Louis, b. Paris 1789, d. Sceaux 1857.

D'ALEMBERT, Jean Baptiste, b. Paris 1717, d. Paris 1783.

DARBOUX, Jean Gaston, b. Nimes 1842, d. Paris 1917.

DE MORGAN, Augustus, b. India 1806, d. London 1871.

DEDEKIND, Julius Wilhelm Richard, b. Braunschweig 1831, d. Braunschweig 1916.

DIRICHLET, Peter Gustav Lejeune, b. Duren 1805, d. Gottingen 1859.

EULER, Leonhard, b. Basel 1707, d. Petrograd 1783.

GAUSS, Carl Friedrich, b. Braunschweig 1777, d. Gottingen 1855.

LAGRANGE, Joseph Louis, b. Turin 1736, d. Paris 1813.

LEIBNIZ, Gottfried Wilhelm, b. Leipzig 1646, d. Hanover 1716.

L'HÔPITAL, Guillaume François (Marquis de), b. Paris 1661, d. Paris 1704.

MACLAURIN, Colin, b. Argyllshire 1698, d. York 1746.

NAPIER, John, b. Edinburgh 1550, d. Edinburgh 1617.

RIEMANN, Georg Friedrich Bernhard, b. Hanover 1826, d. Lake Maggiore 1866.

ROLLE, Michel, b. Ambert (Auvergne) 1652, d. Paris 1719.

RUSSELL, Bertrand (Lord), b. Trelleck (Monmouth) 1872.

TAYLOR, Brook, b. Edmonton 1685, d. London 1731.

WEIERSTRASS, Karl, b. Ostenfelde 1815, d. Berlin 1897.

Index